THE ORIGINS AND GROWTH
OF BIOLOGY

*

EDITED BY ARTHUR ROOK

BASED ON
'MOMENTS OF DISCOVERY'
EDITED BY GEORGE SCHWARTZ
AND PHILIP W. BISHOP

*

WITH EIGHT PLATES

PENGUIN BOOKS

Penguin Books Ltd, Harmondsworth, Middlesex
U.S.A.: Penguin Books Inc., 3300 Clipper Mill Road, Baltimore 11, Md
AUSTRALIA: Penguin Books Pty Ltd, 762 Whitehorse Road,
Mitcham, Victoria

—

Moments of Discovery first published in the U.S.A. 1958
The Origins and Growth of Biology first published in Pelican Books 1964

—

Copyright © Basic Books, Inc., 1958, and Penguin Books Ltd, 1964

Made and printed in Great Britain
by Hazell Watson & Viney Ltd
Aylesbury, Bucks
Set in Linotype Baskerville

PUBLISHER'S NOTE

The Origins and Growth of Biology is one of three Pelican volumes, the other two being *The Origins and Growth of Physical Science*, Vols 1 & 2, edited by D. L. Hurd and J. J. Kipling (Pelicans A534 and A535), based on *Moments of Discovery*, edited by George Schwartz and Philip W. Bishop, and published in America by Basic Books in 1958. The extracts from scientific writings in this volume are, with one exception, the same as those used in the American books, but the introductory material has been partly rewritten.

CONTENTS

7

CONTENTS

CONTENTS

VI
THE DEVELOPMENT AND EVOLUTION OF LIFE

VII
THE CONQUEST OF DISEASE

CONTENTS

ACKNOWLEDGEMENTS

ACKNOWLEDGEMENTS are due to the following for the use of materials from the publications stated: *British Medical Journal*, Joseph Lister, 'On the Antiseptic Principle in the Practice of Surgery', 1867, Sir Ronald Ross, 'On Some Peculiar Pigmented Cells found in Two Mosquitoes Fed on Malarial Blood', 1897; *Bulletin No. 1* of the Bureau of Animal Industry, U.S. Department of Agriculture, 1893 (Theobald Smith); *Bulletin of the History of Medicine*, O. Temkon and W. L. Strauss, Jr, 'Translation of Galen on Muscles Moving the Forearm', 1946; Clarendon Press Oxford, Aristotle (trans. D. W. Thompson), *On Psyche, Histories About Animals, On Parts of Animals*, 1910; Columbia University Press, Vesalius (trans. S. Lambert), *De humani corporis fabrica*, 1935; J. M. Dent, William Harvey, *Anatomical Disquisition on the Motion of the Heart and Blood*, Everyman Library and E. P. Dutton & Co., 1906; Jonathan Cape and G. P. Putnam's Sons, T. H. White, *The Book of Beasts*, 1954; Harvard University Press, *The Hippocratic Collection (On the Sacred Disease; on Airs, Water and Places; Prognostic*) trans. W. H. S. Jones and E. T. Withington),) 1923–31, A Hort, *Theophrastus – Enquiry into Plants*, 1913; *Johns Hopkins Hospital Bulletin*, Henri Dutrochet (trans. A. R. Rich), 1926; Macmillan & Co., J. B. Lamarck, *Zoological Philosophy*, St Martin's Press Incorporated, 1912; The National Tuberculosis Association, Robert Koch (trans. Dr and Mrs Max Pinner), *The Etiology of Tuberculosis*, 1932; New Sydenham Society, Robert Koch (trans. Victor Horsley), *On the Investigation of Pathogenic Organisms*, 1886, Louis Pasteur, *Recent Essays on Bacteria in Relation to Disease*, 1886; Open Court Publishing Co., Hugo DeVries, *The Mutation Theory*, 1909, Francesco Redi (M. A. B. Bigelow), *Experiments on the Generation of Insects*, 1909; *Proceedings of the Royal Society of Medicine*, Andreas Vesalius (B. Farrington), *De humani corporis fabrica,* 1932, Marcello Malpighi (trans. James Young), *De pulmonibus*, 1929; *Proceedings of the Society for Experimental Medicine and Biology* (Ross Harrison), 1907; the Ray Society, Linnaeus (trans. Sir A. Hort), *Critica botanica*, 1938; *The Royal Horticultural Society of London*, Gregor Mendel (trans. W. Bateson), *Proceedings of the Natural History Society of Brünn*, 1866; Staples Press, C.

ACKNOWLEDGEMENTS

Dobell, *Antony van Leeuwenhoek and his 'Little Animals'*, 1932; the Sydenham Society, Theodor Schwann (trans. Henry Smith), *Microscopical Researches into the Accordance in the Structure and Growth of Animals and Plants*, 1847; *Transactions of the Linnaean Society*, Robert Brown, 'Observations on the Organs and Mode of Fecundation in Orchidae and Asclepiadeae', 1833.

Acknowledgements are also due to the Burndy Library for permission to use illustrative material.

INTRODUCTION
THE ORIGINS OF SCIENTIFIC BIOLOGY

MAN'S discoveries about himself and the world around him, put into an orderly form, have created that vast structure of knowledge we now call 'science'. This search for explanations began with his first observation of the 'movement' of the sun or with his question, when he first penetrated the forest behind his cave: 'Why do the leaves die before the snow comes?' And, since pride came no later than the ability to speak, no sooner were the questions phrased than controversy about the explanations began. For it is of the very nature of the scientific mind to question accepted patterns of knowledge, to suggest new explanations, and to defy those who claim to know better. The readings that make up this book have been chosen because each recalls something of the search for truth since the written record began. They commemorate some of the great discoverers, those whose observations proved so much better than their fellows' that the influence of their thought survives to form a part of our culture. As the Biblical writings or the plays of Shakespeare still give life to our language, so the discoveries of Hippocrates and Newton take their place among the influences on an Einstein or a Bohr.

We take science for granted today. Scarcely anything we do or anything we use to make life easy and comfortable is unaffected by science. Scientific research is looked upon now as synonymous with progress; and without progress the elaborate structure of modern life will collapse. Our standard of living depends on science to find new ways of using the resources we have and to find new products among the old raw materials. Science – applied science – may even decide the political future of man.

All this is far removed from the picture of the early scientist, perhaps a lonely man, examining the apparent movement of the stars and trying to find a systematic relationship among them. The spread of education and of the means of communication in the last hundred years has brought science into everyday life. The youngest student can look over the shoulder of the scientist while he works, as he would watch the artist at his easel on the dock of an old fishing port, to observe the progress of the experiments and to criticize the equations. But it is better that the student-critic of the painter learn something of the story of art before he presume to comment on the artist's interpretation of the scene before him; to understand the purpose of art and its methods, he should know something of Michelangelo and of Picasso. So, he who wishes to talk about science, read about science, and, especially, work in science, should examine the sources of modern knowledge and appreciate the long history of man's exploration of the unknown world.

The immensely wide scope of modern science, and the progressively more rapid accumulation of new facts by research workers, have brought about the division of science into innumerable special branches. The broad divisions of physics and chemistry, zoology and botany, familiar since the early nineteenth century, are each now further differentiated, but such specialization is a relatively modern development. Even today the interdependence of the various divisions of science is obvious – the recent studies of virus structure with the electron microscope provide an example. In the past, as in the present, many advances in, for example, what we should now call biology, have resulted from new discoveries in the physical sciences, and the latter in turn have often profited from progress in the observation and recording of the phenomena of life. The history of biology cannot therefore be studied apart from the history of science as a whole. For convenience the extracts concerning discoveries in biology have been gathered together in the present volume, but it should be read in conjunction with the two companion volumes (*The Origins and Growth of Physical Science*). It has proved impossible in the brief introductory survey which follows to avoid occasional reference to the physical sciences and some overlap with the introductions to the other volumes is therefore inevitable. Such repetition will perhaps serve a useful purpose in emphasizing the essential unity of science.

Something is known of the earliest explorations from the tablets left by the Babylonians. These records go back as far as three thousand years before the Christian era. Those of Egypt are generally of a later date. The ancient documents – clay tablets and papyri – show that ancient man observed the regularity of the supposed movements of the sun and the planets and connected them with the rhythm of seed time and harvest. From these observations calendars were evolved and such phenomena as eclipses were predicted.

In the hands of specialists, the science of prediction was, in time, debased into the art of astrology, in which the movements of the stars were alleged to foretell change in the affairs of men, if, indeed, they did not directly influence them. Combined with the rituals and mysteries of the temples, astrology brought science down to the level of the common man. It was perhaps in this form that the early knowledge of the stars was transmitted to later generations and to other peoples.

These records show, too, how the art of counting was developed. The great pyramids of Egypt are the living testimony to the skill of the early priests who evolved the rules of measurement and found ways to use the plumb-line, to construct right-angles, and to shape stone with a mason's square. Ahmes, 'the moonborn', recorded, 3,500 years ago, how to calculate the area of a circle. At sea, the Phoenicians, who sailed the Mediterranean and even the Atlantic when they sought the tin of Cornwall, observed the connexion between the stars and their problem of setting a course and made rules which guided future mariners and helped the first map-makers.

From his earliest days man has been afflicted by many diseases and has injured himself in accidents and in battle. From the study of the customs of peoples still at a primitive stage of civilization we can form a picture of the way in which our ancestors many thousands of years ago must have sought relief from pain and remedies for disease. The tablets and the papyri show us that the Babylonians and the Egyptians had accumulated many observations on the human body in health and in sickness and had devised systems of medical practice which combined empiricism and magical rites.

Direct knowledge of these and similar discoveries by the ancients has come to us only in recent years as the excavations of the archaeologists have found treasures hidden in the sands of centuries; but the influence of earlier cultures came indirectly through the writings of the Greeks, the first people in Europe to produce an organized literature of science. Among the selections that make up this book, the Greek writings are the earliest; and they are chosen as typical of the writings which influenced the growth of knowledge in the rest of Europe after the decline of Greece's own civilization. The first of the writers chosen, Hippocrates, was of the Ionian Colony, which seems to have led the mother country in scientific developments, perhaps because it was in closer contact, geographically, with the older civilizations. Hippocrates was a pioneer in the observation of the ills of the human body. Others of his period put the study of nature generally on a systematic basis.

The Greeks preferred, on the whole, to establish a theory – as, for instance, that all things are made of four 'elements', fire, air, water, and earth – and then fit the facts to the theory. Although Hippocrates showed the value of observation and experiment, much of Greek science depended on an approach typified by such propositions as: God is good; the sphere is the most perfect of forms; therefore, the universe must be spherical. Plato preferred this approach and despised experiment. Aristotle (384–322 B.C.), a student in Plato's Academy in Athens, brought together so great a collection of knowledge in his works that they survived to become, fifteen hundred years later, as we shall see, the basis of learning in the Middle Ages. In biology, embryology, and physiology, Aristotle added to knowledge by collecting facts including those to be found in dissecting – perhaps even in vivisecting – animals. His authority in these fields gave him such influence that, in subjects in which he was less competent, such as physics, his writings held up progress when they were later rediscovered.

The climax of Greek advances in science comes with Archimedes (287–212 B.C.), and with the growth in importance of Alexandria, founded in Egypt by Alexander the Great in 332 B.C. There, a great research library, containing, it is said, some 400,000 manuscripts in literature, mathematics, astronomy, and medicine, later to be destroyed by Christians and Moslems, attracted such scholars as Euclid, Hipparchus, and Ptolemy.

The next great civilization, that of the Romans, which spread all over Europe, has only one representative in the selection below – Galen (c. 129–200). The reason for this is to be found in the preoccupation of the Romans in what we would now call applied science. As farmers, architects, and engineers, the Romans used Greek knowledge and developed the practical arts; and from Rome to the borders of Scotland, roads, walls, aqueducts, and stadiums remain as monuments to their skill. Some, like Lucretius and Pliny the Elder, revived Greek learning or made encyclopedic compilations of the knowledge of the period. A Greek among them, Galen, developed theories of bodily functions which were to dominate physiology for fifteen hundred years. In the main, however, Romans recorded the facts of their widespread observation but did little to advance theoretical science.

With the decline of the Roman Empire, which culminated around the fourth century after the Christian era, the advance of science was transferred into other hands. Europe entered a period of a thousand years during which the ancient classics lay unknown to the West. The Christian religion had, during its earliest years, inherited the traditions of Plato and Aristotle and these survived to maintain some sort of theological link, in Christian Europe, between the old and the new learning; but it was the Arabs and their colonists who, eastward from Constantinople and Alexandria, the last remaining outposts of Western knowledge, carried on the work of the Greeks, making new discoveries in chemistry and astronomy, in physics and mathematics. Omar Khayyám, best known for his *Rubá'iyát* ('A Book of Verses underneath the Bow, a Jug of Wine, a Loaf of Bread – and Thou ...') made important contributions to algebra.

Knowledge of the Arabic culture filtered back into Europe, largely through Spain, by the hands of the Sephardic Jews, and toward the end of the eleventh century there came a revival in that kind of questioning which leads, eventually, to new scientific advance. Averroes (1126–98), a Spanish Moslem, published a commentary on Aristotle which had considerable influence in, for example, the Universities of Paris (founded *c.* 1170) and Oxford (*c.* 1168). His ideas on religion, though regarded as subversive by the Christian Schoolmen, stimulated a new examination of the relations between religion and philosophy. This led, in turn, to a revival of interest in the nature of the universe itself. Through the Arabic versions of Greek texts, translated into Latin during the twelfth and thirteenth centuries, scholars became familiar with the early philosophers and scientists, and especially with the works of Aristotle. Since Aristotle's teachings, helped by such commentators as Averroes, led to conflicts with the doctrines of the Church, it is not surprising that there ensued long and tortuous debates – for example, over such matters as the moment of time at which the soul enters the human embryo. Thomas Aquinas (c. 1225–74), in his *Summa theologiae* and other works, provided a re-conciliation of Aristotelian philosophy with the Christian teachings and so began the influence of the Schoolmen.

Scholasticism held, in effect, that the mysteries of human existence and of our relationship with God could be per-ceived and examined by means of the concepts of natural truths which Plato and Aristotle explained even if they could not be proved by reason. Human reason could, then, give a *description* of the universe, but only the authority of the Catholic Church could provide the final answer. This kind of rationalism was not in sympathy with experi-ments which would lead to the growth of science, and the Renaissance, which is usually said to have begun around 1450, represents the reaction to this restriction on man's natural inquisitiveness.

Roger Bacon (c. 1214–94), who was one of the first to proclaim the importance of experiment, was among the earliest to revolt against the scholastic restraints on the activity of the human mind. Such other scholars as Duns Scotus (c. 1266–1308) and Nicolas of Cusa (1401–64) continued the opposition to scholasticism, the one arguing in favour of the idea of free-will, the other working in mathematics and physical science and, in effect, preparing the way for Copernicus by perceiving the error of Ptolemy.

The Middle Ages were not wholly lacking in contribu-tions to scientific knowledge. In medicine, for example, some progress was made. Roger Bacon promoted the idea of the sphericity of the earth. Alchemy, by which men hoped to change the baser metals into gold, kept alive, at least, the study of chemistry. But it was not until the Renaissance that the horizons of scholars were lifted to-ward real discovery.

Two factors seem to have stimulated the change. The

capture of Constantinople by the Turks in 1453 led to the migration of scholars westward with new manuscripts. Introduction to these encouraged the search for other collections hidden in monasteries for centuries. Moreover, the world suddenly became a larger place as Columbus discovered the New World (1492), Sebastian Cabot discovered Salvador in 1497, Vasco da Gama found the sea route to India (1497), and Magellan sailed around the world (1519).

The spirit of the times began to change. Science entered a new period of development in which its observations would no longer be limited to mere support of the doctrines of the Church. The revolt against the ecclesiastical tradition, led by such men as Martin Luther (1483–1546) and encouraged, for very different motives, by Henry VIII of England (1491–1547), seems to have influenced those men who, otherwise content with their religious environment, began to question the authority of the ancient Greeks. Traditional theory was set against the facts of their observation, and new explanations began to appear, at times tolerated by the Church and at others regarded as defiance of its authority.

Throughout the whole of Europe this rebirth of curiosity, this spirit of discovery, emerged and set in motion with accumulating force that movement we call the Renaissance. Its most spectacular figure was Leonardo da Vinci (1452–1519), a man who is typical of the new age and whose birth date is taken as its beginning. Since he did not publish, during his lifetime, any of his voluminous 'Notes', some of which remained hidden for centuries after his death, the impact of his great intellect came through his personal contacts and through his art. We can imagine, now that we can study his anatomical drawings, his projects in engineering, architecture, hydraulics, and optics, the kind of discussions that went on in his circles at Florence, Milan, and Rome. When one stands beside the great *naviglio* (canal) connecting Milan with the River

Ticino and hears one's Italian friend say proudly, 'That was planned by Leonardo,' one realizes the tremendous force he must have been at a time when the world was emerging from a long millennium of quiescence or mere talk. Leonardo set the pattern for the 'new learning' and by example, if not by writing, forced men to look themselves for the facts of the world around them.

The revival in habits of observation, begun in astronomy and mechanics, spread rapidly to other fields of science. Andreas Vesalius, by the accurate observation and description of the anatomy of the human body, cut biology loose from the fetters imposed by the authority of Galen. It was another of these remarkable coincidences which mark the history of the development of ideas that his monumental book, with extraordinary illustrations, was published the same year (1543) in which Copernicus's revolutionary book appeared in print. Thus the story of the development of modern biology is traced back into the sixteenth century.

This was followed, as is every 'breakthrough', by a vast amount of work carried on by lesser figures who worked in related fields. It was not until the mid nineteenth century that the first great synthesizing concept of biology was proposed – the cell theory, which made it possible to provide coherence in what had become a confusing, chaotic accumulation of data. This concept, too, had its real beginning in the late seventeenth century with the development of the microscope – the tool with which the biologist extended his range of observation.

William Harvey made the second 'breakthrough' in biology by establishing the possibility of investigating the functioning of organs – even though Harvey believed that his discovery was no more than an affirmation of Aristotle's vitalism. Malpighi, Hales, Ingenhousz, and others continued the thread of this development, although it was the nineteenth century that saw the real advances in physiology.

The age of exploration brought back to systematic biologists vast numbers of species of plants and animals, many of which were being seen and studied for the first time. This incredible diversity of living forms (more than a million species of plants and animals have thus far been identified) gave rise to many questions. The most perplexing, and ultimately the most revolutionary in effect, was the problem of the forces and patterns underlying this bewildering array of life forms.

The second great biological synthesis of the nineteenth century was that of Charles Darwin. It established the fact of biological evolution beyond dispute. The explanation of the mechanism by which this vast process had been brought about was a continuation, in a way, of a thread which can be traced back to Thales (*c.* 624–*c.* 548 B.C.) and succeeding philosophers, although its nineteenth-century development buttressed speculation with observations, facts, and even experiment. The impact of this theory on all facets of intellectual activity is difficult to reconstruct without a detailed account of late-nineteenth-century intellectual history.

The next of the great advances in biology to be dealt with in this volume concerns the solution of an ancient problem, the question of the spontaneous generation of life. Redi, and after him Spallanzani, had apparently settled the question with effective experimental demonstrations, but doubt remained, particularly as to the origin of microscopic life, for experimenters seemed to be able to show the origin of living bacteria from inanimate matter. It was at this point that Pasteur entered the controversy, since the problem needed a definitive solution if Pasteur was to develop his theories about the nature of bacteria and their role in a number of life processes.

One of the fruits of Pasteur's classic researches was the germ theory of disease. Koch, Lister, and a host of others rapidly expanded the development of applied bacteriology and were instrumental in relating specific bacteria to specific diseases and to the occurrence of sepsis in the surgical ward. Pasteur himself, and others, were more concerned with the application of these discoveries to the prevention and treatment of such diseases and established the science of immunology. No one interested in lessening human suffering would question the immense value of these discoveries; yet there was something underlying them which is of transcendent value. As Sarton points out: 'The latest results are like the new fruits of a tree; the fruits serve our immediate practical purpose, but for all that it is the tree that matters. The scientist of philosophic mind is not interested so much in the latest results of science as he is in its eternal tendencies, in the living and exuberant and immortal tree.'

I

THE BEGINNINGS OF THE
SCIENTIFIC APPROACH

WE have indications that the civilization of Greece reached the peak of its intellectual development in the fifth century B.C. We know that, during two thousand years before the Greeks, man was solving the problems of practical life with but few attempts to explain why things happened as they did. The Babylonians and Egyptians left their marks as construction engineers capable of solving formidable problems; they systematized methods of counting and measurement; they observed the rhythms of the sun and planets, and made calendars. The Egyptians made progress in the art of medicine.

The climax of Greek achievement was followed by another era in which the practical man reigned supreme. The Romans – soldiers, administrators, lawyers – whose conquests absorbed the Greeks and the body of Greek knowledge, concerned themselves with the practical affairs of their vast Empire. They, in turn, were conquered; cultural growth throughout Europe as we now know it was suspended. The Arabs and the Jews carried on the Greek scientific tradition while the Christian Church struggled for survival and occupied itself with the rationalization of its philosophy. For a thousand years, science remained dormant among the peoples north of the Mediterranean.

What might have happened if the course of history had been diverted? Let us suppose that the Romans had been more modest in their ambitions and had concentrated on building up their strength to a point where they could resist the encroachments of the barbarians. The Greeks among them, inheritors of the great traditions of Aristotle and Archimedes, would have had more opportunity to impress the Romans with their ideas of the scientific approach. Instead of the word 'How?' more would have been heard of 'Why?' And, as in our modern civilization, in which the 'Why?' of the scientist is constantly stimulated by the results of technological progress, Roman empiricism would have been enriched by scientific questioning. Had the Roman era lasted longer than five or six hundred years, is it not possible that the exploitation of the vast natural resources of their Empire (even a smaller empire, more capable of protection against the invader) would have given some Greek citizen, perhaps a follower of Hero, the opportunity to discover how the power of steam could be employed to move a machine? Might not the astrologers have broken loose from superstition and, with the help of Arabic knowledge of glass, found ways to observe the stars and so arrive at those discoveries which, in fact, had to await the coming of Galileo a thousand years later?

It is, indeed, a great mystery why, under the impact of the constant needs for war material, the Roman economy did not call on its scientists – even its Greek scientists – for greater contributions, as we have done, particularly during the last twenty years. Why, for instance, were the alchemists not induced to extend their experiments; to defer attempts to transform base metals into gold and to find a way of making an iron capable of taking a keener edge – in fact, to make cheaper steel?

Attempts to explain the Romans' failure to make use of the specialists among them must take into account a great array of influences that discouraged inquiry. Perhaps, as in the Middle Ages, too much emphasis was placed on religion. Education was the privilege of the few, and the fundamentals upon which they could have exercised their ingenuity were withheld from *hoi polloi*. Perhaps even among the Greeks themselves this exclusiveness of education took its toll, limiting the development of inquiring minds. Another theory, proposed by Sarton, suggests that the decline of science was the inevitable result of a basic lack of moral character among the Greeks.

Whatever the explanation, the fact remains that the structure of scientific accomplishment built up by the Greeks disappeared. Modern science had to be laboriously rebuilt from its foundations, while men argued, often wastefully, as to the meaning of the words the Greeks had left behind them. A great gap was created in the steady stream of progress.

Are these inquiries into the 'what might have been' justified? How valuable, after all, was the Greek contribution to science? Were the foundations they laid actually as sound as this approach assumes? Is it possible that the modern reader of the classical writings, too much influenced by his inherited fund of knowledge, attributes too high an accomplishment to the Greeks by reading into the writings more than is, in fact, there?

In order to assess the value of the Greek contributions to science, we must recall that the idea of positive activity is implicit in the definition of the term *contribution*. Science does not develop from observation alone; the scientist must pursue an objective, study and select his data, organize it systematically, and attempt a synthesis. Even a wrong hypothesis may be useful to the scientist by leading him into a better method of obtaining his experimental data. There can be a contribution to science, therefore, even if the conclusions are incorrect, provided the scientist or his successor is prepared always to question the results and to proceed from one stage to another towards the truth. By this standard, the Greeks could be described, correctly, as scientists. They made mistakes, but, within their own era, progress can be observed; and, perhaps more significantly, the records of their work provided the impetus to a resumption of scientific work when Europe at last found time not only to study but also to criticize them.

Sarton's great *Introduction to the History of Science*

lists hundreds of Greeks who contributed, in one way or another, to the growth of science. We can cite but a few. A hundred years before Hippocrates the Ionian school of natural philosophy came into being, founded by Thales (c. 640–546 B.C.). Thales had lived in Egypt, and he set up the first system of abstract geometry out of the practice of mathematics and astronomy which he learned there. His was the first attempt to provide a general explanation of the universe. He is said to have predicted the eclipse of the sun that occurred in 585 B.C. One of his pupils, Anaximander (610–c. 545 B.C.), attempted to explain organic evolution and produced a map of the world, perhaps the first Greek to do so.

Farther west, in the Greek colony in Southern Italy, Pythagoras (c. 566–c. 497 B.C.) founded his brotherhood, which developed into a scientific school. The Egyptians had discovered how to lay out a right-angle, a necessary preliminary to building a pyramid, but it was Pythagoras who produced the first deductive proof – the *pons asinorum* of schooldays – that the square on the hypotenuse of a right-angled triangle is equal to the sum of the squares on the other two sides. The Pythagoreans placed such emphasis on the theory of numbers that the school ultimately found itself involved in a world of mystical abstractions. Their influence was felt especially in the period of scholasticism, when their conception of a numbered order in geometry, arithmetic, music, and astronomy caused these four subjects to become the fundamental courses in medieval education. More immediately, their ideas were a powerful influence on Plato; however, before discussing him, we should note a trio of experimenters whose work represents a peak in this first period of Greek science.

Empedocles (c. 493–c. 433 B.C.), a physicist and physician as well as poet and philosopher, recognized four elements (fire, air, water, and earth), over combinations of which two moving forces (love and strife) ruled; but he also developed a theory of the movement of the blood to and from the heart and made the first reference in Greek literature to the use of water-clocks. Democritus (*c.* 470–*c.* 400 B.C.) was renowned for his atomic theory. Hippocrates, the first great medical scientist, has already been mentioned. These men were important influences in medieval studies, and, by the standard we have suggested, they clearly rank as scientists entitled to their position in the great evolution of the species.

With Socrates and Plato came a pause in the rate of development. The former (470–399 B.C.) developed in his philosophical discussions the idea of the inductive method in science. Although, like his pupil Plato (427–347 B.C.), he distrusted experimentation, he taught the virtues of clear definition and reasoned scepticism. Plato, more interested in mathematics and much influenced by Pythagorean ideas, is said to have regarded experiments as offensive to the gods. His theories, especially those recorded in the *Timaeus*, had a tremendous influence on medieval thought and brought him into a later disrepute which sometimes overshadowed his real contributions to mathematics and astronomy. Equally known for his development of the analytical method, in which one assumes the problem solved and then works back through the various presumptions until one reaches a premise, the truth or falsehood of which is known, he showed in effect that analysis as well as synthesis is an important tool of scientific investigation.

Aristotle and Theophrastus, who followed Plato, will also be discussed below in the introductions to their writings.

After these men the centre of interest shifts from Athens to Alexandria. With the collapse of Alexander's empire after his death Ptolemy became the ruler of Egypt and so managed the development of scientific studies that Alexandria became the cultural centre of the Mediterranean world. The physiologist Erasistratus and the anatomist

Hierophilus dissected the human body and made important contributions to their sciences.

During the long period of Roman domination the three most important figures for the history of biology and medicine were Dioscorides, Pliny, and Galen. Dioscorides was a surgeon in Nero's army. His studies and descriptions of plants had a profound influence on the development of botany. Pliny was an industrious and uncritical compiler whose *Natural History*, unscientific and replete with folklore and romantic tales, was a standard work for many centuries. To it can be traced many of the fables and superstitions of the medieval Bestiaries (see p. 61). Galen and his work and influence are discussed in the introduction to the extracts from his writings.

HIPPOCRATES
c. 460–*c.* 375 B.C.

A SCIENTIFIC APPROACH TO THE STUDY AND TREATMENT OF DISEASE IS INTRODUCED

NATURAL philosophy was born of man's search for an explanation of the events that affected his daily life. In the course of time the priests constructed a mythology in which the control over man's destiny was assigned to various gods. In solemn ceremonies the favour of the gods was sought and their anger propitiated.

Before the emergence of the Greek civilization the eastern shores of the Mediterranean were inhabited by a civilized people in close contact with the ancient culture of the Middle East. The invading Greek tribes displaced or merged with the existing people after 1000 B.C. and gradually built up their own distinctive civilization. Although Socrates suffered because it was alleged that he had been disrespectful of the gods the Greeks in general encouraged inquiry and speculation and their philosophers were unwilling to accept supernatural explanations of natural events.

About 600 B.C. a medical school developed on the Island of Cos. Hippocrates was its greatest physician. The Hippocratic school sought a natural explanation for disease. They rejected the priests' interpretation of disease as the consequences of the anger of the gods to be combated with offerings, spells, and incantations. They encouraged the accurate observation of the patient and the recording of the symptoms and signs of his disease and of the response to treatment in the individual case, arguing logically that only by the accumulation of such information would the physician be enabled to evaluate the treatment and to predict the course of the disease in other patients. Epilepsy, perhaps because the convulsions appeared to have no rational cause, was known as the 'sacred disease', but the Hippocratic physicians in a book devoted to the disease, considered it no more divine than any other ... 'men think it divine because they do not understand it'.

The Hippocratic Collection consists of more than a hundred books, the earliest of which were written about 500 B.C. It is disputed which were the work of Hippocrates himself but this is not important, for they are certainly all the work of his School. The writings are among the first to show a scientific approach to disease and to other biological phenomena, for the biological sciences were first studied in relation to medicine. They are pervaded by a spirit of enlightened humanity and they lay down a code of behaviour governing the relations between the physician and his patients which still forms the basis of the ethical ideals of physicians in most countries of the world.

The rediscovery of the Hippocratic writings in the Middle Ages tended at first to discourage original thought and research. The numerous commentaries on the writings treated them as the final authority and devoted volumes to scholastic wrangling in marked contrast to the spirit of the writings themselves. After the Renaissance this spirit reasserted itself and inspired a new generation of physicians, of which Sydenham was the greatest, to observe and record disease in the patient.

The extracts that follow, which are from the translations by W. H. S. Jones and E. T. Withington for the Loeb Classical Library (1923–31), show something of the quality of scientific methods propounded by Hippocrates and will suggest why they retained their power to guide physicians even in the seventeenth century. 'On the Sacred Disease' brings observation and experiment into conflict with superstition and magic. 'On Airs, Waters, and Places' shows how study of the environment is significant to diagnosis. The 'Prognostic' guides the physician into the difficult area of forecasting the course of disease from his interpretation of the symptoms.

———

¶ *On the Sacred Disease*

5. But this disease [epilepsy] is in my opinion no more divine than any other; it has the same nature as other diseases, and the cause that gives rise to individual diseases. It is also curable, no less than other illnesses, unless by long lapse of time it be so ingrained as to be more powerful than the remedies that are applied. Its origin, like that of other diseases, lies in heredity. For if a phlegmatic parent has a phlegmatic child, a bilious parent a bilious child, a consumptive parent a consumptive child, and a splenetic parent a splenetic child, there is nothing to prevent some of the children suffering from this disease when one or the other parent suffered from it; for the seed comes from every part of the body, healthy seed from the healthy parts, diseased seed from the diseased parts. Another strong proof that this disease is no more divine than any other is that it affects the naturally phlegmatic, but does not attack the bilious. Yet, if it were more divine than others, this disease ought to have attacked all equally, without making any difference between bilious and phlegmatic.

21. This disease styled sacred comes from the same causes as others, from the things that come to and go from the body, from cold, sun, and from the changing restlessness of winds. These things are divine. So that there is no need to put the disease in a special class and to consider it more divine than the others; they are all divine and all human. Each has a nature and power of its own; none is hopeless or incapable of treatment. Most are cured by the same things as caused them. One thing is food for one thing, and another for another, though occasionally it does it harm. So the physician must know how, by distinguishing the seasons for individual things, he may assign to one

thing nutriment and growth, and to another diminution and harm. For in this disease as in all others it is necessary, not to increase the illness, but to wear it down by applying to each what is most hostile to it, not that to which it is accustomed. For what is customary gives vigour and increase; what is hostile causes weakness and decay. Whoever knows how to cause in men by regimen moist or dry, hot or cold, he can cure this disease also, if he distinguish the seasons for useful treatment, without having recourse to purifications and magic.

¶ On Airs, Waters, and Places

1. Whoever wishes to pursue properly the science of medicine must proceed thus. First he ought to consider what effects each season of the year can produce; for the seasons are not at all alike, but differ widely both in themselves and at their changes. The next point is the hot winds and the cold, especially those that are universal, but also those that are peculiar to each particular region. He must also consider the properties of the waters; for as these differ in taste and in weight, so the property of each is far different from that of any other. Therefore, on arrival at a town with which he is unfamiliar, a physician should examine its position with respect to the winds and to the risings of the sun. For a northern, a southern, an eastern, and a western aspect has each its own individual property. He must consider with the greatest care both these things and how the natives are off for water, whether they use marshy, soft waters, or such as are hard and come from rocky heights, or brackish and harsh. The soil, too, whether bare and dry or wooded and watered, hollow and hot, or high and cold. The mode of life also of the inhabitants that is pleasing to them, whether they are heavy drinkers, taking lunch, and inactive, or athletic, industrious, eating much, and drinking little.

2. Using this evidence he must examine the several problems that arise. For if a physician know these things

well, by preference all of them, but at any rate most, he will not, on arrival at a town with which he is unfamiliar, be ignorant of the local diseases, or of the nature of those that commonly prevail; so that he will not be at a loss in the treatment of diseases, or make blunders, as is likely to be the case if he have not this knowledge before he consider his several problems. As time and the year passes he will be able to tell what epidemic diseases will attack the city either in summer or in winter, as well as those peculiar to the individual which are likely to occur through change in mode of life. For knowing the changes of the seasons, and the risings and settings of the stars, with the circumstances of each of these phenomena, he will know beforehand the nature of the year that is coming. Through these considerations and by learning the times beforehand, he will have full knowledge of each particular case, will succeed best in securing health, and will achieve the greatest triumphs in the practice of his art. If it be thought that all this belongs to meteorology, he will find out, on second thoughts, that the contribution of astronomy to medicine is not a very small one but a very great one indeed. For with the seasons men's diseases, like their digestive organs, suffer change.

3. I will now set forth clearly how each of the foregoing questions ought to be investigated, and the tests to be applied. A city that lies exposed to the hot winds – these are those between the winter rising of the sun and its winter setting – when subject to these and sheltered from the north winds, the waters here are plentiful and brackish, and must be near the surface, hot in summer, and cold in winter. The heads of the inhabitants are moist and full of phlegm, and their digestive organs are frequently deranged from the phlegm that runs down into them from the head. Most of them have a rather flabby physique, and they are poor eaters and poor drinkers. For men with weak heads will be poor drinkers, as the after-effects are more distressing to them. The endemic diseases are these. In the

first place, the women are unhealthy and subject to excessive fluxes. Then many are barren through disease and not by nature, while abortions are frequent. Children are liable to convulsions and asthma, and to what they think causes the disease of childhood, and to be a sacred disease. Men suffer from dysentery, diarrhoea, ague, chronic fevers in winter, many attacks of eczema, and from hemorrhoids. Cases of pleurisy, pneumonia, ardent fever, and of diseases considered acute rarely occur. These diseases cannot prevail where the bowels are loose. Inflammations of the eyes occur with running, but are not serious; they are of short duration, unless a general epidemic take place after a violent change. When they are more than fifty years old, they are paralysed by catarrhs supervening from the brain, when the sun suddenly strikes their head or they are chilled. These are their endemic diseases, but besides, they are liable to any epidemic disease that prevails through the change of the seasons.

¶ Prognostic

1. I hold that it is an excellent thing for a physician to practise forecasting. For if he discover and declare unaided by the side of his patients the present, the past, and the future, and fill in the gaps in the account given by the sick, he will be the more believed to understand the cases, so that men will confidently entrust themselves to him for treatment. Furthermore, he will carry out the treatment best if he know beforehand from the present symptoms what will take place later. Now to restore every patient to health is impossible. To do so indeed would have been better even than forecasting the future. But as a matter of fact men do die, some owing to the severity of the disease before they summon the physician, others expiring immediately after calling him in – living one day or a little longer – before the physician by his art can combat each disease. It is necessary, therefore, to learn the natures of such diseases, how much they exceed the strength of men's

bodies, and to learn how to forecast them. For in this way you will justly win respect and be an able physician. For the longer time you plan to meet each emergency the greater your power to save those who have a chance of recovery, while you will be blameless if you learn and declare beforehand those who will die and those who will get better.

2. In acute diseases the physician must conduct his inquiries in the following way. First he must examine the face of the patient, and see whether it is like the faces of healthy people, and especially whether it is like its usual self. Such likeness will be the best sign, and the greatest unlikeness will be the most dangerous sign. The latter will be as follows. Nose sharp, eyes hollow, temples sunken, ears cold and contracted with their lobes turned outwards, the skin about the face hard and tense and parched, the colour of the face as a whole being yellow or black. If at the beginning of the disease the face be like this, and if it be not yet possible with the other symptoms to make a complete prognosis, you must go on to inquire whether the patient has been sleepless, whether his bowels have been very loose, and whether he suffers at all from hunger. And if anything of the kind be confessed you must consider the danger to be less. The crisis comes after a day and a night if through these causes the face has such an appearance. But should no such confession be made, and should a recovery not take place within this period, know that it is a sign of death. If the disease be of longer standing than three days when the face has these characteristics, go on to make the same inquiries as I ordered in the previous case, and also examine the other symptoms, both of the body generally and those of the eyes. For if they shun the light, or weep involuntarily, or are distorted, or if one becomes less than the other, if the whites be red or livid or have black veins in them, should rheum appear round the eyeballs, should they be restless or protruding, or very sunken, or if the complexion of the whole face be changed – all

39

these symptoms must be considered bad, in fact fatal. You must also examine the partial appearance of the eyes in sleep. For if a part of the white appear when the lids are closed, should the cause not be diarrhoea or purging, or should the patient not be in the habit of so sleeping, it is an unfavourable, in fact a very deadly symptom. But if, along with one of the other symptoms, eyelid, lip, or nose be bent or livid, you must know that death is close at hand. It is also a deadly sign when the lips are loose, hanging, cold, and very white.

ARISTOTLE

384–322 B.C.

THE HABITS OF A NUMBER OF MARINE ANIMALS ARE DESCRIBED

ARISTOTLE was born at Stagira, a Greek settlement on the frontier of the State of Macedon. His father was physician to Amyntas II, King of Macedon. At seventeen Aristotle was sent to Athens where he became a pupil of Plato, the philosopher and mathematician. Although Aristotle's interests lay in biology rather than mathematics he remained a member of Plato's school until the latter's death in 347 B.C. Aristotle, who may have hoped to succeed his master, did not do so and left Athens. For five years he lived on the coast of Asia Minor near Lesbos with leisure and opportunity for the systematic study of the habits of marine animals. So accurate were many of his observations that little has been added to his descriptions. His account of the breeding of the catfish was regarded as too imaginative until twenty-two centuries later a catfish showing precisely the behaviour described by Aristotle was discovered.

In 342 B.C. Aristotle became tutor to Alexander of Macedon, then a boy of thirteen or fourteen, and remained with him until, nearly seven years later, Alexander succeeded his father Philip on the throne of Macedon. Aristotle certainly aroused the interest of the future Alexander the Great in science, although master and pupil are said not to have been on the best of terms.

Returning to Athens, Aristotle set up his own school, the Lyceum, where he taught until 323, when he thought it wise to leave Athens as in the disturbances which followed the sudden death of Alexander at Babylon the party most opposed to Macedon had gained power. Aristotle died a year later and his pupil Theophrastus succeeded him as head of the Lyceum. Other scholars trained in the Lyceum were later established in Alexander's new city of Alexandria. The great library at Alexandria, one of the wonders of the world, was to provide the link between Greek culture and that of the Arabs.

Aristotle is among the greatest of all biologists. He arranged and classified all existing knowledge and added to it the fruits of his own accurate observation. A profound and original thinker, he speculated on the nature of life and the distinction he made between the vegetable or nutritive, the animal or sensitive, and the human or rational soul constantly recurs in the writings of later centuries. His arrangement of living things to demonstrate their relationships suggests that he was advancing towards a belief in evolution. He was interested in function as well as in the observation of structure, but he was not an experimentalist and his work in what we now call physiology is of less importance than his other studies.

No writer has ever had greater influence. The authority of his works was undisputed and his errors were perpetuated. In his studies of the nature of matter and of the physical world Aristotle did not accept the atomic theory of Democritus but adopted the older concept of the four elements – earth, air, fire, and water – to which he added a fifth, aether, as the component of celestial bodies. His explanation of the universe was treated with the same respect as his more substantial contributions to scientific knowledge and method and retained its influence until the time of Galileo. That his works were abused and that observation of nature and the inductive approach which he taught were so long neglected is the fault of the Schoolmen of the Middle Ages and not of Aristotle.

The most important of the surviving biological works of Aristotle are *On Psyche, Histories About Animals,* and *On the Parts of Animals,* from which the following passages have been selected (from D. W. Thompson's translation, published by the Oxford University Press).

———

In marine creatures, also, one may observe many ingenious devices adapted to the circumstances of their lives. For the accounts commonly given of the so-called fishing-frog are quite true; as are also those given of the torpedo. The fishing-frog has a set of filaments that project in front of its eyes; they are long and thin like hairs, and are round at the tips; they lie on either side, and are used as baits. Accordingly, when the animal stirs up a place full of sand and mud and conceals itself therein, it raises the filaments, and, when the little fish strike against them, it draws them in underneath into its mouth. The torpedo narcotizes the creatures that it wants to catch, overpowering them by the power of shock that is resident in its body, and feeds upon them; it also hides in the sand and mud, and catches all the creatures that swim in its way and come under its narcotizing influence. This phenomenon has been actually observed in operation. The sting-ray also conceals itself, but not exactly in the same way. That the creatures get their living by this means is obvious from the fact that, whereas they are peculiarly inactive, they are often caught with mullets in their interior, the swiftest of fishes. Furthermore, the fishing-frog is unusually thin when he is caught after losing the tips of his filaments, and the torpedo is known to cause a numbness even in human beings. Again, the hake, the ray, the flat-fish, and the angel-fish burrow in the sand, and after concealing themselves angle with the filaments on their mouths, that fishermen call their fishing-rods, and the little creatures on which they feed swim up to the filaments taking them for bits of sea-weed, such as they feed upon.

Wherever an anthias-fish is seen, there will be no dangerous creatures in the vicinity, and sponge-divers will dive in security, and they call these signal-fishes 'holy-fish'.

It is a sort of perpetual coincidence, like the fact that wherever snails are present you may be sure there is neither pig nor partridge in the neighbourhood; for both pig and partridge eat up the snails.

The sea-serpent resembles the conger in colour and shape, but is of lesser bulk and more rapid in its movements. If it be caught and thrown away, it will bore a hole with its snout and burrow rapidly in the sand; its snout, by the way, is sharper than that of ordinary serpents. The so-called sea-scolopendra,* after swallowing the hook, turns itself inside out until it ejects it, and then it again turns itself outside in. The sea-scolopendra, like the land-scolopendra, will come to a savoury bait; the creature does not bite with its teeth, but stings by contact with its entire body, like the so-called sea-nettle. The so-called fox-shark, when it finds it has swallowed the hook, tries to get rid of it as the scolopendra does, but not in the same way; in other words, it runs up the fishing-line, and bites it off short; it is caught in some districts in deep and rapid waters, with night-lines.

The bonitos swarm together when they espy a dangerous creature, and the largest of them swim round it, and if it touches one of the shoal they try to repel it; they have strong teeth. Amongst other large fish, a lamia shark, after falling in amongst a shoal, has been seen to be covered with wounds.

Of river-fish, the male of the sheat-fish is remarkably attentive to the young. The female after parturition goes away; the male stays and keeps on guard where the spawn is most abundant, contenting himself with keeping off all other little fishes that might steal the spawn or fry, and this he does for forty or fifty days, until the young are sufficiently grown to make away from the other fishes for themselves. The fishermen can tell where he is on guard: for, in warding off the little fishes, he makes a rush in the water and gives utterance to a kind of muttering noise. He is so earn-

* It is not clear what animal Aristotle was describing here.

44

est in the performance of his parental duties that the fishermen at times, if the eggs be attached to the roots of water-plants deep in the water, drag them into as shallow a place as possible; the male fish will still keep by the young, and, if it so happen, will be caught by the hook when snapping at the little fish that come by; if, however, he be sensible by experience of the danger of the hook, he will still keep by his charge, and with his extremely strong teeth will bite the hook to pieces.

*

Of molluscs the sepia is the most cunning, and is the only species that employs its dark liquid for the sake of concealment as well as from fear: the octopus and calamary make the discharge solely from fear. These creatures never discharge the pigment in its entirety; and after a discharge the pigment accumulates again. The sepia, as has been said, often uses its colouring pigment for concealment; it shows itself in front of the pigment and then retreats back into it; it also hunts with its long tentacles not only little fishes, but oftentimes even mullets. The octopus is a stupid creature, for it will approach a man's hand if it be lowered in the water; but it is neat and thrifty in its habits: that is, it lays up stores in its nest, and, after eating up all that is eatable, it ejects the shells and sheaths of crabs and shellfish, and the skeletons of little fishes. It seeks its prey by so changing its colour as to render it like the colour of the stones adjacent to it; it does so also when alarmed. By some the sepia is said to perform the same trick; that is, they say it can change its colour so as to make it resemble the colour of its habitat. The only fish that can do this is the angel-fish, that is, it can change its colour like the octopus.

*

The dolphin, the whale, and all the rest of the Cetacea, all, that is to say, that are provided with a blow-hole instead of gills, are viviparous. That is to say, no one of all

45

these fishes is ever seen to be supplied with eggs, but directly with an embryo from whose differentiation comes the fish, just as in the case of mankind and the viviparous quadrupeds.

The dolphin bears one at a time generally, but occasionally two. The whale bears one or at the most two, generally two. The porpoise in this respect resembles the dolphin, and, by the way, it is in form like a little dolphin, and is found in the Euxine; it differs, however, from the dolphin as being less in size and broader in the back; its colour is leaden-black. Many people are of opinion that the porpoise is a variety of the dolphin.

All creatures that have a blow-hole respire and inspire, for they are provided with lungs. The dolphin has been seen asleep with his nose above water, and when asleep he snores.

The dolphin and the porpoise are provided with milk, and suckle their young. They also take their young, when small, inside them. The young of the dolphin grows rapidly, being full-grown at ten years of age. Its period of gestation is ten months. It brings forth its young in summer, and never at any other season (and, singularly enough, under the Dog-star it disappears for about thirty days). Its young accompany it for a considerable period; and, in fact, the creature is remarkable for the strength of its parental affection. It lives for many years; some are known to have lived for more than twenty-five, and some for thirty years; the fact is fishermen nick their tails sometimes and set them adrift again, and by this expedient their ages are ascertained.

The seal is an amphibious animal: that is to say, it cannot take in water, but breathes and sleeps and brings forth on dry land – only close to the shore – as being an animal furnished with feet; it spends, however, the greater part of its time in the sea and derives its food from it, so that it must be classed in the category of marine animals. It is viviparous by immediate conception and brings forth its young alive, and exhibits an after-birth, and all else just like a ewe. It bears one or two at a time, and three at the most. It has two teats, and suckles its young like a quadruped. Like the human species, it brings forth at all seasons of the year, but especially at the time when the earliest kids are forthcoming. It conducts its young ones, when they are about twelve days old, over and over again during the day down to the sea, accustoming them by slow degrees to the water. It slips down steep places instead of walking, from the fact that it cannot steady itself by its feet. It can contract and draw itself in, for it is fleshy and soft and its bones are gristly. Owing to the flabbiness of its body it is difficult to kill a seal by a blow, unless you strike it on the temple. It looks like a cow. The female in regard to its genital organs resembles the female of the ray; in all other respects it resembles the female of the human species.

So much for the phenomena of generation and of parturition in animals that live in water and are viviparous either internally or externally.

THEOPHRASTUS

c. 370–287 B.C.

SOME METHODS OF PLANT PROPAGATION AND GROWTH ARE DESCRIBED

THEOPHRASTUS was born on the Island of Lesbos and may first have met Aristotle there. He subsequently became Aristotle's favourite pupil and successor at the Lyceum. He was a man of wide interests, an industrious compiler, and an accurate observer. Most of Aristotle's writings on botany have not survived, but the work of Theophrastus probably represents his master's opinions for the two men were very closely associated. However, Theophrastus did not accept Aristotle's teleological view that developments are due to the purpose that will in fact be fulfilled by them (as, for example, the assumption that plants and animals exist only for their use to human beings), but seems to have preferred to leave such questions to be decided by the evidence.

Theophrastus wrote on climate, minerals, and geography; but he is best known for his work on plant propagation and seed germination. Theophrastus's work in botany, which established the basic concepts of botanical science, is unusual for the extent of his observations, his interest in scientific agriculture, and, especially, for the data he accumulated on the strange (to the Greeks) new specimens from India. Of these, he collected his information from Alexander and his officers. His descriptions of plants often attain a high level of accuracy, even by modern standards, if it be remembered that he was handicapped by the lack of any standardized terminology. Like all other scientists until the seventeenth century he believed in spontaneous generation. The distinction between the male and female parts of plants has only recently been fully understood.

Theophrastus restored the Hippocratic assumption that the brain was the centre of intelligence. (Aristotle had decreed that the seat of the intelligence was the heart, the brain providing it with a cooling system by secreting phlegm.) His work in arithmetic and geometry, of which he is believed to have written a history, has been lost, but we know that he had no sympathy for the idea that natural phenomena could be expressed in the artificial language of mathematics.

The selection is from the A. Hort translation of *The History of Plants* in the Loeb Classical Library.

———

¶ *Propagation: Germination and Growth*

1. The ways in which trees and plants in general originate are these: spontaneous growth, from seed, from a root, from a piece torn off, from a branch or twig, from the trunk itself; or again from small pieces into which the wood is cut up (for some trees can be produced even in this manner). Of these methods spontaneous growth comes first, one may say, but growth from seed or root would seem most natural; indeed these methods too may be called spontaneous; wherefore they are found even in wild kinds, while the remaining methods depend on human skill or at least on human choice.

However all plants start in one or other of these ways, and most of them in more than one. Thus the olive is grown in all the ways mentioned, except from a twig; for an olive-twig will not grow if it is set in the ground, as a fig or pomegranate will grow from their young shoots. Not but what some say that cases have been known in which, when a stake of olive-wood was planted to support ivy, it actually lived along with it and became a tree; but such an instance is a rare exception, while the other methods of growth are in most cases the natural ones. The fig grows in all the ways mentioned, except from root-stock and cleft wood; apple and pear grow also from branches, but rarely. However, it appears that most, if not practically all, trees may grow from branches, if these are smooth, young, and vigorous. But the other methods, one may say, are more natural, and we must reckon what may occasionally occur as a mere possibility.

In fact there are quite few plants which grow and are brought into being more easily from the upper parts, as the vine is grown from branches; for this, though it cannot be grown from the 'head', yet can be grown from the branch, as can all similar trees and under-shrubs, for instance, as it appears, rue, gilliflower, bergamot-mint, tufted thyme, calamint. So the commonest ways of growth with all plants are from a piece torn off or from seed; for all plants that have seeds grow also from seed. And they say that the bay too grows from a piece torn off, if one takes off the young shoots and plants them; but it is necessary that the piece torn off should have part of the root or stock attached to it. However, the pomegranate and 'spring apple' will grow even without this, and a slip of almond grows if it is planted. The olive grows, one may say, in more ways than any other plant; it grows from a piece of the trunk or of the stock, from the root, from a twig, and from a stake, as has been said. Of other plants the myrtle also can be propagated in several ways; for this too grows from pieces of wood and also from pieces of the stock. It is necessary, however, with this, as with the olive, to cut up the wood into pieces not less than a span long and not to strip off the bark.

Trees then grow and come into being in the above-mentioned ways; for as to methods of grafting and inoculation, these are, as it were, combinations of different kinds of trees; or at all events these are methods of growth of quite different class and must be treated of at a later stage.

2. Of under-shrubs and herbaceous plants the greater

part grow from seed or a root, and some in both ways; some of them also grow from cuttings, as has been said, while roses and lilies grow from pieces of the stems, as also does dog's-tooth grass. Lilies and roses also grow when the whole stem is set. Most peculiar is the method of growth from an exudation; for it appears that the lily grows in this way too, when the exudation that has been produced has dried up. They say the same of alexanders, for this too produces an exudation. There is a certain reed also which grows if one cuts it in lengths from joint to joint, and sets them sideways, burying it in dung and soil. Again they say that plants which have a bulbous root are peculiar in their way of growing from the root.

The capacity for growth being shown in so many ways, most trees, as was said before, originate in several ways; but some come only from seed, as silver-fir, fir, Aleppo pine, and in general all those that bear cones; also the date-palm, except that in Babylon it may be that, as some say, they take cuttings from it. The cypress in most regions grows from seed but in Crete from the trunk also, for instance in the hill country about Tarra; for there grows the cypress which they clip, and when cut it shoots in every possible way, from the part which has been cut, from the ground, from the middle, and from the upper parts; and occasionally, but rarely, it shoots from the roots also.

About the oak accounts differ; some say it only grows from seed, some from the root also, but not vigorously, others again that it grows from the trunk itself, when this is cut. But no trees grow from a piece torn off or from a root except those which make side-growths.

———

GALEN

c. 129–200

THE DISSECTION OF A BARBARY APE PROVIDES THE MATERIAL FOR A DESCRIPTION OF THE MUSCLES OF THE FOREARM

ALTHOUGH Galen is recognized as one of the greatest scientific minds of his period, and indeed of antiquity, it is well to bear in mind his limitations as well as his accomplishments; for his later influence on the medieval mind had often more to do with his dogmatism than with his discoveries.

Galen was born in Asia Minor but practised medicine in Rome until his death around A.D. 200. As he was physician to the greatest of the Roman Emperors, Marcus Aurelius, it is probable that he was under the influence of Stoics, whose philosophy reached the climax of its influence at this time. If so, this would account not only for his scientific interests – which Stoicism encouraged – but also for his teleological approach – that is, his fundamental assumption that the body was designed to fulfill the purposes of divine law. He did not become a Christian but he believed in one God and insisted that every organ was created in the most perfect possible form for the functions assigned to it by God. He also referred favourably to Christianity. His acceptance of a monotheistic religion accounts for the extraordinary veneration in which his writings were held until the Renaissance. He was indeed regarded as infallible. This was the more unfortunate because he had never dissected the human body, and his accounts of human anatomy were based on his findings in the Barbary ape.

For Galen, the blood was formed in the liver and ebbed and flowed rather than circulated through the body.

Mixed, in the heart, with 'vital spirits', the blood flowed into the brain, where it was converted into 'animal spirits' in a form capable of transmission through the nerves to stimulate the functions of the body. The general movement of the blood was from the veins into the arteries, a reversal of the actual system. So influential was Galen's teaching on this subject that it is said that medieval dissectors believed that the actual flows they observed were an effect on the body of the dissection itself. What they saw was abnormal; Galen's theory was the true one!

These negative aspects of Galen's work are emphasized for the reason already given: that his teaching had more importance than the body of the experimental data he recorded. But he left a great mass of material that was valuable in all aspects of anatomy, physiology, and pathology. He brought together the existing Greek medical and anatomical knowledge and contributed further by his own experimentation and observation – adding to knowledge of the functions of the kidneys, the spinal cord, and the brain.

The present selection is a good sample of his style of exposition, which, even in translation, is clear and precise. This translation of 'On the Muscles Moving the Forearm' was done by O. Temkon and W. L. Strauss, Jr, and published in the *Bulletin of the History of Medicine* in 1946.

———

You will not be able to observe accurately the movements of the forearm towards the upper arm, in flexion or in extension, before you lay the whole upper arm bare of all the surrounding muscles. So let us do it, keeping in mind that we said that the muscle lying upon the radius reaches up to the humerus and that the muscle underneath this one, viz. the muscle that inserts into the metacarpus before the index and middle finger, also reaches up to the humerus a little distance away. As I said, it is better to preserve the heads of these muscles, or at least that of the one lying upon the radius. For it will only become clearly visible to you when you have laid bare the foremost muscle of the upper arm. You will expose this muscle by paying attention to the following two marks: the vein that runs along the whole upper arm and is called the 'shoulder' vein, and the muscle that occupies the upper part of the shoulder – perhaps it would be better to say that 'forms' the upper part of the shoulder, since it is the only muscle that lies upon this part. You should make the incision along the vein downwards and, of course, after having taken away the entire skin of this region, as well as all the membranes around the muscles. The incision in the upper part of the shoulder should be made by paying attention to the likeness and unlikeness of the fibres, whereby you will perceive that the whole circumference of the muscle reaches up to one apex and, like a triangle, is inserted into the upper arm. This muscle belongs to the shoulder joint, and it alone among the muscles moving the shoulder joint has now to be removed, in order that the double head of the foremost muscle of the upper arm become visible. . . .

The foremost muscle of the upper arm which, even before dissection, is clearly visible along the shoulder vein in all people, particularly in athletes, has two heads, one of which is attached to the rim of the neck of the scapula, the other to the apophysis which some people call ancyroeides [i.e. similar to an anchor], others coracoeides [i.e. similar to a raven's beak]. The ligament of each head is rather strong and not quite round. Now you should follow these heads as they extend downwards along the upper arm. For at the point where they unite, they produce this muscle which, however, is no longer lifted nor distant from the bones like its heads, but is forthwith grown to the bone of the upper arm, together with the other smaller muscle which lies underneath, and on top of which it rides as far as the elbow joint. Here it forms its aponeurosis and brings forth a strong tendon by means of which it grows to the radius. Moreover, it takes a share in the membranous ligament around the joint, by means of which it also flexes the joint, bending it slightly to the inner side.

If this muscle is taken away, you will find another one lying underneath. This muscle too clings to the upper arm from two fleshy origins, one in the back of the upper arm, the other one more in the front. The posterior head, however, reaches much higher. You will see that these heads also unite and form a muscle which becomes tendinous and, with the tendon produced, attaches to the ulnar bone, flexing the joint and bending it slightly outwards. But when both muscles function exactly, the flexion of the joint is not inclined to either side. Thus there are two anterior muscles which, as has been said, flex the elbow joint, while three others, grown to one another, extend this articulation. They should also be prepared as follows.

First one has to dissect the muscle which lies in the inner parts of the upper arm below the skin. It has its head near the limit of the posterior muscle of the arm-pit (whose nature will be discussed in the anatomy of the muscles moving the shoulder joint). Its end reaches the elbow joint near the inner condyle of the upper arm and is membranous and thin. After this muscle has been removed, study two origins of the muscles which extend the whole forearm. One of their origins grows out from the inside of the shoulder blade, not from the whole but from approximately half of its upper part. The other one grows out from the posterior part of the upper arm below its head. Advancing, these origins grow together at the upper arm and in their further advance they become attached to the bend of the ulna by means of a broad tendon. If you follow the fibres from above in a longitudinal direction, this tendon will appear double to you, taking its external part from the first muscle mentioned before, and the internal part from the second. If you separate them from each other and endeavour to pull each part of the muscle, you will see that each of them extends the whole forearm, but that there is a difference regarding lateral inclination. For the first of the muscles mentioned effects an oblique inclination outwards, the second inwards. Beneath this one there is another muscle which surrounds the bone of the upper arm. It is united with the second muscle and believed to be part of it by the anatomists. Thus it is if one considers this whole muscle as a double muscle. Nevertheless, it is possible to separate them from each other along the length of the fibres. And if you do this, you will find that this muscle remains entirely fleshy and grows into the posterior part of the elbow. If this muscle is pulled, sometimes a straight and direct tension around the elbow joint seemed to me to take place, sometimes it seemed to incline a little inwards.

II

THE DARK AGES

FOR almost a thousand years after the death of Galen there was no advance in the biological sciences. As Charles Singer has said, 'Nothing was added to Galen except misunderstanding.' Even the works of Galen himself and of the authors of the Alexandrian school show a decline from the standards of Hippocrates and Aristotle. This degeneration cannot therefore be attributed to the influence of the Christian Church or to any other single factor; rather was it the result of that complex of factors, social, political, and religious, which determined the intellectual climate of the age.

During the Dark Ages the lamp of learning was kept alight by the Christian monks and by the philosophers and scientists of the Arab world. The monks transcribed and commented on such of the works of the Graeco-Roman period as came into their hands. Copies of copies became increasingly corrupt and little attempt was made to check the recorded facts by experiment or observation.

Greek science passed to the Arab world largely through the foundation of the Greek city of Alexandria. Greek texts were translated into Arabic. Commentaries on these texts were produced and later original observations, many of great importance, were added. The most lasting contributions of the Arabs were to chemistry and pharmacology. Although much of the work was undertaken in the vain search for the elixir of life or the philosopher's stone the many solid facts accumulated are among the foundations of modern chemistry. The greatest of the chemists was Jebir ibn Hayzan, commonly known as Geber, who flourished about 775.

At its widest extent the Moslem empire included all the

countries of the Middle East and North Africa as well as Spain and Portugal. Not all of the great men of this empire were of Arab nationality and not all were of the Islamic faith. The most notable of the physicians, Rhazes (865–925) and Avicenna (980–1037), were both born in Persia. Both compiled encyclopedias of medicine, and the *Liber continens* of Rhazes and the *Canon* of Avicenna, containing much careful clinical observation, had a wide circulation in Europe in Latin translation. Rhazes was known as the Arabic Hippocrates.

The Dark Ages then were not wholly dark. No doubt many of the manuscripts of this period before the invention of printing have perished, and our knowledge of its achievements is limited. Technological advances were made and empirical knowledge was accumulated. Increasing travel, particularly by pilgrims and crusaders, brought Europe into closer and beneficial contact with the Arab world. The extract given below shows the sterility of the monastic approach to science and in this respect is a characteristic work of the period. It cannot however be taken as representative of an entire millennium. To give a fair picture many extracts from monastic and Arab writers would be needed. These would however only emphasize the truth of the statement that during this period there was no significant advance in the biological sciences.

THE BOOK OF BEASTS

TWELFTH-CENTURY LATIN BESTIARY

SOME FABULOUS ANIMALS ARE DESCRIBED ALONG WITH SOME FACTS AND MISCONCEPTIONS ABOUT REAL ANIMALS

SCIENCE depends on observation as well as experiment, and the progress of science depends heavily on the proper recording of observational data. The Greeks and the Romans were fond of compiling encyclopedias of existing knowledge. In some fields, such as anatomy or astronomy, it was reasonably easy for the facts, as reported in such works, to be verified by personal observation of the reader; but where the compilation included travellers' tales of things seen in far countries, doubt could not be eliminated. In this way, legends become established as realities, to survive generally for many centuries until other explorers brought back new and sometimes equally fantastic tales.

This was specially true of zoology. Pliny the Elder indiscriminately accepted the fabulous along with the real, and his descriptions of the characteristics of animals provided material for the medieval compilers. Towards the end of the second century, the scholars of Alexandria accepted these and other descriptions and, combining them with Christian teachings, produced a series of allegorical tales (the *Physiologos*) which became as popular as science-fiction is today and was translated from the Greek into many languages.

The selection included below is enough to indicate the attractions of the theme for the artists of the early Christian period, some of whose interpretations remain in use today in the form of heraldic devices. The unicorn and the griffin are as much a part of modern life as they were in the Middle Ages. A hypocrite still sheds 'crocodile tears'. We may laugh at the crudities of the bestiaries, but we must be careful not to overlook the fact that they contain much that was scientific. Unverified report and theological analogy were combined with the data of active observation. Perhaps the scientific aspects would have survived with more effect if the unknown had not overstimulated the artists' imaginations.

It has been suggested by H. T. Pledge (*Science Since 1500*) that the first difficulty in connexion with zoological studies was that of preserving specimens (other than the skin). The corrective to the bestiaries came when increasing wealth and expanded travel permitted the collection of live specimens and the establishment of zoological gardens, so that personal observation could finally winnow fact from fiction about the giraffe or the elephant.

The following extracts are taken from T. H. White's translation of *The Book of Beasts* published by Jonathan Cape, 1954.

======

TIGRIS THE TIGER gets his name from his speedy pace; for the Persians, Greeks, and Medes used to call an arrow 'tygris'.

The beast can be distinguished by his manifold specklings, by his courage, and by his wonderful velocity. And from him the River Tigris is named, because it is the most rapid of all rivers.

Hyrcania is his principal home.

Now the Tigress, when she finds the empty lair of one of her cubs that has been stolen, instantly presses along the tracks of the thief. But this person who has stolen the cub, seeing that even though carried by a swiftly galloping horse he is on the point of being destroyed by the speed of the tigress, and seeing that no safety can be expected from flight, cunningly invents the following ruse. When he perceives that the mother is close, he throws down a glass ball, and she, taken in by her own reflection, assumes that the image of herself in the glass is her little one. She pulls up, hoping to collect the infant. But after she has been delayed by the hollow mockery, she again throws herself with all her might into the pursuit of the horseman, and, goaded by rage, quickly threatens to catch up with the fugitive. Again he delays the pursuer by throwing down a second ball, nor does the memory of his former trick prevent the mother's tender care. She curls herself round the vain reflection and lies down as if to suckle the cub. And so, deceived by the zeal of her own dutifulness, she loses both her revenge and her baby.

A STAG is called 'Cervus' from its habit of snuffing up the Cerastes – which are horned snakes – or else from being 'horn-bearing', for horns are called 'cerata' in Greek.

These creatures are enemies to serpents. When they feel themselves to be weighed down by illness, they suck snakes from their holes with a snort of the nostrils and, the danger of their venom having been survived, the stags are restored to health by a meal of them.

The plant called Dittany offers them the same sort of medical food, for, when they have fed on it, they can shake off any arrows which they may have received.

Stags listen admiringly to the music of rustic pipes. With their ears pricked, they hear acutely; with the ears lowered, not at all.

Also these animals have the following peculiarity: that when they change their feeding grounds for love of a foreign pasture, and browse along on the way there, if by any chance they have to cross huge rivers or seas, each rests his head on the haunches of the one in front, and, since the one behind does the same thing for him in turn, they suffer no trouble from the weight. And, when they have mounted their heads upon those parts, they hurry across with the greatest possible speed for fear of getting befouled.

Stags have another feature too, for, after a dinner of snake, they shed their coats and all their old age with them.

This is called a COCODRYLLUS from its crocus or saffron colour. It breeds in the River Nile: an animal with four feet, amphibious, generally about thirty feet long, armed with horrible teeth and claws. So great is the hardness of its skin that no blow can hurt a crocodile, not even if hefty stones are bounced on its back. It lies in the water by night, on land by day.

It incubates its eggs in the earth. The male and female take turns. Certain fishes which have a saw-like dorsal fin destroy it, ripping up the tender parts of its belly. More-over, alone among animals, it moves its upper jaw, keeping the lower one quite motionless. Its dung provides an oint-ment with which old and wrinkled whores anoint their figures and are made beautiful, until the flowing sweat of their efforts washes it away.

Hypocritical, dissolute, and avaricious people have the same nature as this brute – also any people who are puffed up with the vice of pride, dirtied with the corruption of luxury, or haunted with the disease of avarice – even if they do make a show of falling in with the justifications of the Law, pretending in the sight of men to be upright and indeed very saintly.

Crocodiles lie by night in the water, by day on land, be-cause hypocrites, however luxuriously they live by night, delight to be said to live holily and justly by day. Con-scious of their wickedness in doing so, they beat their breasts: yes, but with use, habit always brings to light the things which they have done.

The monster moves his upper jaws because these people hold up the higher examples of the Fathers and an abundance of precepts in speech to others, while they show in their lower selves all too little of what they say.

An ointment is made of its evil dung because bad people

are often admired and praised by the inexperienced for the evil they have done, and extolled by the plaudits of this world, as if beautified by an ointment. But when the Judgement, sweated out by the evils perpetrated, moves its anger to the striking, then all that elegance of flattery vanishes like a smoke.

This is called a GRIFFIN* because it is a winged quadruped. This kind of wild animal is born in Hyperborean parts, or in mountains. All its bodily members are like a lion's but its wings and mask are like an eagle's.

It is vehemently hostile to horses. But it will also tear to pieces any human beings which it happens to come across.

A beast gets born in India called the LEUCROTA, and it exceeds in velocity all the wild animals there are. It has the size of a donkey, the haunches of a stag, the breast and shins of a lion, the head of a horse, a cloven hoof, and a mouth opening as far as its ears. Instead of teeth, there is one continuous bone: but this is only as to shape, for in voice it comes near to the sounds of people talking.

————

* [See Plate 2.]

III

THE ORIGIN OF LIFE

DURING the past twenty-five centuries scientists have attempted to solve many of the riddles of life. The routine of observation, hypothesis, experiment, analysis, and synthesis, when it has not provided a solution, has often at least led to discoveries which reassure the scientist that he is working along the right lines. He is able to plan further experiments to check his findings and to correct previous errors of observation. He is well aware that his solutions are never conclusive and that at any time new advances, often in a field of science remote from his own, may compel him to untie his neat package of solutions and start his work again. But at least he knows where to start. Other problems remain tantalizingly unsolved and the accumulated observations from years of research merely increase the number of unanswered questions.

*

Perhaps the most challenging question of all is: 'How did life begin?' The science of geology, by the examination of rocks and the fossils found in them, now indicates that, although the earth is between three and five thousand million years old, life itself has existed for less than one thousand million. But if, for two or four thousand million years, the state of the earth was such that life could not exist on it, by what means did life appear when, at last, conditions became favourable? How, indeed, did life *begin*? The readings which follow describe some of the discoveries which have upset ancient ideas and set us on the road toward the final answer.

The first task of the biologists, after Galileo and others presented them with a practical microscope, was to show the error of the first answer given to this question. Because live animals had frequently been discovered in decaying timber, in rotting vegetation and dung, in mud, and even in the dew, the idea developed that under the influence of heat, water, air, and putrefaction, life was generated spontaneously. Much of this belief was crystallized by Aristotle in his *Historia animalium*, in which he gathered much so-called first-hand observation in apparent support of it. Like so many of Aristotle's ideas, this one dominated the thinking of Western man for more than 2,000 years. As we have already seen, to doubt the Aristotelian doctrine was to defy the evidence of the senses and the processes of reason and, what was much worse, to challenge the constituted religious authorities of the time.

In his *Georgics*, Virgil (70–19 B.C.) gives a graphic account of the generation of living bees from the carcass of a dead calf. And, as late as the sixteenth century, Van Helmont provided a recipe for producing mice from rags and wheat grains. Even Harvey and Newton found it possible to accept some features of spontaneous generation. The work of Pasteur and Tyndall in the nineteenth century apparently settled two hundred years of controversy on the subject, but even to the present day the erroneous belief persists among laymen that some smaller living things are spontaneously generated.

The first attempt to examine the question in a modern manner was made late in the seventeenth century by Francesco Redi. Redi was pre-eminently an experimenter who showed an intuitive grasp of the significance of the scientific method. The selection from his writings reflects an amazingly modern way of putting questions to nature and of eliciting answers. Redi was perceptive enough to limit both his experiments and the conclusions he drew from them. He thought he had proved that the maggots found in decaying meat did not originate spontaneously but developed from eggs deposited in the meat by flies. He also showed that the maggots ultimately developed into flies – flies of the same type that had originally laid eggs in the meat. Redi erected no broad theories on the origin of living things, although his experiments unquestionably were responsible for overthrowing the notion of the spontaneous generation of the larger forms of life. Yet his acuteness in this direction did not prevent him from concluding that the worm-like larvae found in plant galls arose spontaneously in the gall – a view that was corrected by Vallisnieri (1661–1730), a favourite pupil of Redi. Vallisnieri and others finally established that all the large forms of life originated from other living things by some reproductive process.

The development and use of microscopes by Leeuwenhoek reopened the question of spontaneous generation, for it revealed the existence of a world of microscopic life. It was inevitable that the question be asked again – where do the myriad microscopic plants and animals come from? And just as inevitably the answer seemed to be that they arose spontaneously from the water or other substances in which they were found. Early in the eighteenth century Joblot performed experiments on heated infusions to see whether they could produce microscopic life. He concluded that the teeming animalcules he found entered the infusion from the air and reproduced more animalcules like themselves.

Despite this experimental demonstration that microbes originated from pre-existing life just as do the larger plants and animals, the idea of spontaneous generation of microscopic plants and animals persisted and even flourished. It was particularly supported by the experiments of Needham (1713–81) and Buffon (1707–88) among others. It was these experiments that stimulated the efforts of Spallanzani, who repeated many of Needham's experiments and showed that heating an infusion effectively prevents the appearance of microscopic life.

Spallanzani's experiments were brilliantly conceived

and performed and should have dispelled the notion of spontaneous generation. The doctrine persisted, however, for almost another century, and scores of investigators applied themselves to the question, often with techniques which were primitive against the standard set by Spallanzani. By the middle of the nineteenth century, the question had aroused such keen interest that some new experimental refutation or confirmation was imperative. Pasteur, in a series of researches remarkable for their clarity, simplicity, and experimental skill, finally refuted the theory of spontaneous generation of microorganisms, and found that living things can arise only from other living things by a process of reproduction. Pasteur's work had the greatest influence in establishing the germ theory of disease.

Although the theory of spontaneous generation had been disposed of, the answer to the question 'How did life begin?' remained elusive. The study of certain viruses has revealed the existence of large molecules showing some of the attributes of living matter.

FRANCESCO REDI

1626–97

THE DEVELOPMENT OF MAGGOTS IS SHOWN BY EXPERIMENT TO RESULT FROM THE EGGS OF FLIES

DISTINGUISHED scholar, philologist, physician, and poet, but pre-eminently a naturalist of wide interests, Redi is best remembered today for his experimental investigation of the concept of spontaneous generation. He was a physician to the Dukes of Tuscany, but his main interest was in investigation, and his *Esperienze intorno alla generazione degli insetti* is the record of an experimental examination of a biological problem which reaches almost to modern standards.

Redi attempted no universal explanation. He tried to demonstrate the simple hypothesis that maggots found in decaying flesh were not the product of the putrefaction of the flesh but were produced by natural means by living animals (flies) which laid their eggs in the meat. His conclusion was: 'Thus the flesh of dead animals cannot engender worms unless the eggs of the living be deposited therein.' Redi fully recognized the limits of his experiments but they soon became accepted as proof that, for large animals at least, 'if living causes be excluded, no living things arise'.

Redi was evidently not a wholehearted opponent of the idea of spontaneous generation, for he used it to explain the origin of insect larvae found in many plant galls. Some galls have an obvious opening by which the egg of the insect could be deposited within the plant tissues before the gall developed. Many galls do not reveal this point of entrance and it was these which puzzled Redi. It remained for one of Redi's students, Vallisnieri (1661–1730), utilizing the techniques of his teacher, to explain the natural origin of these insect larvae and thus demonstrate the wider application of Redi's statement.

Redi's method of investigation was an early form of 'control experiment' now almost standard practice in biological experimentation. The technique takes account of the number of variables in a problem and examines the results of testing one variable while keeping the others unchanged. A 'control' case is established as a standard of comparison so that the investigator can ensure that only the variable being tested affects the results. The number of controls used will depend on the number of possible conditions to be accounted for. If, for example, two rats are kept under identical conditions except that one (the control) is fed normal food and the other a vitamin-reinforced diet, the effects of the diet can be observed and precise conclusion reached without fear of intrusion of unknown factors. Redi's sealed and open flasks, described in the following selection, were an insurance that his experiment with the closed flask was not affected by some internal condition which would have brought about a similar result in an open flask at that particular time.

Redi's application of the method of 'control experiment' was not to be generally adopted in the biological sciences for two hundred years, but his general influence on contemporary science is shown by the fact that his *Esperienze*, first published in 1668, went through five editions before 1688. Nine men, of whom he was one, formed the Accademia del Cimento in 1657, actually providing a model for the Royal Society of London and similar groups of scientifically-minded men. The Accademia went out of existence before Redi published his work, but the channels of communication had been well enough established for Redi's reports to become rapidly available in London, Paris, and Amsterdam.

The following selection is taken from the M. A. B.

Bigelow translation of *Esperienze*, entitled *Experiments on the Generation of Insects* by Francesco Redi (Open Court, 1909).

———

Although content to be corrected by any one wiser than myself, if I should make erroneous statements, I shall express my belief that the Earth, after having brought forth the first plants and animals at the beginning by order of the Supreme and Omnipotent Creator, has never since produced any kinds of plants or animals, either perfect or imperfect, and everything which we know in past or present times that she has produced, came solely from the true seeds of the plants and animals themselves, which thus, through means of their own, preserve their species. And, although it be a matter of daily observation that infinite numbers of worms are produced in dead bodies and decayed plants, I feel, I say, inclined to believe that these worms are all generated by insemination and that the putrefied matter in which they are found has no other office than that of serving as a place, or suitable nest where animals deposit their eggs at the breeding season, and in which they also find nourishment; otherwise, I assert that nothing is ever generated therein. And, in order, Signor Carlo, to demonstrate to you the truth of what I say, I will describe to you some of those insects which, being most common, are best known to us.

It being thus, as I have said, the dictum of ancients and moderns, and the popular belief, that the putrescence of a dead body, or the filth of any sort of decayed matter engenders worms; and being desirous of tracing the truth in the case, I made the following experiment:

At the beginning of June I ordered to be killed three snakes, the kind called Eels of Aesculapius. As soon as they were dead, I placed them in an open box to decay. Not long afterwards I saw that they were covered with worms of a conical shape and apparently without legs. These worms were intent on devouring the meat, increasing meanwhile in size, and from day to day I observed that they likewise increased in number; but, although of the same shape, they differed in size, having been born on different days. But all, little and big, after having consumed the meat, leaving only the bones intact, escaped from a small aperture in the closed box, and I was unable to discover their hiding place. Being curious, therefore, to know their fate, I again prepared three of the same snakes, which in three days were covered with small worms. These increased daily in number and size remaining alike in form, though not in colour. Of these, the largest were white outside, and the smallest ones, pink. When the meat was all consumed, the worms eagerly sought an exit, but I had closed every aperture. On the nineteenth day of the same month some of the worms ceased all movements, as if they were asleep, and appeared to shrink and gradually assume a shape like an egg. On the twentieth day all the worms had assumed the egg shape, and had taken on a golden white colour, turning to red, which in some darkened, becoming almost black. At this point the red, as well as the black ones, changed from soft to hard, resembling somewhat those chrysalides formed by caterpillars, silkworms, and similar insects. My curiosity being thus aroused, I noticed that there was some difference in shape between the red and the black eggs (pupae), though it was clear that all were formed alike of many rings joined together; nevertheless, these rings were more sharply outlined, and more apparent in the black than in the red, which last were almost smooth and without a slight depression at one end, like that in a lemon picked from its stalk, which further distinguished the black egg-like balls. I placed these balls separately in glass vessels, well covered with paper, and at the end of eight days, every shell of the red balls was broken, and from each came forth a fly of grey colour, torpid and dull, misshapen as if half finished, with closed wings; but after a few minutes they commenced to unfold and to expand in exact proportion to the tiny body, which also in the meantime had acquired symmetry in all its parts. Then the whole creature, as if made anew, having lost its grey colour, took on a most brilliant and vivid green; and the whole body had expanded and grown so that it seemed incredible that it could ever have been contained in the small shell. Though the red eggs (pupae) brought forth green flies at the end of eight days, the black ones laboured fourteen days to produce certain large black flies striped with white, having a hairy abdomen, of the kind that we see daily buzzing about the butchers' stalls.

Having considered these things, I began to believe that all worms found in meat were derived directly from the droppings of flies, and not from the putrefaction of the meat, and I was still more confirmed in this belief by having observed that, before the meat grew wormy, flies had hovered over it, of the same kind as those that later bred in it. Belief would be vain without the confirmation of experiment, hence in the middle of July, I put a snake, some fish, some eels of the Arno, and a slice of milk-fed veal in four large, wide-mouthed flasks; having well closed and sealed them, I then filled the same number of flasks in the same way, only leaving these open. It was not long before the meat and the fish, in these second vessels, became wormy and flies were seen entering and leaving at will; but in the closed flasks I did not see a worm, though many days had passed since the dead flesh had been put in them. Outside on the paper cover there was now and then a deposit, or a maggot that eagerly sought some crevice by which to enter and obtain nourishment. Meanwhile the different things placed in the flasks had become putrid and stinking.

Not content with these experiments, I tried many others at different seasons, using different vessels. In order to leave nothing undone, I even had pieces of meat put under ground, but though remaining buried for weeks, they never bred worms, as was always the case when flies had been allowed to light on the meat. One day a large number of worms, which had bred in some buffalo-meat, were killed by my order; having placed part in a closed dish, and part in an open one, nothing appeared in the first dish, but in the second worms had hatched, which changing as usual into egg-shaped balls (pupae), finally became flies of the common kind. In the same experiment tried with dead flies, I never saw anything breed in the closed vessel.

Hence I might conjecture that Father Kircher, though a man worthy of esteem, was led into erroneous statements in the twelfth book of *The Subterranean World*, where he describes the experiment of breeding flies in the dead bodies of the same. 'The dead flies', says the good man, 'should be besprinkled and soaked with honey-water, and then placed on a copper-plate exposed to the tepid heat of ashes; afterwards very minute worms, only visible through the microscope, will appear, which little by little grow wings on the back and assume the shape of very small flies, that slowly attain perfect size.' I believe, however, that the aforesaid honey-water only serves to attract the living flies to breed in the corpses of their comrades and to drop their eggs therein. . . .

Leaving this long digression and returning to my argument, it is necessary to tell you that although I thought I had proved that the flesh of dead animals could not engender worms unless the semina of live ones were deposited therein, still, to remove all doubt, as the trial had been made with closed vessels into which the air could not penetrate or circulate, I wished to attempt a new experiment by putting meat and fish in a large vase closed only with a fine Naples veil, that allowed the air to enter. For further protection against flies, I placed the vessel in a frame covered with the same net. I never saw any worms in the meat, though many were to be seen moving about on the net-covered frame. These, attracted by the odour of the meat, succeeded at last in penetrating the fine meshes and would have entered the vase had I not speedily removed them. It was interesting, in the meanwhile, to notice the number of flies buzzing about which, every now and then, would light on the outside net and deposit worms there. I noted that some left six or seven at a time there and others dropped them in the air before reaching the net. Perhaps these were of the same breed mentioned by Scaliger, in whose hand, by a lucky accident, a large fly deposited some small worms, whence he drew the conclusion that all flies bring forth live worms directly and not eggs. But what I have already said on the subject proves how much this learned man was in error. It is true that some kinds of flies bring forth live worms and some others eggs, as I have proved by experiment.

ANTONY VAN LEEUWENHOEK

1632–1723

BACTERIA AND PROTOZOA ARE SEEN AND
ACCURATELY DESCRIBED FOR THE FIRST TIME

VAN LEEUWENHOEK was a gifted amateur, enjoying a
modest income and the leisure to indulge his curiosity.
Such men, amongst whom are reckoned Boyle and Darwin,
have in the past contributed greatly to the advance of
science. By increasing specialization and the need for the
elaborate facilities of a modern laboratory and a long
formal training they have now been virtually excluded
from the pursuit of discovery in most branches of
science.

Born in Delft ten years before the death of Galileo into
a period which saw the foundation of many of the great
scientific societies, Leeuwenhoek was the son of a basket-
worker and received only an elementary education. He
was apprenticed to a shopkeeper in Amsterdam but soon
returned to Delft, where he opened a shop of his own and
held municipal office as Chamberlain to the Sheriffs and
wine-gauger. He remained modest and unworldly.

His hobby, which he pursued with passionate devotion,
was the magnifying glass. The compound microscope had
been developed but remained unsatisfactory until the
discovery of the achromatic lens in the nineteenth century.
Leeuwenhoek concentrated on the improvement of the
single-lens or simple microscope which was easier to make
but difficult to use as the area in focus becomes very small
as the magnification is increased. He made more than 400
lenses, some of them magnifying up to 270 times.

Having produced his lenses, Leeuwenhoek went on to
observe a wide range of materials. Although untrained in
science he was a most careful observer, and left a record

of his observations in a series of hundreds of letters written in his native Dutch, for he knew no other language, and sent to the secretary of the Royal Society of England, who published them in Latin and English translations.

A whole world of microscopic life was first seen and reported by Leeuwenhoek – protozoa, bacteria, and countless other small animals and plants. The descriptions were so accurate that it is possible for the reader today to identify the objects described. Some were represented by drawings which are even more strikingly accurate. Leeuwenhoek observed circulation in both eels and fish; he saw the blood cells and confirmed Malpighi's discovery of the capillaries, thus completing the theory of circulation as developed by Harvey (1578–1657) some fifty-five years before. He recognized that the aphid could be developed by parthenogenesis – that is without the intervention of the male; he made particularly accurate observations on the development of the ant and on the spinning and poison apparatus of spiders. Not least of his accomplishments was to take unusually accurate micrometric measurements.

Leeuwenhoek gave some of his microscopes away but never sold one and kept the best for himself. He did not even permit anyone to look through his best microscopes. On his death many of his microscopes were bequeathed to the Royal Society, but most of these have disappeared. The letters used in these readings are his most famous ones and record his discovery of protozoa and of bacteria.

The life of Leeuwenhoek illustrates the thesis, recently presented to the American Chemical Society by Dr W. S. Knoll, that 'very great discoveries ... are still so close to the surface that they can be unearthed with little expense by nonconformists with an inquisitive mind, with knowledge, the urge to create, and who are prepared to accept sacrifice as a way of life.' (*Nature*, London, Vol. 181, p. 160).

The selection that follows has been taken from *Antony*

van Leeuwenhoek and his 'Little Animals' (1932) by C. Dobell, who translated the letters from the original Dutch.

———

¶ *First Observation of Rain-water*

In the year 1675, about half-way through September (being busy with studying air, when I had much compressed it by means of water), I discovered living creatures in rain, which had stood but a few days in a new tub that was painted blue within. This observation provoked me to investigate this water more narrowly; and especially because these little animals were, to my eye, more than 10,000 times smaller than the animalcule which Swammerdam has portrayed, and called by the name of water-flea or water-louse, which you can see alive and moving in water with the bare eye. [Obviously Daphnia.]

Of the first sort that I discovered in the said water [Obviously Vorticella sp.], I saw, after divers observations, that the bodies consisted of 5, 6, 7, or 8 very clear globules, but without being able to discern any membrane or skin that held these globules together, or in which they were enclosed. When these animalcules bestirred 'emselves, they sometimes stuck out two little horns, which were continually moved, after the fashion of horse's ears. The part between these little horns was flat, their body else being roundish, save only that it ran somewhat to a point at the hind end; at which pointed end it had a tail, near four times as long as the whole body, and looking as thick, when viewed through my microscope, as a spider's web. At the end of this tail there was a pellet, of the bigness of one of the globules of the body; and this tail I could not perceive to be used by them for their movements in very clear water. These little animals were the most wretched creatures that I have ever seen; for when, with the pellet, they did but hit on any particles or little filaments (of which there are many in water, especially if it hath but stood some days), they stuck entangled in them; and then pulled their body out into an oval, and did struggle by strongly stretching themselves, to get their tail loose; whereby their whole body then sprang back towards the pellet of the tail, and their tails then coiled up serpent-wise, after the fashion of a copper or iron wire that, having been wound close about a round stick, and then taken off, kept all its windings. This motion of stretching out and pulling together the tail continued; and I have seen several hundred animalcules, caught fast by one another in a few filaments, lying within the compass of a coarse grain of sand.

I also discovered a second sort of animalcule, whose figure was an oval; and I imagined that their head was placed at the pointed end. These were a little bit bigger than the animalcules first mentioned. Their belly is flat, provided with divers incredibly thin little feet, or little legs [cilia], which were moved very nimbly, and which I was able to discover only after sundry great efforts, and wherewith they brought off incredibly quick motions. The upper part of their body was round, and furnished inside with 8, 10, or 12 globules. Otherwise these animalcules were very clear. . . . Their body was also very yielding: for if they so much as brushed against a tiny filament, their body bent in, which bend presently sprang out again; just as if you stuck your finger into a bladder-full of water, and then, on removing the finger, the inpitting went away. Yet the greatest marvel was when I brought any of the animalcules on a dry place, for I then saw them change themselves at last into a round, and then the upper part of the body rose up pyramid-like, with a point jutting out in the middle; and after having thus lain moving with their feet for a little while, they burst asunder, and the globules and a watery humour flowed away on all sides, without my being able to discern even the least sign of any skin wherein these globules and the liquid had to all appearance been enclosed; and at such times I could discern more globules than when they were alive.

¶Letter 39 Dated 17 September 1683 to F. Aston

I have ere this sent you my observations concerning spittle, which I see have been made public in print in the 'Lecture and Collections' published by Mr Robert Hooke, Secretary of the Royal Society, in the year 1678. Since that time I have made divers further observations on my spittle, with the idea that if there be any animalcules lying about in the body, they would get into the mouth, sooner or later, through the spit-ducts; but in what observations I made to this end, I could make out no animalcules there, nor could I say aught else but what I have hitherto writ.

'Tis my wont of a morning to rub my teeth with salt, and then swill my mouth out with water: and often, after eating, to clean my back teeth with a toothpick, as well as rubbing them hard with a cloth: wherefore my teeth, back and front, remain as clean and white as falleth to the lot of few men of my years [fifty-one at the time], and my gums (no matter how hard the salt be that I rub them with) never start bleeding. Yet notwithstanding, my teeth are not so cleaned thereby, but what there sticketh or groweth between some of my front ones and my grinders (whenever I inspected them with a magnifying mirror), a little white matter, which is as thick as if 'twere batter. On examining this, I judged (albeit I could discern nought a-moving in it) that there yet were living animalcules therein. I have therefore mixed it, at divers times, with clean rain water (in which there were no animalcules), and also with spittle, that I took out of my mouth, after ridding it of air bubbles (lest the bubbles should make any motion in the spittle): and I then most always saw, with great wonder, that in the said matter there were many little living animalcules, very prettily a-moving. The biggest sort had the shape of Figure A *: these had a very strong and swift motion and

* [See Plate 3.]

shot through the water (or spittle) like a pike does through the water. These were most always few in number.

The second sort had the shape of Figure B. These ofttime spun around like a top, and every now and then took a course like that shown between C and D: and these were far more in number.

To the third sort I could assign no figure: for at times they seemed to be oblong, while anon they look perfectly round. These were so small that I could see them no bigger than Figure E: yet therewithal they went ahead so nimbly, and hovered so together, that you might imagine them to be a big swarm of gnats or flies, flying in and out among one another. These last seemed to me e'en as if they were, in my judgement, several thousand of 'em in an amount of water or spittle (mixed with the matter aforesaid) no bigger than a sand-grain; albeit there were quite nine parts of water, or spittle, to one part of the matter that I took from betwixt my front teeth, or my grinders.

Furthermore, the most part of this matter consisted of a huge number of little streaks, some greatly differing from others in their length, but of one and the same thickness withal; one being bent crooked, another straight, like Figure F, and which lay disorderly ravelled together. And because I had formerly seen, in water, live animalcules that had the same figure, I did make every endeavour to see if there was any life in them; but I could make out not the least motion, that looked like anything alive in any of 'em.

LAZARO SPALLANZANI

1729-99

IT IS DEMONSTRATED BY EXPERIMENTS THAT MICROBES DO NOT ORIGINATE SPONTANEOUSLY

THE problem of the origin of life was not settled by Redi's experiment, or by Vallisnieri's extension of it; indeed the spontaneous generation controversy was not to be settled until the mid nineteenth century. A hundred years after Redi the controversy flared up again, this time to receive the attention of one of the first of the great experimental physiologists, Lazaro Spallanzani.

Educated as a lawyer, Spallanzani entered the Catholic priesthood (eventually becoming an abbot) and began teaching in Northern Italy. He was primarily a biologist, but his active investigations extended into physics and mineralogy. His experimental techniques were remarkably advanced, and he followed, deliberately or otherwise, the advice of Vallisnieri 'to carry out experiments and observations again and again, and never to tire of collecting and comparing them in order to find out the truth'.

Spallanzani's interests ranged over all the animal functions: the processes of fertilization, reproduction, and development; the nature of the digestive process; the circulation of the blood; and the phenomena of respiration. He used for his experiments all kinds of animal life, and especially the creatures of the rivers and streams, so easily available to him in the rich valley of the Po.

The occasion for Spallanzani's intervention in the controversy over spontaneous generation was his study of the experiments of J. T. Needham (1713–81), an English priest, reported in 1748. Needham was interested in testing the application of Redi's conclusions to microscopic organisms. His experiment consisted in boiling a meat broth, then sealing the flask to exclude airborne organisms. Inspecting the infusions after various periods of time, he found the broth contained 'animalcules' and, assuming that by his boiling he had destroyed all the organisms originally present, and that his seals were adequate to exclude the air, he concluded that the new life had originated spontaneously from lifeless matter.

Spallanzani was not convinced by these demonstrations. Supposing that Needham had not boiled his infusions long enough, he repeated the experiments, varying the length of boiling time and hermetically sealing his containers. Though the procedures were simple, they were disciplined and controlled, and the results were precisely interpreted. He found that various sorts of animalcula could withstand different boiling periods, some resisting for up to forty-five minutes, but that adequate boiling would destroy them. The infusions, thus treated, could be kept indefinitely without the appearance of microorganisms; but restored to contact with the air, the contents of his flasks soon contained microscopic life. Needham's supporters contended that Spallanzani's boiling had destroyed the 'vital principle' in the air in the flasks, spoiling it for the purposes of generation, and they refused to accept these findings as conclusive and the debate continued well into the nineteenth century until Pasteur and Tyndall finally established the doctrine of biogenesis.

The selection that follows is taken from *Tracts on the Natural History of Animals and Vegetables*, translated by J. G. Dalyell in 1799.

¶ *Whether, According to a New Theory of Generation, Animalcula are Produced by a Vegetative Power in Matter*

§ *Infusions and Infused Substances Exposed to Heat*

Nothing is more common with philosophers who have invented any theory, or given a new form to one already established, and universally known, than to republish it on some other occasion, corrected, improved, or illustrated, with additional information. If we would review our discoveries, if we would examine them profoundly and with impartiality, we should in general find defects unnoticed before, which arise from the want of connexion in sentiment, from the want of a necessary and laudable perspicuity, or because they are discordant with more recent discoveries.

A certain vegetative power some have conceived to reside in matter, appropriated to the formation and regulation of organized existence; that by it are the numberless combinations of the animal machine affected; the operation of nutrition and perspiration, the variety of constitution, the animal appetites, and dimensions of the human frame. By the same means has it been explained why a blind or a maimed person may have children vigorous and entire; because the vegetative power will restore to them the members defective in the parent.

Not only has it been supposed to be destined for the organization of matter in animated beings, but that it might change an animal to the vegetable state, and the vegetable again to an animal; that it acts on plants while living, and when dead regenerates them in new beings; these are the animalcula of infusions, which cannot strictly be called animals, but beings simply *vital*.

One proof adduced in support of this hypothesis, is derived from the origin of animalcula. We are told they must either come from specific seeds, or be produced by the vegetative power; that the first cannot take place, because they are found in close vessels subjected to the action of heat, equally as in open vessels, whereas the included germs, if there were any, ought not to survive. Therefore, they must originate from the vegetative power alone. Nothing has been omitted to obtain favourable arguments for this opinion, and to give it that clearness, elegance, and simplicity most likely to gain converts.

Nineteen vessels, containing infused substances, were hermetically sealed, and kept an hour in boiling water. Being opened at a proper time, not a single animalcule was to be seen. To this experiment of mine, it was objected that the long continuance of heat had perhaps entirely destroyed the vegetative power of the infused substances, or materially injured the elasticity of the air remaining included in the vessels; thus, it was not surprising if animalcula did not appear.

To estimate the weight of these objections, I conceived an experiment apparently decisive; which was, to make nineteen infusions, and boil some of them a short time, others longer, and the rest very long. If it was founded, the number of animalcula would be less according to the duration of boiling, if not, the number would be alike in all cases.

Vegetable seeds, being the most fit for producing animalcula, were preferred to other substances, and those that never failed to produce them though they had experienced the influence of heat. White kidney beans, vetches, buckwheat, barley, maize, the seeds of mallows, and beets were infused; and, that the experiment might be the more accurate, I endeavoured as much as possible to take each species of seed from the same plant. As the yolk of an egg in maceration abounds with animalcula, one was also infused.

Experiment has demonstrated, that the heat of boiling water is not always the same, but greater, if the atmosphere is heavier; and less, if lighter : therefore, water will acquire more heat at one time than another, which will be proportioned to the state of the atmosphere. In this, and my other experiments, the seven different kinds of seeds, and the yolk, were all boiled an equal time, that they might acquire the same degree of heat. Here the experiment was diversified, by boiling a certain quantity of each infusion half an hour; another quantity, an hour; a third, an hour and a half; and a fourth, two hours. Thus, four classes of infusion, and the egg, could be formed. The same water, in which the seeds had boiled, was taken for the infusions, and what had boiled half an hour alone taken for the seeds that had boiled half an hour. The like proportions of time were preserved in the water for the other three classes of infusions; that is, an hour, one and a half, and two hours.

Each of the four classes was marked with a different number, to avoid all hazard of confusion or error: and, because an equal temperature was most essential, all were deposited in the same place. The vessels, containing the infusions, were not hermetically sealed, but loosely stopped with corks; the only object of this examination being to discover, whether long protracted ebullition would prejudice or destroy the property of infused substances in producing animalcula; if it did, there would be no difference whether the vessels were open or closed.

The examination of one, or of few drops, will often induce an observer to suppose the infusion quite deserted, or very thinly inhabited, while the observation of many drops proves it to be otherwise. I was not content with one drop only, but uniformly took a considerable number from each infusion.

The surface of infusions is generally covered with a gelatinous scum, thin at first, and easily broken, which, in process of time, acquires consistence. Here, animalcula are always most numerous, as may be seen by a method I have constantly practised, examining with a magnifier a portion placed in a strong light.

Where the animalcula are minute, or rare, the thickness of the infusion often prevents the observer from distinguishing whether any are there or not. It is then necessary to dilute the drops with water. Elsewhere it has been remarked, that distilled water was taken to make the infusions; common water might introduce some latent animalcule. In the course of these observations and experiments, distilled water has also been employed for dilution, when required; and, for greater security, examined with a magnifier before being used. In particular cases, the accidental concealment of a single animalcule might vitiate the truth of the experiment.

I conceive it my duty to mention precautions so essential, and to put it in every individual's power to judge not only of the experiments and observations themselves, but of the mode of conducting them in matters so nice and important.

On the 15 of September, I made thirty-two infusions; and on the twenty-three examined them for the first time. Animalcula were in all; but the number and species different in each. In the maize infusions, they were smaller, and proportionally more rare, according to the duration of boiling.

From this it may seem, that although long continued heat had not prevented the production of animalcula, it had contributed to diminish the number, or alter the kind. But with the rest of the infusions it was otherwise: the kidney beans, vetches, barley, and mallow seeds, were in a better condition, after sustaining the violent impression of heat two hours, than those that had been exposed to it less. Let us enter on that detail which the subject merits.

In the infusion of kidney beans, boiled two hours, were three species of animalcula; very large; middle-sized; and very small. The figure of the first, partly umbellated and attached to long filaments dragged along in their progress; the second were cylindrical; and the third, globular. All three were incredibly numerous.

In the infusion boiled two hours, were animalcula of the largest and smallest class, but few in number; still fewer, in that boiled an hour; and fewest of all, in that boiled half an hour.

The infusion of mallows, boiled two hours, produced middle-sized circular animalcula; and some very large, with the head extremity hooked. In two infusions, boiled an hour, and an hour and a half, the number and species were the same: and though they might be surpassed by those of the infusions boiled two hours, still they were much more numerous than in those boiled half an hour.

In vetches, boiled half an hour, was an immense number of semicircular bell-shaped animalcula, all of considerable size, while in those boiled an hour and a half, they were small and rare. Some bell-shaped animalcula might be seen in an infusion boiled an hour, but it gave the eye pain to discover a few, and these most minute, when it had boiled only half an hour.

Those in a barley infusion boiled two hours were numerous beyond description, and large; part of an elliptic figure, others oblong. The infusions boiled an hour and a half had but a moderate number of animalcula very minute; and some appeared when boiled half an hour.

There was no fixed rule with the remaining infusions. In buck-wheat boiled an hour and a half were many more animalcula than in any other infusions of it. This also happened in the egg and beet seed boiled an hour; but it is to be remarked, that fewer animalcula were in these two infusions boiled half an hour than in any of the rest.

Hitherto, the figure of these legions of animalcula has been cursorily alluded to. A circumstantial account is in my Dissertations, and it will be spoken of more at large in the course of the Tract.

Thus, it is clearly evident, that long boiling of seed infusions does not prevent the production of animalcula; and, notwithstanding the maize does not seem to favour it, four infusions strongly corroborate the fact.

What is the cause that infusions boiled least have fewest animalcula? I cannot think myself mistaken in assigning the following reason. That animalcula should appear, it is necessary that the macerating substances give some indication of the dissolution of their parts; and, in proportion as dissolution advances, at least for a limited time, the number of animalcula will increase. The uniformity of this has been shown in another place, and would be confirmed, was it requisite, by further experiments and observations, in these new inquiries. Now, as seeds have boiled a shorter time, so are they less invested and penetrated by the dissolving power of heat; therefore, when set apart to macerate, they are not so soon decomposed as those longer boiled. Thus, there is no occasion for surprise if some infusions swarm with animalcula while others have very few: And this I do believe the reason why, when two infusions are made at the same time, one of unboiled, the other of boiled seeds, animalcula are frequently observed much sooner in the latter than in the former. A little boiling will not decompose vegetable seeds, for decomposition is effected by slow and gradual maceration.

Some days after these experiments, the number of animalcula always became greater; and towards the middle of October increased so much, that each of the thirty-two infusions was equally swarming. The only difference was in size, figure, and motion: I enjoyed this pleasing microscopic scene uninterrupted until the 10 of November; and it might have amused me longer had I continued to examine the infusions.

It ought not to be omitted, that experiments exactly similar were soon afterwards made with pease, lentils, beans, and hemp seed. Except in the beans, the result so far corresponded, that a greater number of animalcula appeared in the infusions that had boiled most.

It is a fact established by the universal concurrence of philosophers, that, after water has come to the state of ebullition, it cannot acquire a greater degree of heat, however much the action of the fire may be augmented, provided it can evaporate. Therefore, when I say the seeds boiled longest have acquired greater heat, I mean it to be understood in *time* and not *intensity*, by supposing that the duration of boiling increased the intensity of heat the seeds would be exposed to.

Recourse was had to another experiment to learn whether an increase of heat would obstruct the production of animalcula. The eleven species of seeds were slowly heated in a coffee roaster till they became pretty well roasted, and eleven infusions formed of them with water previously boiled as usual. But this heat, so much more intense, neither prevented the origin of animalcula nor lessened the number. They were rare at first; but about the middle of October, that is, twenty days after making the infusions, the fluid was so full as absolutely to appear animated.

The constancy of their appearing even here excited my curiosity to augment the heat still more. The seeds were burnt and ground the same as we burn and grind coffee. Of the dust, which resembled soot, I made as many infusions as different kinds of seed: likewise, an infusion was made of the yolk of an egg, which by the thermometer had suffered 279° of heat. What followed? Animalcula equally appeared in these infusions, only a little more time elapsed before they became so numerous, because the weather was colder; and they uniformly inhabit infusions sooner or later according to the temperature of the atmosphere.

Vegetable seeds were exposed to trials more severe: they were exposed to the greatest heat that can be excited by common fires, or fire augmented by art. Burning coals, and the flame of the blow-pipe, were the two agents exercising their power on them. And, in the first place, I kept them on an iron plate above burning coals until entirely consumed by the violence of the flames, and converted to a dry cinder, which was reduced to powder, and as many infusions formed as there were seeds. A cinder was also made by the blow-pipe, which, besides excessive aridity, had acquired considerable hardness. I must acknowledge I did not in the least expect to find animalcula in this new infusion. After viewing them once and again, hardly able to credit my eyes, I repeated the experiment twice. Some suspicion arose that the animalcula might come from the water used rather than the burnt seeds; therefore, on repeating the experiment, the same as what formed the infusions was put in other vessels. Both times, however, they re-appeared in the burnt seeds, while not one was seen in the water.

These facts fully convinced me that vegetable seeds never fail to produce animalcula, though exposed to any degree of heat; whence arises a direct conclusion, that the *vegetative power* is nothing but the work of imagination; and if no animalcula appear in vessels hermetically sealed and kept an hour in boiling water, their absence must proceed from some other cause.

*

We are therefore induced to believe, that those animalcula originate from germs there included, which, for a certain time, withstand the effects of heat, but at length yield under it; and, since animalcula of the higher classes only exist when the heat is less intense, we must imagine they are much sooner affected by it, than those of the lower classes. Whence, we should conclude, that this multitude of the superior animalcula, seen in the infusions of open vessels, exposed not only to the heat of boiling water, but to the flame of a blow-pipe, appears there, not because their germs have withstood so great a degree of heat, but because new germs come to the infusions, after cessation of the heat.

IV

THE STRUCTURE OF LIVING THINGS

IT was largely the influence of the Arab world which brought about the revival of learning in Europe in the thirteenth century. Latin translations from the Arabic of the works of Aristotle, Hippocrates, and Galen, among others, slowly stimulated the intellects of the Western world. During the first phase of the revival, the period of Scholasticism, textual criticism and commentary were the predominating interest and retained their importance for some centuries in the curricula of many of the older universities which were founded at that time. In the medical schools the studies were often entirely academic and were limited to discussing and committing to memory the writings of Aristotle and Galen, whose authority was regarded as absolute and infallible. As both the Christian and Islamic faiths forbade dissection of the human body no anatomical investigations were carried out during the thousand years after the death of Galen. When in the early days of the universities demonstrations on the human body began occasionally to be given, these were superficial and cursory. The demonstrator pointed at the parts as they were mentioned by the Reader. Where there was some obvious difference between the body and Galen's account, the condition in the body was considered to be abnormal, although most of Galen's anatomical knowledge was based on the dissection of the Barbary ape and not of man.

In the fourteenth century there began a revolt against this authoritarian approach to scientific questions, especially at the University of Bologna. The dissection of the human body was resumed with particular skill by one Mondino (c. 1316), a professor of anatomy in that university. Others followed, and the Universities of Bologna and of Padua became centres of the anatomical revival for the next two centuries. The urge towards direct knowledge of the body was further stimulated by the naturalist movement in art, which culminated in the fifteenth century. Artists such as Michelangelo, Raphael, Dürer, and Leonardo da Vinci strove to represent the human form with accuracy and did not hesitate to resort to dissection to discover the basic structure of the body. They left a record of their studies in their superb anatomical drawings.

The great synthesis of this revival was produced by Vesalius, who in one magnificent work laid the foundation for the anatomical side of medicine and effectively discredited the authoritarian approach. The publication of Vesalius's monumental work in the same year (1543) as Copernicus's *magnum opus* is a reminder of the extent of the forces then at work which led, in due course, to the scientific revolution. The contribution of Vesalius will be considered in detail later. Other great anatomists of this period – such men as Fabricius (1537–1619), Fallopius (1523–62), and Eustachius (*c.* 1524–74) – made important contributions towards the science of anatomy.

During the sixteenth century a similar revival in the anatomical study of plants, especially those having medicinal value, was begun in northern Europe. A number of fine herbals were produced at this time – particularly those of Brunfels (1489–1534), Bock (1498–1554), and Fuchs (1501–66) – which were especially distinguished for the fine quality of illustration, although they were not yet distinguished for the accuracy of their minute observations and representations.

The development of the microscope in the middle of the seventeenth century provided a new tool for observation and added a new dimension to the study of the structure of plants and animals. One of its immediate consequences was, as we have seen, the discovery of the world of microscopic life by Leeuwenhoek. The anatomy of some of the smaller forms of life was studied with great skill by Hooke and Grew in England, Malpighi in Italy, and Swammerdam in Holland.

Most important of all were the anatomical studies of the parts of larger plants and animals for which the science of microscopic anatomy, now called histology, supplemented the study of gross anatomy. The culminating achievement of the microscopic approach was the enunciation of the cell theory, which recognized the basic unity of the structure of all living things and provided the biologist with his equivalent of the chemist's atoms and molecules. The early microscopists unquestionably saw cells, as their drawings attest, and Hooke coined the term *cell* to describe the microscopic structure of a piece of cork; yet more than a century and a half elapsed before the cell theory was firmly established. There are, of course, many more names associated with the development of this fundamental generalization than those whose writings are included in this volume. Hooke, Brown, Dutrochet, and Schwann are included here together with one contemporary, Ross Harrison, whose work reveals the possibilities for the extension of basic biological studies into fields at present unexplored.

The cell theory was largely a nineteenth-century development, which together with the establishment of the physiology of both plants and animals as distinct sciences, the theory of natural selection, and the germ theory of disease, marked the nineteenth century as the time of the revolution in biology, just as the seventeenth was the century of the revolution in physics and the end of the eighteenth witnessed the revolution in chemistry. The cell concept provided the spark and direction for much of the development of modern biology and has led to a most fruitful analysis of many fundamental biological problems, including those of reproduction and development, heredity, and growth.

The development of the electron microscope has now

extended research to the subcellular level, and other improvements in the study of cellular chemistry and function may, indeed, have led the biologist to the threshold of the mystery of the nature of life itself. Whether or not he will succeed in penetrating its veil remains to be seen.

ANDREAS VESALIUS

1514–64

THE DISSECTION OF THE HUMAN BODY
PROVIDES THE FOUNDATION OF MODERN
MEDICINE

THE position of Vesalius in intellectual history is secure, and medical historians agree that his *De humani corporis fabrica* represents the foundation of the modern study of anatomy and hence modern medicine. Clearly the work of a great mind, it was published before Vesalius was thirty years old, in 1543, the same year that saw Copernicus's great work. Vesalius upset the authority of Galen much as Copernicus destroyed the influence of Ptolemy. Of the two works, that of Vesalius is the more modern in temper and in its departure from tradition. The work of Copernicus still needed the refinements of Galileo, Kepler, and Newton before the revolution in astronomy could be completed.

Born in Brussels to a family of physicians, Vesalius showed an early interest in anatomy and as a young boy dissected the bodies of dead birds, mice, and other animals. He was educated at the University of Louvain in the classical tradition and then went to Paris to study medicine. His teachers of anatomy, including Jacobus Sylvius (1478–1555), were Galenists and taught anatomy in the manner of the times. The professor occupied a chair high above the class and read the appropriate passages from Galen. Below him a demonstrator dissected the appropriate structure when specimens were used and pointed out the parts described by the reader. If the specimen varied from the descriptions, it was explained that the human body had changed since Galen's time or that the specimen was abnormal – Galen was never to be doubted.

Dissatisfied with this type of instruction, Vesalius, at great personal risk, 'snatched' bodies for dissection. He developed special instruments and would never permit anyone to perform dissections for him; he wanted to see for himself. His method was to read the appropriate passage of Galen and follow his descriptions of structure; but he allowed his own observations to replace Galen's without hesitation whenever the facts so dictated. All his anatomical studies are distinguished by this careful, objective approach.

On one occasion, Vesalius found outside the city walls the skeleton of a criminal, complete even to the ligaments, which were intact. He cut it down and managed to get it to his home, where it served as the basis for his studies of the human skeleton which became a part of his great work.

At the age of twenty-three, Vesalius was appointed professor of surgery and anatomy at Padua; within five years he had completed his own anatomical studies in spite of the demands of his overflowing classes of medical students, to whom he gave his own demonstrations. He solved the serious problem of obtaining material for dissection by body snatching, a practice which has uncomfortable connotations and which in the eighteenth century led to grave-robbing and even murder, to provide the anatomists with their specimens.

In addition to the great merits of Vesalius's anatomical descriptions, the plates which were produced to illustrate them are probably the finest anatomical drawings ever made. Made by Jan Stephen van Calcar, a Fleming and a student of Titian, they are more than accurate representations of human anatomy; they were drawn with an effort to represent the body in natural positions, with the organs as they probably functioned. This is especially true of the plates of the skeleton and the musculature, as can be seen in Plate 1.

Publication of the *Fabrica* exposed Vesalius to vigorous opposition by many anatomists as well as to heated and bitter controversy. He himself was a difficult character, and his reluctance to tolerate academic jealousies led him to resign his chair at Padua to become physician to Charles V of Spain (to whom he dedicated the *Fabrica*) and then to Philip II, son of Charles. Thereafter he did no more work in anatomy.

Vesalius is represented here by two readings. The first, from the preface to his work, reveals the nature of his approach to anatomy. It was translated by B. Farrington (*Proceedings of the Royal Society of Medicine*, Vol. 25, 1932). The second reading, from Chapter 19 of Book VII of the *Fabrica*, deals with the dissection of living animals and the value thereof. It was translated by S. Lambert in 1935 (Columbia University Press).

¶ *The Preface of Andreas Vesalius. His Own Books on the Mechanism of the Human Body addressed to The Most Great and Invincible Emperor The Divine Charles V*

Those engaged in the arts and sciences, Most Gracious Emperor Charles, find many serious obstacles to the exact study and successful application of them. In the first place, no slight inconvenience results from too great separation between branches of study which serve for the perfection of one art. But much worse is the mischievous distribution among different practitioners of the practical applications of the art. This has been carried so far that those who have set before themselves the attainment of an art embrace one part of it to the neglect of the rest, although they are intimately bound up with it and can by no means be separated from it. Such never achieve any notable result; they never attain their goal or succeed in basing their art upon a proper foundation.

I shall pass over all the other arts in silence and confine myself to a few remarks on that which presides over the health of mankind. This, of all the arts which the mind of man has discovered, is by far the most beneficial, necessary, abstruse, and laborious. But in bygone times, that is to say [in the West] after the Gothic deluge and [in the East] after the reign of Mansur at Bochara in Persia, under whom, as we know, the Arabs still lived as was right on terms of familiarity with the Greeks, medicine began to be sore distempered. Its primary instrument, the employment of the hand in healing, was so neglected that it was relegated to vulgar fellows with no instruction whatsoever in the branches of knowledge that subserve the art of medicine.

In ancient times there were three medical sects, to wit, the Dogmatic, the Empirical, and the Methodical, but the exponents of each of these embraced the whole of the art as the means to preserve health and war against disease. To this end they referred all that they individually thought necessary in their particular sects, and employed the service of a threefold aid to health: first, a theory of diet; secondly, the whole use of drugs; and thirdly, manual operation. This last, above the rest, nicely proves the saying that medicine is the addition of that which is defective and the removal of that which is in excess; as often as we resort to the art of medicine for the treatment of disease we have occasion to employ it; and time and experience have taught, by the benefits it has conferred, that it is the greatest aid to human health.

This triple manner of treatment was equally familiar to the doctors of each sect; and those who applied manual operation according to the nature of the affection expended no less care in training their hands than in establishing a theory of diet, or in learning to recognize and compound drugs. This, not to mention his other books, is clearly shown by those most perfect of the compositions of Hippocrates: *On the Function of the Doctor, On Fractures of Bones, On Dislocations of Joints and Similar Ailments*. Nay, more, Galen, after Hippocrates the prince of medicine, in addition to the fact that he boasts from time to time that the care of the gladiators of Pergamum was entrusted to his sole charge, and that when age was now becoming a burden he was reluctant for the monkeys he had for dissection to be skinned by the help of slaves, frequently impresses on us his joy in manual dexterity and how zealously he, in common with the other doctors of Asia, employed it. Indeed, there is no one of the ancients who does not seem as solicitous to hand down to posterity the method of cure which is effected by the hand as those methods which depend on diet and drugs.

But it was especially after the ruin spread by the Goths, when all the sciences, which before had flourished gloriously and were practised as was fitting, went to ruin, that more fashionable doctors, first in Italy, in imitation of the old Romans, despising the work of the hand, began to delegate to slaves the manual attentions which they judged needful for their patients, and themselves merely to stand over them like master builders. Then, when all the rest also who practised the true art of healing gradually declined the unpleasant duties of their profession, without, however, abating any of their claim to money or honour, they quickly fell away from the standard of the doctors of old. Methods of cooking, and all the preparation of food for the sick, they left to nurses; compounding of drugs they left to the apothecaries; manual operation to barbers. Thus in course of time the art of healing has been so wretchedly rent asunder that certain doctors, advertising themselves under the name of physicians, have arrogated to themselves alone the prescription of drugs and diet for obscure diseases, and have relegated the rest of medicine to those whom they call surgeons and scarcely regard as slaves, disgracefully banishing from themselves the chief and most ancient branch of the medical art, and that which principally (if indeed there be any other) bases itself upon the investigation of nature. Yet among the Indians today it is the kings that chiefly exercise this [surgical] art; the Persians hand it down as an obligatory inheritance to their children, as formerly did the whole family of the Asclepiads; the Thracians, with many other nations, cultivate and honour it above other arts, to the neglect almost of that part of the art [the prescription of drugs] which formerly many proscribed from the state, as devised for the deception and destruction of men; for it, refusing the aid of nature, gives no deep relief, but rather endeavouring to help nature while it is in any case overwrought by the effort to cast off the disease, it often destroys it quite and utterly distracts it from its normal function. Consequently it is to it in particular we owe the fact that so many scoffs are wont to be cast at doctors, and this most holy art is made a mock, though all the time one part of it, which those trained in liberal studies allow basely to be torn from them, could adorn it forever with peculiar praise.

For when Homer, that wellspring of genius, declares that a man that is a doctor is better than a host, and together with all the poets of Greece celebrates Podalirius and Machaon, truly these divine sons of Aesculapius are thus praised not for the reason that they banished a touch of fever or other ailments which nature usually cures, unaided, and without the assistance of the doctor more easily than with his aid, nor because they pandered to the appetites of men in obscure and desperate affections, but because they devoted themselves in particular to the cure of dislocations, fractures, bruises, wounds, and other breaches of continuity, and to fluxions of blood, and because they freed the noble warriors of Agamemnon from javelins, darts, and other evils of that kind, which wars particularly occasion, and which always demand the careful attention of the doctor.

But it was not at all my purpose to set one instrument of medicine above the rest, since the triple art of healing, as it is called, cannot at all be disunited and wrenched asunder, but belongs in its entirety to the same practitioner; and for the due attainment of this triple art, all the parts of medicine have been established and prepared on an equal footing, so that the individual parts are brought into use with a success proportioned to the degree in which one combines the cumulative force of all. How rarely indeed a disease occurs which does not at once require the triple manner of treatment; that is to say, a proper diet must be prescribed, some service must be rendered by medicine, and some by the hand. Therefore the tyros in this art must by every means be exhorted to follow the Greeks in despising the whisperings of those physicians (save the mark!), and, as the fundamental nature and rational basis of the art prescribes, to apply their hands also to the treatment, lest they should rend the body of medicine and make of it a force destructive of the common life of man.

And they must be urged to this with all the greater earnestness because men today who have had an irreproachable training in the art are seen to abstain from the use of the hand as from the plague, and for this very reason, lest they should be slandered by the masters of the profession as barbers before the ignorant mob, and should henceforth lack equal gain and honour with those less than half doctors, losing their standing both with the uneducated commonalty and with princes. For it is indeed above all other things the wide prevalence of this hateful error that prevents us even in our age from taking up the healing art as a whole, makes us confine ourselves merely to the treatment of internal complaints, and, if I may utter the blunt truth once for all, causes us, to the great detriment of mankind, to study to be healers only in a very limited degree.

For when, in the first place, the whole compounding of drugs was handed over to the apothecaries, then the doctors promptly lost the knowledge of simple medicines which is absolutely essential to them; and they became responsible for the fact that the druggists' shops were filled with barbarous terms and false remedies, and also that so many elegant compositions of the ancients were lost to us, several of which have not yet come to light; and, finally, they prepared an endless task for the learned men, not only of our own age, but for those who preceded it by some years, who devoted themselves with indefatigable zeal to research in simple medicines; so much so that they may be regarded as having gone far to restore the knowledge of them to its former brilliance.

But this perverse distribution of the instruments of healing among a variety of craftsmen inflicted a much more odious shipwreck and a far more cruel blow upon the chief branch of natural philosophy [anatomy], to which, since it comprises the natural history of man and should rightly be regarded as the firm foundation of the whole art of medicine and its essential preliminary, Hippocrates and Plato attached so much importance that they did not hesitate to put it first among the parts of medicine. For though originally it was the prime object of the doctors' care, and though they strained every nerve to acquire it, it finally began to perish miserably when the doctors themselves, by resigning manual operations to others, ruined anatomy. For when the doctors supposed that only the care of internal complaints concerned them, considering a mere knowledge of the viscera as more than enough for them, they neglected the structure of the bones and muscles, as well as of the nerves, veins, and arteries which run through bones and muscles, as of no importance for them. And further, when the whole conduct of manual operations was entrusted to barbers, not only did doctors lose the true knowledge of the viscera, but the practice of dissection soon died out, doubtless for the reason that the doctors did not attempt to operate, while those to whom the manual skill was resigned were too ignorant to read the writings of the teachers of anatomy.

It is thus utterly impossible for this class of men to preserve for us a difficult art which they have acquired only mechanically. And equally inevitably this deplorable dismemberment of the art of healing has introduced into our schools the detestable procedure now in vogue, that one man should carry out the dissection of the human body, and another give the description of the parts. These latter are perched up aloft in a pulpit like jackdaws, and with a notable air of disdain they drone out information about facts they have never approached at first hand, but which they merely commit to memory from the books of others, or of which they have descriptions before their eyes; the former are so ignorant of languages that they are unable to explain their dissections to the onlookers and botch what ought to be exhibited in accordance with the instruction of the physician, who never applies his hand to the dissection, and contemptuously steers the ship out of the manual, as the saying goes. Thus everything is wrongly taught, days are wasted in absurd questions, and in the confusion less is offered to the onlooker than a butcher in his stall could teach a doctor. I omit all mention of those schools in which there is scarcely even a thought of opening a human body to exhibit its structure. So far had ancient medicine fallen some years ago from its pristine glory.

But when medicine in the great blessedness of this age, which the gods will to entrust to the wise guidance of your divine power, had, together with all studies, begun to live again and to lift its head up from its utter darkness (so much so, indeed, that it might without fear of contradiction be regarded in some academies as having well-nigh recovered its ancient brilliance); and when there was nothing of which the need was now so urgently felt as the resurrection of the science of anatomy, then I, challenged by the example of so many eminent men, insofar as I could and with what means I could command, thought I should lend my aid. And lest, when all others for the sake of our common studies were engaged in some attempt and with such great success, I alone should be idle, or lest I should fall below the level of my forebears, doctors to be sure not unknown to fame, I thought that this branch of natural philosophy should be recalled from the dead, so that if it did not achieve with us a greater perfection than at any other place or time among the old teachers of anatomy, it might at least reach such a point that one could with confidence assert that our modern science of anatomy was equal to that of old, and that in this age anatomy was unique both in the level to which it had sunk and in the completeness of its subsequent restoration.

But this effort could by no manner of means have succeeded if, when I was studying medicine at Paris, I had not myself applied my hand to this business, but had acquiesced in the casual and superficial display to me and my fellow students by certain barbers of a few organs at one or two public dissections. For in such a perfunctory manner was anatomy then treated in the place where we have lived to see medicine happily reborn that I myself, having trained myself without guidance in the dissection of brute creatures, at the third dissection at which it was my fortune ever to be present (this, as was the custom there, was concerned exclusively or principally with the viscera), led on by the encouragement of my fellow students and teachers, performed in public a more thorough dissection than was wont to be done. Later I attempted a second dissection, my purpose being to exhibit the muscles of the hand together with a more accurate dissection of the viscera. For except for eight muscles of the abdomen, disgracefully mangled and in the wrong order, no one (I speak the simple truth) ever demonstrated to me any single muscle, or any single bone, much less the network of nerves, veins, and arteries.

Subsequently at Louvain, where I had to return on account of the disturbance of war, because during eighteen years the doctors there had not even dreamed of anatomy, and in order that I might help the students of that academy, and that I myself might acquire greater skill in a matter both obscure and in my judgement of prime importance for the whole of medicine, I did somewhat more accurately than at Paris expound the whole structure of the human body in the course of dissecting, with the result that the younger teachers of that academy now appear to spend great and very serious study in acquiring a knowledge of the parts of man, clearly understanding what invaluable material for philosophizing is presented to them from this knowledge. Furthermore at Padua, in the most famous gymnasium of the whole world, I had been charged with the teaching of surgical medicine five years by the illustrious Senate of Venice, which is far the most liberal in the endowment of the higher branches of learning. And since the carrying out of anatomical inquiry is of importance for surgical medicine, I devoted much effort to the investigation of the structure of man, and so directed my inquiries, and exploding the ridiculous fashion of the schools, so taught the subject that we could not find in my procedure anything that fell short of the tradition of the ancients.

However, the supineness of the medical profession has seen to it only too well that the writings of Eudemus, Herophilus, Marinus, Andreas, Lycus, and other princes of anatomy should not be preserved to us, since not even a fragment of any page has survived of all those famous writers whom Galen mentions, to the number of more than twenty, in his second commentary to the book of Hippocrates on *The Nature of Man*. Nay, even of his own anatomical writings scarcely the half has been saved from destruction. But those who followed Galen, among whom I place Oribasius, Theophilus, the Arabs, and all our own writers whom I have read to date, all of them (and they must pardon me for saying this), if they handed on anything worth reading, borrowed it from him. And, believe me, the careful reader will discover that there is nothing they were further from attempting than the dissection of bodies. They placed an absolute trust in I know not what quality of the writing of their chief, and in the neglect of dissection of the rest, and shamefully reduced Galen to convenient summaries, never departing from him by so much as the breadth of a nail, that is, supposing they succeed in arriving at his meaning. Nay, they place it in the forefront of their books that their own writings are pieced together from the teachings of Galen, and that all that is theirs is his. And so completely have all surrendered to his authority that no doctor has been found to declare that in the anatomical books of Galen even the slightest error has ever been found, much less could now be found; though all the time (apart from the fact that Galen frequently corrects himself, and in later books, after acquiring more experience, removes oversights that he had committed in earlier books, and sometimes teaches contradictory views) it is quite clear to us, from the revival of the art of dissection, from a painstaking perusal of the works of Galen, and from a restoration of them in several places, of which we have no reason to be ashamed, that Galen himself never dissected a human body lately dead. Nay, more, deceived by his monkeys (although it is admitted that human bodies dried, and prepared as it were for an inspection of the bones, did come under his observation), he frequently wrongly controverts the ancient doctors who had trained themselves by dissecting human corpses.

And again, how many false observations you will find him to have made even on his monkeys. I shall say nothing about the astonishing fact that in the manifold and infinite divergences of the organs of the human body from those of the monkey Galen hardly noticed anything except in the fingers and the bend of the knee – which he would certainly have passed over with the rest, if they had not been obvious to him without dissection. But at the moment I do not propose to criticize the false statements of Galen, easily the foremost among the teachers of anatomy; and much less would I wish to be regarded now in the beginning as disloyal to the author of all good things and lacking in respect for his authority. For I am not unaware how the medical profession (in this so different from the followers of Aristotle) are wont to be upset when in more than two hundred instances, in the conduct of the single course of anatomy I now exhibit in the schools, they see that Galen has failed to give a true description of the interrelation, use, and function of the parts of man – how they scowl at times, and examine every inch of the dissection in their determination to defend him. Yet they too, drawn by the love of truth, gradually abandon that attitude and, growing less emphatic, begin to put faith in their own not ineffectual sight and powers of reason rather than in the writings of Galen. These true paradoxes, won not by slavish reliance on the efforts of others, nor supported merely by masses of authorities, they eagerly communicate in their correspondence to their friends; they exhort them so earnestly and so friendly-wise to examine them for themselves, and to come at last to a true knowledge of anatomy, that there is ground for hope that anatomy will ere long be cultivated in all our academies as it was of old in Alexandria.

And that the muses might the more smile upon this hope, I have, so far as in me lay, and in addition to my other publications on this subject – which certain plagiarists, thinking me far away from Germany, have put out there as their own – made a completely fresh arrangement in seven books of my information about the parts of the human body in the order in which I am wont to lay the same before that learned assembly in this city, as well as at Bologna and at Pisa. Thus those present at the dissections will have a record of what was there demonstrated, and will be able to expound anatomy to others with less trouble. And also the books will be by no means useless to those who have no opportunity for personal examination, for they relate with sufficient fullness the number, position, shape, substance, connexion wih other parts, use and function of each part of the human body, together with many similar facts which we are wont to unravel during dissection concerning the nature of the parts, and also the method of dissection applicable to dead and living animals. Moreover, the books contain representations of all the parts inserted in the text of the discourse, in such a way that they place before the eyes of the student of nature's works, as it were, a dissected corpse.

Thus in the first book I have described the nature of all bones and cartilages, which, since the other parts are supported by them, and must be described in accordance with them, are the first to be known by students of anatomy. The second book treats of the ligaments by which bones and cartilages are linked one with another, and then the muscles that effect the movements that depend upon our will. The third comprises the close network of veins which carry to the muscles and bones and the other parts the ordinary blood by which they are nourished, and of arteries which control the mixture of innate heat and vital spirit. The fourth treats of the branches not only of the nerves which convey the animal spirit to the muscles, but of all the other nerves as well. The fifth explains the structure of the organs that subserve nutrition effected through food and drink; and furthermore, on account of the proximity of their position, it contains also the instruments designed by the Most High Creator for the propagation of the species. The sixth is devoted to the heart, the *fomes* of the vital faculty, and the parts that subserve it. The seventh describes the harmony between the structure of the brain and the organs of sense, without, however, repeating from the fourth book the description of the network of nerves arising from the brain. . . .

But here there comes into my mind the judgement of certain men who vehemently condemn the practice of setting before the eyes of students, as we do with the parts of plants, delineations, be they never so accurate, of the parts of the human body. These, they say, ought to be learned not by pictures but by careful dissection and examination of the things themselves. As if, forsooth, my object in adding to the text of my discourse images of the parts, which are most faithful, and which I wish could be free from the risk of being spoiled by the printers, was that students should rely upon them and refrain from dissecting bodies; whereas my practice has rather been to encourage students of medicine in every way I could to perform dissections with their own hands. Assuredly, if the practice of the ancients had lasted down to our day, namely, to train boys at home in carrying out dissections, just as in making their letters and in reading, I would gladly consent to our dispensing not only with pictures but with all commentaries. For the ancients only began to write about dissection when they decided that honour demanded that they should communicate the art not only to their children but to strangers whom they respected for their virtue. For, as soon as boys were no longer trained in dissection, the inevitable consequence at once followed that they learned anatomy less well, since the training had been abolished with which they had been wont to begin in youth. So much so that when the art had deserted the family of the Asclepiads, and had been now for many centuries on the decline, books were needed to preserve a completed view of it. Yet how greatly pictures aid the understanding of these things, and how much more accurately they put the things before the eyes than even the clearest language, nobody can have failed to experience in geometry and the other mathematical disciplines.

But, however that may be, I have done my best to this single end, namely, in an equally recondite and laborious matter, to aid as many as possible, and truly and completely to describe the structure of the human body – which is built up not of some ten or twelve parts (as seems to those who give it a passing glance) but of some thousands of different parts – and to bring to students of medicine a substantial contribution toward the understanding of those books of Galen treating of this branch of learning, which of all his writings most require the assistance of a teacher.

Moreover, I am aware [first] how little authority my efforts will carry by reason of my youth (I am still in my twenty-eighth year); and [secondly] how little, on account of the frequency with which I draw attention to the falsity of Galen's pronouncements, I shall be sheltered from the attacks of those who have not – as I have done in the schools of Italy – applied themselves earnestly to anatomy, and who, being now old men devoured by envy at the true discoveries of youths, will be ashamed, together with all the other sectaries of Galen, that they have been hitherto so purblind, failing to notice what I now set forth, yet arrogating to themselves a mighty reputation in the art – [I know, I say, how little authority my efforts will carry] unless they come forth auspiciously into the light, commended by the great patronage of some divine power. And, inasmuch as it cannot be more safely sheltered or more splendidly adorned than by the imperishable name of the Divine Charles, the Most Great and Invincible Emperor, I beseech Your Majesty to allow this useful work of mine, which on many accounts and for many reasons is dangerous to itself, to circulate for a short time under Your Majesty's auspices, glory, and patronage, until through experience of the facts, through judgement which matures with time, and through learning, I may make the fruit of my toil worthy of the Most High and Best Prince, or may offer another gift worthy of acceptance on another subject chosen from our art.

PADUA, *1 August*, A.D *1542.*

¶ *On Dissection of the Living*

§ *What may be Learned by Dissection of the Dead and What of the Living*

Quite as the dissection of the dead teaches well the number, position, and shape of each part, and most accurately the nature and composition of its material substance, thus also the dissection of a living animal clearly demonstrates at once the function itself, at another time it shows very clearly the reasons for the existence of the parts. Therefore, even though students deservedly first come to be skilled in the study of dead animals, afterward when about to investigate the action and use of the parts of the body they must become acquainted with the living animal.

On the other hand since very small parts of the body are endowed with different uses and functions, it is fitting that no one doubt that dissections of the living present also many contradictions. ...

The Use and Function of the Muscles Which May Be Seen

In a proper dissection thou shalt see the function of the muscles; notice during their own action they contract and become thick where they are most fleshy, and again they lengthen and become thin according as they in combination draw up a limb, either letting themselves go back and having been drawn out permit the limb to be pulled in an opposite direction by another muscle, or at other times indeed they do not put in action their own combination. ...

Examination of the Uses of the Veins and Arteries

Also when inquiring into the use of the veins the work is scarcely one for the dissection of the living, since we shall become sufficiently acquainted in the case of the dead with the fact that these veins carry the blood through the whole body and that any part is not nourished in which a prominent vein has been severed in wounds.

Likewise concerning the arteries we scarcely require a dissection of the living although it will be allowable for anyone to lay bare the artery running into the groin and to obstruct it with a band, and to observe that the part of the artery cut off by the band pulsates no longer.

And thus it is observed by the easy experiment of opening an artery at any time in living animals that blood is contained in the arteries naturally.

In order that on the other hand we may be more certain that the force of pulsation does not belong to the artery or that the material contained in the arteries is not the producer of the pulsation, for in truth this force depends for its strength upon the heart. Besides, because we see that an artery bound by a cord no longer beats under the cord, it will be permitted to undertake an extensive dissection of the artery of the groin or of the thigh, and to take a small tube made of a reed of such a thickness as is the capacity of the artery and to insert it by cutting in such a way that the upper part of the tube reaches higher into the cavity of the artery than the upper part of the dissection, and in the same manner also that the lower portion of the tube is introduced downward farther than the lower part of the dissection, and thus the ligature of the artery which constricts its calibre above the cannula is passed by a circuit.

To be sure when this is done the blood and likewise the vital spirit run through the artery even as far as the foot; in fact the whole portion of the artery replaced by the cannula beats no longer. Moreover when the ligature has been cut, that part of the artery which is beyond the cannula shows no less pulsation than the portion above.

We shall see next how much force is actually carried to the brain from the heart by the arteries. Now in this demonstration thou shalt wonder greatly at a vivisection of Galen in which he advises that all things be cut off which are common to the brain and heart, always excepting the arteries which seek the head through the transverse processes of the cervical vertebrae and carry also besides a substantial portion of the vital spirit into the primary sinuses of the *dura mater* and also in like manner into the brain. So much so that it is not surprising that the brain performs its functions under these conditions for a long time, which Galen observed could easily be done, for the animal breathes for a long time during this dissection, and sometimes moves about. If indeed it runs, and therefore requires much breath, it falls not long afterwards although the brain will still afterwards receive the essence of the animal spirit from those arteries which I have closely observed seek the skull through the transverse processes of the cervical vertebrae. . . .

We see that the peritoneum is a wrapper for all the organs enclosed in it; that the omentum and likewise the mesentery serve in the best manner for the conduction and distribution of the blood vessels; that the stomach prepares the food and drink, and passes these through the stomach onward.

§ *Examination of the Function of those Parts Which are Contained in the Peritoneum*

And however nothing may prevent our taking living dogs which have consumed food at less or greater intervals previously and examine them alive, and thus investigating the functions of the intestines. But on the contrary we are able to behold the functioning of the liver as also of the spleen or of the kidneys or of the bladder during the dissection of the living, scarcely better than in that of the dead; unless someone shall wish to excise the spleen in the living dog which I have once done, and have preserved the dog (alive) for some days ...

In truth these operations, just as the dislocations and fractures of bones, which we sometimes do on brute beasts, serve more for training the hands and for determining correct treatment rather than for investigating the functions of organs. . . .

ROBERT HOOKE

1635–1703

THE TERM *CELL* IS USED TO DESCRIBE THE MICROSCOPIC STRUCTURE OF CORK

ROBERT HOOKE'S most important researches were in the physical sciences but he was also one of the greatest of the early microscopists. His health in childhood was delicate and he did not receive a normal education, but his precocity and intelligence at Oxford attracted the attention of Robert Boyle and led to his appointment as curator of instruments to the newly founded Royal Society. He showed great originality and ingenuity in devising and constructing new instruments, including air-pumps, diving bells, micrometers, hygroscopes, triple-writing machines, and rain and wind gauges. Another of these instruments was the compound microscope shown on Plate 4.

In his *Micrographia*, published in 1665, he recorded his microscopic observations, mainly of plant structures. The work was illustrated by meticulously engraved plates, of great accuracy and beauty. They include drawings of the stinging hairs of the nettle, a leaf fungus, the sting of a bee, a flea, a slice of cork (Plate 5), and a foraminiferan, probably the first drawing of a protozoan. There were eighty-three plates in all.

The most important from the historical point of view was the drawing of a slice of cork, for it was in this connexion that the word *cell* was first used in its modern biological sense. He applied it to the dead walls of the cells and was unaware of their living contents. He failed to observe cells in seeds although his contemporaries Grew and Malpighi saw and drew them.

The selection here included is taken from the *Micrographia*.

━━━━━

The Microscopic Structure of Cork

I took a good clear piece of cork, and with a Pen-knife sharpen'd as keen as a Razor, I cut a piece of it off, and thereby left the surface of it exceeding smooth, then examining it very diligently with a *Microscope*, me thought I could perceive it to appear a little porous; but I could not so plainly distinguish them, as to be sure that they were pores, much less what Figure they were of: But judging from the lightness and yielding quality of the Cork, that certainly the texture could not be so curious, but that possibly, if I could use some further diligence, I might find it to be discernible with a *Microscope*, I with the same sharp Pen-knife, cut off from the former smooth surface an exceeding thin piece of it, and placing it on a black object Plate, because it was it self a white body, and casting the light on it with a deep *plano-convex Glass*, I could exceeding plainly perceive it to be all perforated and porous, much like a Honey-comb, but that the pores of it were not regular; yet it was not unlike a Honey-comb in these particulars.

First, in that it had a very little solid substance, in comparison of the empty cavity that was contain'd between, for the *Interstitia*, or walls (as I may so call them) or partitions of those pores were neer as thin in proportion to their pores, as those thin films of Wax in a Honey-comb (which enclose and constitute the *sexangular cells*) are to theirs.

Next, in that these pores, or cells, were not very deep, but consisted of a great many little Boxes, separated out of one continued long pore, by certain *Diaphragms*. ...

I no sooner discern'd these (which were indeed the first *microscopical* pores I ever saw, and perhaps, that were ever seen, for I had not met with any Writer or Person, that had made any mention of them before this), but me thought I had with the discovery of them, presently hinted to me the true and intelligible reason of all the *Phaenomena* of Cork; As,

First, if I enquir'd why it was so exceedingly light a body? my *Microscope* could presently inform me that here was the same reason evident that there is found for the lightness of froth, an empty Honey-comb, Wool, a Spunge, a Pumice-stone, or the like: namely a very small quantity, of a solid body, extended into exceedingly large dimensions.

Next, it seem'd nothing more difficult to give an intelligible reason, why Cork is a body so very unapt to suck and drink in Water and consequently preserves itself, floating on the top of Water, though left on it never so long: and why it is able to stop and hold air in a Bottle, though it be there very much condens'd and consequently presses very strongly to get a passage out, without suffering the least bubble to pass through its substance. For, as to the first, since our *Microscope* informs us that the substance of Cork is altogether fill'd with Air, and that that Air is perfectly enclosed in little Boxes or Cells distinct from one another. It seems very plain, why neither the Water nor any other Air can easily insinuate itself into them, since there is already within them an *intus existens*, and consequently, why the pieces of Cork become so good floats for Nets, and stopples for Viols, or other close Vessels. . . . Our *Microscope* will easily inform us, that the whole mass consists of an infinite company of small Boxes or Bladders of Air, which is a substance of a springy nature, and that will suffer a considerable condensation (as I have several times found by divers trials, by which I have most evidently condens'd it into less than a twentieth part of its usual dimensions neer the Earth, and that with no other strength then that of my hands without any kind of forcing Engine, such as Racks, Leavers, Wheels, Pullies, or the like, but this onely by and by) and besides, it seems very probable that those very films or sides of the pores have in them a springing quality, as almost all other kind of Vegetable substances have, so as to help to restore themselves to their former position. . . .

But, to return to our Observation. I told several lines of these pores, and found that there were usually about three-score of these small Cells placed end-ways in the eighteenth part of an Inch in length, whence I concluded there must be neer eleven hundred of them, or somewhat more than a thousand in the length of an inch and therefore in a square inch above a Million, or 1166400, and in a Cubick Inch, above twelve hundred Millions, or 1259712000, a thing almost incredible, did not our *Microscope* assure us of it by ocular demonstration; nay, did it not discover to us the pores of a body, which were they *diaphragm'd*, like those of Cork, would afford us in one Cubick Inch, more than ten times as many little Cells, as is evident in several charr'd Vegetables; so prodigiously curious are the works of Nature that even these conspicuous pores of bodies, which seem to be the channels or pipes through which the *Succus nutritius*, or natural juices of Vegetables are convey'd, and seem to correspond to the veins, arteries and other Vessels in sensible creatures, that these pores I say, which seem to be the Vessels of nutrition to the vastest body in the World, are yet so exceeding small that the Atoms which *Epicurus* fancy'd would go neer to prove too bigg to enter them, much more to constitute a fluid body in them. . . .

But though I could not with my *Microscope*, nor with my breath, nor any other way I have yet try'd, discover a passage out of one of those cavities into another, yet I cannot thence conclude, that therefore there are none such, by which the *Succus nutritius*, or appropriate juices of Vegetables, may pass through them; for, in several of those Vegetables, whil'st green, I have with my *Microscope*, plainly enough discover'd these Cells or Holes fill'd with juices, and by degrees sweating them out: as I have also observed in green Wood all those long *Microscopical* pores which appear in Charcoal perfectly empty of any thing but Air.

Now, though I have with great diligence endeavoured to find whether there be any such thing in those *Microscopical* pores of Wood or Piths, as the *Valves* in the heart, veins, and other passages of Animals, that open and give passage to the contain'd fluid juices one way, and shut themselves, and impede the passage of such liquors back again, yet have I not hitherto been able to say any thing positive in it; though, me thinks, it seems very probable, that Nature has in these passages, as well as in those of Animal bodies, very many appropriated Instruments and contrivances, whereby to bring her designs and end to pass, which 'tis not improbable, but that some diligent Observer, if help'd with better *Microscopes*, may in time detect. . . .

═══════

JAN SWAMMERDAM

1637–80

THE ANATOMY OF AN INSECT IS DESCRIBED IN A SERIES OF DISSECTIONS AND DRAWINGS

As L. C. Miall points out, 'The *Biblia naturae* (of Swammerdam) is of permanent interest as a collection of facts, as a monument of industry and sagacity, and as a measure of the high level which biological knowledge had attained in the latter half of the seventeenth century.' Indeed, Swammerdam's accuracy and skill in describing the anatomy of small animals, especially insects, ranks with the best work done in modern times.

Jan Swammerdam was born in Amsterdam, where his father, an apothecary, had assembled from the Dutch trade with the Indies a magnificent museum which included many specimens in natural history. With such an opportunity, it is not surprising that Swammerdam became interested in the subject at an early age. It was originally intended that he study for the Protestant ministry, but Swammerdam preferred medicine and was permitted to begin studies at Leyden.

There he became friendly with the Dane Stensen, and with the Frenchman de Graaf, all three being students of the great medical teacher Franciscus Sylvius. In 1667 Swammerdam was awarded his degree, but he did not take to the practice of medicine seriously, preferring to return to his studies in natural history. These he pursued with almost superhuman efforts, despite the fact that his health was impaired. He regularly worked from dawn until well into the night dissecting, studying, and drawing.

Swammerdam used lenses for most of his dissections, and he had a special brass dissecting table built with two movable arms, one to hold his specimen, the other to hold the lens. He made his own dissecting instruments, such as special scissors, forceps, scalpels, and needles so small that they had to be honed and sharpened under a magnifying glass.

In the course of his work, Swammerdam compiled a mass of detailed and accurate information on the structure and minute anatomy as well as the life history of the mayfly, dragonfly, bee, gnat, ant, rhinoceros beetle, gall insects, water flea, tadpole, snail, and many others. The drawings he made were remarkable for their detail and were never surpassed (Plate 6); they were equalled only by the drawings of Lyonet on the anatomy of the goat moth, published some seventy years after Swammerdam's book.

The last six or seven years of Swammerdam's life were unproductive and were marked by illness, financial cares, and religious fanaticism. He was a strange, disturbed man, and the enormous output of his relatively short working life is a monument to his fantastic drive and energy. His manuscripts, unpublished for fifty-seven years, were finally published in 1737 as *Biblia naturae*. German and English (1758) translations were also available, and it is from the English translation, entitled *The Bible of Nature*, that the abridged account of the life history and structure of a mayfly, *Palinginea*, is taken (see Plate 6).

─────

¶ *Structure and Life History of Palinginea*

The winged Palinginea is an Insect with four wings, two small antennae, six feet, and two long, hairy filaments, which stand straight out from the hinder end of the body. It lives at most five hours in the winged state. Every year it appears on the banks of the Rhine, the Maas, the Waal, the Leck, and the Yssel, appearing on the surface of the water about the feast of St Olof and St John. The flies may be seen in the air for three days together. Those which appear on the first day die the same evening, and the same thing happens on the second and third days. Then a whole year has to elapse before they are seen again.

When the female has emerged from the water and cast off her skin, she passes the contents of the double ovary into the water, but first she moves to and fro on the surface of the water as if in sport, and flits about with rapid exploring movements. Immediately after the eggs are passed into the water, they are fertilized by the male, which has previously emerged and cast off a delicate membranous skin. The eggs, thus passed into the water and fertilized, sink slowly, and are scattered over the mud at the bottom of the stream. The form of the eggs contributes to this mode of dispersal; they are rounded discs, which sink at different rates; hence if a number of the eggs are gently lowered into the water on the point of a knife, they are seen to spread as they descend.

How long the eggs lie on the bottom of the river, and how many days elapse before the larvae emerge, is known only to God. Something might be made out upon these points if anyone would search the bottom of the stream at frequent intervals, or keep the eggs in a basin with water and mud.

Some time after the descent of the eggs, a crowd of minute worms, each with six legs, makes its appearance. These do not differ in shape from the older larvae. Their growth is so slow that after a year, viz., in the following June, they are only a third of the length of the larvae then ready to enter the winged state. At the end of another year the larvae are twice as long, but three years are required before they attain their full size. Not only do these larvae of different ages differ in size, but also in the degree of development of the wings. The small larvae, a year old, exhibit no trace of wings; after two years the wings are visible, and enclosed in special sheaths; at the end of the third year they are quite plain and ready to burst forth.

These larvae are rarely, if ever, seen swimming in the

water. It is true that they can swim by a kind of serpentine movement, bending the head now down, now up, but they always keep to the banks out of reach of the current. They can very rarely be seen out of the mud, in which they make for themselves long cylindrical and horizontal burrows.

As the Bees in their own wonderful way make homes out of wax, so the larvae of the Ephemera excavate out of mud the tubes in which they dwell. If they are taken out of their tubes, they can only creep readily when the bottom is so flat as to support the whole length of the body. Although they are ordinarily immersed in water and can swim, I have found on taking a number of them out of their tubes, that they at once fall on their backs as if paralyzed, and are not able to right themselves. But within their burrows they can move quickly backwards and forwards. The same is true of various other larvae which burrow in trees, fruits, leaves, or galls. The Cossus when taken from its hole in a tree covers its whole body with a web, and supported by this, it is able to make a new hole in the wood, but if left without support, or some fixed object against which the body can be pressed, it is quite unable to bore. The larva of the Ephemera is so helpless outside its tube, that if while swimming in the water it ceases to exert itself, it falls at once to the bottom, and there lies upon its back.

As soon as the larvae escape from the egg, they set about making their burrows, and these are gradually increased in size as the larva grows. The All-wise Creator has provided them with limbs suitable to their work. The forelimbs are fitted for digging, as in the Mole or Mole-cricket. Besides their feet, the larvae are also provided with jaws, each with two teeth, like the pincers of Crabs, and these are well suited for working in the mud. The larvae may be seen at work if they are placed in water mixed with a little mud. If the mud is not sufficient to cover the whole body, they conceal first the head, then the body, and then the tail, endeavouring all the time to complete their dwelling. Anglers assure us that when the water of the rivers sinks, the larvae work deeper and deeper into the mud, rising again as the water rises. This, I suppose, is indispensable for their breathing. They are provided with many air-tubes for distributing the air throughout the body. Access of air would be stopped if they remained below after the water had risen. I have often found that when taken out of their tubes and placed on wet sand, they much prefer creeping out of the water to burying themselves in the sand. The reason of this may be that the warmth of the water is injurious to them, as well as the want of mud.

As to the food of these larvae, it would be hard to say what it was without the help of dissection, but by this means I have discovered that they feed upon mud only. Whenever the body is opened, mud is found in the stomach and intestine. In the same way certain caterpillars feed upon the same substance of which they make their homes.

The full-fed larvae pass from their burrows into the water, and thence into the air, but as no animal is without its enemies, so these larvae, as soon as they enter the water are pursued by Fishes, and when they leave the water for the air, they are immediately liable to be devoured by Birds. All anglers know that the larvae make excellent bait for Fishes. When they emerge from the water, they are often thick as falling flakes of snow. Hence the Dutch proverb, *Het isser soo digt, als Haft* (as thick as Mayflies). At all times of the year when the weather is favourable for fishing, these larvae form an excellent bait. When the waters are high, it is not easy to fetch them out of the mud, and it becomes necessary for someone to strip himself naked and go down after them. I have sometimes sent a man into the water to procure a supply of larvae for dissection. The larvae are tenacious of life, and live long on the hook, but when taken out of their tubes and placed in water mixed with earth, they do not live more than two days. To keep them alive, they should be placed in wet sand or mud. In this may I have seen the older larvae live four days, the younger ones eight days; but when completely submerged, they cannot long be kept alive. If it is desired to send live larvae to a distance, there is no better way than tying together stems of the great reed, and causing the larvae to creep into them.

The body of the larva is divided into fourteen distinct segments. The first forms the head, the three next the thorax, and the remaining ten the abdomen. Upon the head are seen the eyes, and just beneath them the delicate antennae, divided each into five joints; below these are the mandibles, and again below these the hairy, membraneous maxillae, which are like those of Crabs or Shrimps. The first pair of thoracic limbs are adapted by their shape for digging. Their most powerful action is outward, and in this way they are able to throw the mud as a Mole throws out earth. Each of the fore-feet is formed of four joints and a single claw. The second thoracic segment is protected above and below by a shield-like plate; it bears a pair of limbs, each consisting of five joints and a claw, and on the sides of the segment [in advanced larvae] are the sheaths of the wings. Air-tubes ramify upon the sheaths, and shortly before a moult, the wings may be seen within them, folded up in a wonderful and beautiful manner. The third thoracic segment bears the second pair of wings, which are much smaller than the first, and also a pair of five-jointed legs. The first segment of the abdomen is smooth and provided with no appendages, the next six segments are furnished with gills, which are in incessant movement. In the Lobster, Crab, and Sepia, which in many respects approach the structures of Insects, we find the gills formed and arranged in nearly the same manner, though with this difference that in Crabs and Lobsters the gills are enclosed by a hard carapace, while both in them and in the Sepia they are more concealed than in the Palinginea larva. The eighth and ninth segments of the abdomen are simple and smooth. The tenth or last abdominal segment is furnished with three hairy filaments; besides these, there are two small curved appendages (claspers) which are not so conspicuous in the female. To these are added in the male yet another pair of small appendages beneath the others.

The colour of the larvae, when very small, is pale blue, verging upon green. This colour belongs rather to the viscera than to the skin. The eyes are dark brown, and the back speckled with dark spots, which become larger with age.

The male larvae are distinguished in the first place by the eyes, which are twice as large as in the female. The body of the male, however, is much smaller than that of the female, as in all other Insects which I have observed. The effect of this difference in size, is that space is allowed for the vast number of eggs formed in the female. The male has longer tail filaments, and possesses moreover three or four appendages, placed partly on the sides and partly beneath, which in the female are inconspicuous or wanting altogether.

The larva is harmless and inoffensive. If roughly handled, it bends its head towards the breast, and stiffens its body. There is nothing more wonderful in these creatures than the play of the branchiae which stand out from both sides of the body. They move so regularly, distinctly, and incessantly, as to excite admiration in the beholder.

I come next to consider the transformation of this Insect. The change is effected so rapidly that it seems to consist merely in slipping off two integuments and unfolding certain appendages. In order to make it quite plain what is the difference between the swimming larva and the flying Insect, I will first describe the internal organs as they occur in both stages. Here I follow a path trodden by no one before. I will not however lament, with Clutius, the rarity of books dealing with this subject. Nature is the best revealer of her own wonders. Though books may be useful, if they truly represent the phenomena of nature, I pity those who trust to the observations of others, and impose fictions upon themselves and their readers.

I will describe the methods which in the year 1670 I employed to investigate the anatomy of the larva.

The male, which is easily distinguished by its large eyes, is fastened with the finest needles, back downwards, upon black paper or linen in a wooden dish. Then having cut through the skin, we see a watery fluid flow out, which is the true blood of the animal, though it is not red in colour as in the Earthworm or in Quadrupeds. I have found nothing better for opening the skin than fine scissors, for lancets, however sharp, tear the parts. Then with the finest scalpel, or the point of a needle, the skin is gently separated from the parts beneath. Under the skin is found a delicate membrane, and beneath this the muscles of the body-wall, some of which pass directly from one segment to another, others obliquely or transversely. Others again serve for moving the limbs. Within the muscles is a very delicate membrane, upon and within which lies the fat, consisting of minute white vesicles. Next we find the oesophagus, stomach, and intestine. The oesophagus, like a thin thread, passes from the mouth into the thorax, and expands to form the crop. The crop, when distended with food, or with air injected from a fine glass tube, is smooth externally, but internally it is thrown into a reticulation of folds. It appears to be provided with multitudes of fine vessels, but if these are carefully examined with a magnifying glass, it will be found that they are really air-tubes, which supply all parts of the body, whether external or internal. Beyond the crop comes the stomach, then the small intestine, the large intestine or colon, and lastly the rectum. The small intestine is provided internally with a number of folds resembling the valvular folds of the small intestine of man. In the colon are longitudinal muscular valves, rather like those which form the manyplies of the ruminant stomach. The delicate rectum leads to the exterior of the body. A pair of muscles is attached, one on each side, to the rectum, and serve for pressing out its contents. Since the larva feeds upon mud, we commonly find the crop and intestine filled with mud. When the time of transformation is approaching, the animal ceases to feed, as also do the Cossus, the larva of the Bee, and the Silkworm. Hence the intestine becomes transparent at the time of transformation.

A pair of tracheal trunks wind in a serpentine manner along the sides, and send branches to all the organs. The trachae consist of numerous rings held together by delicate membranes. At the time of moult the lining of the air tubes is cast, though I have not seen this in Palinginea. It is, however, very conspicuous in the Silkworm, where, at the time of moult, hundreds of the delicate air-tubes cast their lining membrane. I find it difficult to discover the external openings of the air-tubes, since they do not open into the mouth or throat as in other animals. After long examination, I believe that I have discovered the openings on the under side of the thorax, nearly in the same place as I afterwards found them in Grasshoppers, where, however, they are easily seen. Since the Palinginea larva lives in water and mud, it is natural that the openings should be narrow and hard to discover. From these observations it is clear why the Palinginea larvae, when the water of the river rises, creep upwards and betake themselves to new tubes, in order that they may get the air which they require to breathe. For the same reason they follow the water as it sinks, lest they should be surrounded with air, and dried up. When the air-tubes are examined in an Insect which has been dead some days, so that the viscera have turned black, they appear like pearls, or bright silver on a dark ground. The firmness of their texture prevents them from rapid decay, and they preserve their shape for a considerable time. To make sure whether air is really contained in these vessels or not, it is only necessary to compress them with the point of a needle under water, when bubbles of air will be seen to issue. In a dried larva torn across, the air-tubes are very easily seen, for they retain their shape, and remain open when all the other parts have dried up. The six large gills which stand out from each side of the body are all provided with large air-tubes, three to each gill, as also are the five pairs of golden-yellow fins beneath, by means of which the larvae swim. Some other observations which I had made upon the gills and their vessels have been lost, and I cannot recollect what they were. I do not know, for instance, what is the use of the plume attached to the first pair of gills, and I can now give no more information about them than can be gathered from the figure.

The heart lies on the dorsal surface as in other Insects. It swells out in the middle of each segment, just as Malpighi represents it in the Silkworm. I do not agree with this author in saying that the larva is furnished with more than one heart, and I have only very rarely seen any contraction of the heart in the larva of Palinginea.

The nerve-cord consists of eleven ganglia. From the first of these, or brain, the optic nerve can be seen to spring. In the same way the nerves of the body are given off from the ten other ganglia. Paired connectives issue from each ganglion, and unite it to the next, so that the cord appears to be divided along a considerable part of its length. The nerve-cord may be demonstrated in an uninjured larva, by inflating the body with air from behind. By this means the cord is pressed against the integument, and can be seen with a lens, or even with the naked eye.

There are two ovaries in the female, resembling the ovaries of Fishes. Each is supplied with innumerable air-tubes. The eggs are so small that they cannot well be observed without the aid of a lens. They are of a flattened oval form, and of white colour. Their small size in comparison with that of the adult Insect is explained by the fact that the larvae grow for three years before they arrive at maturity.

The emergence of the fly takes place in warm and still weather. Shortly before emergence, the wings are observed to become prominent, though still enclosed within the larval skin. The intestine is emptied, and the colour of the animal changes in consequence.

When all is ready, the larvae quit their burrows, and swim freely in the water. The time of emergence is usually towards evening, and always in the summer months. In the year 1671, I saw the Palinginea flying about from the 13th of June.

ROBERT BROWN
1773–1858

THE PRESENCE OF A NUCLEUS IS REPORTED
IN THE CELLS OF A NUMBER OF PLANTS

ROBERT BROWN is chiefly remembered for a number of
his meticulous observations, one of which was significant
in the development of the cell concept, and another of
which is discussed in every chemistry textbook. Brown, the
son of a Scottish clergyman, studied medicine at Edin-
burgh and then became an army surgeon. He practised
medicine for about five years but gave up the profession
when, through the influence of Sir Joseph Banks, President of the Royal Society, he was offered a post as
naturalist to an expedition to Australia and Tasmania.

After spending four years in Australia collecting and
studying plants, he decided to devote the rest of his life
to botanical studies. Soon after his return to England, he
became librarian to the Linnaean Society and to Sir
Joseph Banks. When Banks died in 1820 he left Brown his
house in London and the use of his large library and
herbarium for life. In 1827 Brown allowed the books and
collection to be stored in the British Museum where they
are still to be found. He devoted the rest of his life to a
long series of botanical researches. He made detailed
studies of a number of plant families. He investigated
fertilization in plants, and he made original contributions
to plant geography and to the microscopical study of fossil
plants. He is credited with the discovery of the movement
of microscopic particles in fluids, which was named after
him (Brownian Movement) and which is now known to be
the result of molecular bombardment of these particles.

Although the protoplasm concept was not to be developed for many years, Brown clearly described the

flowing movement of the granular material in certain plant cells which we know today as protoplasmic streaming. He discovered, as the reading that follows indicates, the nucleus of the cell. He seems also to have recognized the possible importance of this structure to the cell. Subsequent developments in cell studies have confirmed Brown's prescience, and to this day the nucleus and its activities represent the major focus of study in cellular chemistry. The selection is from Brown's paper 'Observations on the Organs and Mode of Fecundation in Orchideae and Asclepiadeae', in the *Transactions of the Linnaean Society*, 1833.

━━━━━━━

¶ *Observations on the Presence of a Nucleus in Cells*

I shall conclude my observations on Orchideae with a notice of some points of their general structure, which chiefly relate to the cellular tissue.

In each cell of the epidermis of a great part of this family, especially of those with membranaceous leaves, a single circular areola, generally somewhat more opake than the membrane of the cell, is observable. This areola, which is more or less distinctly granular, is slightly convex, and although it seems to be on the surface is in reality covered by the outer lamina of the cell. There is no regularity as to its place in the cell; it is not unfrequently however central or nearly so.

As only one areola belongs to each cell, and as in many cases where it exists in the common cells of the epidermis it is also visible in the cutaneous glands or stomata, and in these is always double – one being on each side of the limb – it is highly probable that the cutaneous gland is in all cases composed of two cells of peculiar form, the line of union being the longitudinal axis of the disk or pore.

This areola, or nucleus of the cell as perhaps it might be termed, is not confined to the epidermis, being also found not only in the pubescence of the surface, particularly when jointed, as in Cypripedium, but in many cases in the parenchyma or internal cells of the tissue, especially when these are free from deposition of granular matter.

In the compressed cells of the epidermis the nucleus is in a corresponding degree flattened; but in the internal tissue it is often nearly spherical, more or less firmly adhering to one of the walls, and projecting into the cavity of the cell. In this state it may not unfrequently be found in the substance of the column, and in that of the perianthium.

The nucleus is manifest also in the tissue of the stigma, where, in accordance with the compression of the utriculi, it has an intermediate form, being neither so much flattened as in the epidermis, nor so convex as it is in the internal tissue of the column.

I may here remark, that I am acquainted with one case of apparent exception to the nucleus being solitary in each utriculus or cell, namely in *Bletia Tankervilliae*.

In the utriculi of the stigma of this plant I have generally, though not always, found a second areola apparently on the surface, and composed of much larger granules than the ordinary nucleus, which is formed of very minute granular matter, and seems to be deep seated.

Mr Bauer has represented the tissue of the stigma in this species of Bletia, both before and as he believes after impregnation; and in the latter state the utriculi are marked with from one to three areolae of similar appearance.

The nucleus may even be supposed to exist in the pollen of this family. In the early stages of its formation at least a minute areola is often visible in the simple grain, and in each of the constituent parts or cells of the compound grain. But these areolae may perhaps rather be considered as merely the points of production of the tubes.

This nucleus of the cell is not confined to Orchideae, but is equally manifest in many other Monocotyledonous families; and I have even found it, hitherto however in very few cases, in the epidermis of Dicotyledonous plants; though in this primary division it may perhaps be said to exist in the early stages of development of the pollen. Among Monocotyledones the orders in which it is most remarkable are Liliaceae, Hemerocallideae, Asphodeleae, Irideae, and Commelineae.

In some plants belonging to this last-mentioned family, especially in *Tradescantia virginica* and several nearly related species, it is uncommonly distinct, not only in the epidermis and in the jointed hairs of the filaments, but in the tissue of stigma, in the cells of the ovulum even before impregnation, and in all the stages of formation of the grains of pollen, the evolution of which is so remarkable in those species of Tradescantia.

═══════

HENRI DUTROCHET
1776–1847

THE CELL THEORY IS ANTICIPATED, AND AN EXPLANATION OF CELL FUNCTION IS OFFERED

WE have already noted that in the history of science discoveries do not arise *de novo*. Most advances are the result of the efforts of many individuals in conscious or unconscious collaboration. The cell concept is certainly one of these developments; its course can be followed like a river and as it is traced back to its source countless tributaries are revealed.

Robert Hooke was unquestionably the first to use the word *cell*. He used it to describe the units making up the structure of cork, but he was not, in fact, referring to the unit of structure and function now recognized as a cell; he was, rather, describing the boundaries of the true cells which in plants are not living but are produced by the living substance of the cell. Leeuwenhoek, Swammerdam, Malpighi, Grew, Brown, and others also saw cells, and some used the term, but there was as yet no clear-cut recognition of the universal nature of cellular organization.

Henri Dutrochet went far beyond his predecessors and for the first time clearly stated that all living things are composed of cells. He arrived at this generalization as a result of many microscopic observations of plant structures and macerated plant materials. He also recognized that growth results from an increase in the volume of cells and from the addition of new small cells which increase in volume – a modern and mature statement of the nature of growth.

Some historians of biology have claimed priority for Dutrochet in the chronology of the cell theory, since his researches were published in 1824, a full fifteen years before the epochal pronouncement of the cell theory of Schwann and Schleiden in 1839. Others insist that the development of evidence by Schwann and Schleiden was much more detailed and complete, and the credit is generally given to them.

Dutrochet was born in the old French province of Poitou. He was educated in medicine, and in addition to some private practice he served as a military surgeon with the French army in the campaign in Spain in 1808 and 1809. Soon after leaving the army he retired from the active practice of medicine and moved to Touraine, where he devoted himself to study and to experimentation. These were fruitful years, and his interests ranged over a wide area, including embryology, the physiology of plants, and photosynthesis, as well as the structural studies of plants which led him to his cell concepts.

Dutrochet made several other important findings, one of which is included in this collection. He recognized the importance of the transfer of materials between the cell and its environment, and he provided the word *osmosis* for this process. This is the first use in the biological literature of this term, which has now acquired a much more limited meaning, referring only to the passage of water into and out of the cell. Dutrochet was one of the first biologists to recognize the connexion between chlorophyll and the plants' ability to utilize carbon dioxide.

Both selections below are taken from the translation by A. R. Rich in the *Johns Hopkins Hospital Bulletin*, Vol. 39, 1926.

---

§ *Observations of Cells in Plants and Animals*

I must repeat here that which I have stated above regarding the organic texture of plants: we have seen that plants are composed entirely of cells, or of organs which are obviously derived from cells; we have seen that these cells are merely contiguous and adherent to each other by cohesion, but that they do not form a tissue actually continuous. The organic being has appeared to us, therefore, to be composed of an infinite number of microscopic parts, which are related only by proximity. Now, the observations on animals which we have just described obviously confirm this.

In the organs of vertebrates, the globular corpuscles are so small that it is impossible to know whether they are solid or vesicular bodies; but in molluscs that is very easy to determine. When one examines microscopically the tissues of the liver, the testis, or the salivary glands of Helix, or of Limax, one sees that these secretory organs are composed, like those of vertebrates, of little globular bodies assembled in a confused manner; but here these little globular bodies are not so excessively small. They are indeed quite large (if one may use such an expression in speaking of microscopic objects), and one can see in the clearest manner that they are vesicular bodies or true cells, the walls of which contain other very minute corpuscles. ... One can therefore draw the general conclusion that the globular corpuscles which make up all the organic tissues of animals are really globular cells of an extreme smallness, which are united only by cohesion. Thus all the tissues, all the organs of animals are really only a cellular tissue diversely modified. This uniformity of ultimate structure proves that organs really differ one from the other only in the nature of the substances which are contained in the vesicular cells of which they are composed.

All of the organic tissues of plants are made of cells and observation has now demonstrated to us that the same is true of animals.

*

It is within the cell that the secretion of the fluid peculiar to each organ is effected. These fluids are probably transmitted by transudation into the excretory canal. ... Thus the cell is the secreting organ *par excellence*. It secretes, inside itself, substances which are, in some cases, destined to be transported to the outside of the body by way of the excretory ducts, and, in other cases, destined to remain within the cell which has produced them, thus playing specific roles in the vital economy. . . .

One can scarcely doubt that parenchymatous organs (such as the spleen) which have no excretory duct must also manufacture in their cells substances which are destined either to remain within those cells, or to pass into the blood vessels by transduction.

In each organ, the cells must have different characteristics, since such different substances are secreted within them. In this connexion, one cannot help admiring the prodigious diversity of the products of living beings – a diversity which is even greater in the plant kingdom. What a variety in the physical and chemical qualities of the substances secreted by the cells which make up the parenchyma of fruits, stems, roots, leaves, and flowers in all the plants which cover the surface of the globe! One can scarcely conceive that such an amazing diversity of products results from the activity of a single organ – the cell. When one compares the extreme simplicity of this organ with the extraordinary diversity of its internal powers, it becomes evident that the cell is truly the piece *fondamentale* of the living organism. . . .

§ *On Osmosis*

In a bowl of water I had a little fish, the tail of which I had cut off. On the surface of the wound there developed a sort of aquatic mould with rather long filaments, at the end of each of which there was a bulbous swelling easily visible to the naked eye. I was stirred with the curiosity to observe with the microscope this plant which was growing upon a living animal. The filaments of the mould were transparent, but the terminal swellings, which were pointed at the end and resembled the capsules of plants, were completely opaque. I cut off a few of these filaments and placed them in a watch-glass containing water in order to study them under the microscope. I saw that soon a multitude of little globules were expelled from an opening at the tip of each of the opaque capsules. As these globules were expelled, the lower part of the capsule (that part opposite the tip from which the globules were discharged) became empty. The globules remaining in the upper part of the capsular cavity seemed compressed together and forcibly driven upward by an accumulation of water in the lower part of the capsule. The fact that this empty part of the capsule had not decreased in size made it clear to me that the expulsion of the globules was not due to a contraction of the capsule. The water, which had entered the lower part of the capsule, seemed to have acted like the piston of a syringe in the driving upward and forcing out from the tip some of the globules with which the capsules were originally completely filled. After a few seconds all of the globules were driven out of the capsules, which were then filled only with water, having lost none of their original size. . . . Whence came this water? What was the force that made it enter the capsules? . . . It was necessary for me to place this phenomenon in the category of those of which the cause is entirely unknown. Since the observation was made with the microscope, its accuracy could be questioned by those who are familiar with the many optical illusions of which that instrument is the source. I contented myself, therefore, with making a note of it; and I thought no more about it until a similar observation, this time not requiring the use of a microscope, presented itself. It was, in this instance, the animal kingdom which furnished the material.

*

These were the two observations which led me to establish the existence of a new physico-organic force. . . . I shall designate this force . . . by the term 'endosmosis', a word derived from ἔνδον meaning 'within' and ὠσμος meaning 'impulsion'.

The soft tissues are aggregates of cells, filled ordinarily with a pasty substance which is more dense than the blood plasma which bathes their walls, or is separated from them only by the extremely thin walls of the capillaries. As a result of this arrangement the blood plasma must tend continually to enter the cells, which become then the seats of two electric currents, one, the stronger, producing endosmosis, and another, the weaker, producing exosmosis. Through the effect of endosmosis the substances in the blood are forced into the cells; exosmosis brings it about that the cells return to the blood-stream a part of the solution which they contain.

The physiological connexions which I have established between plants and animals make it clear that there is but a single physiology, a general science dealing with the functions of living beings – functions which vary in their mode of execution but which are fundamentally identical in all organized beings. I hope that some day, out of these first attempts, there will be born a new science – general physiology.

THEODOR SCHWANN

1810–82

THE CELL THEORY IS ANNOUNCED

THE cell theory is probably the most important biological generalization of the first half of the nineteenth century. It has grown in importance and serves as a unifying principle in the continued development of modern biology. Earlier readings in this section have emphasized that the cell concept derived from the work of many microscopists and that there were several claimants for priority of discovery. A number of biologists before Schwann and Schleiden wrote about the cellular organization of plants and animals, but it is clear that the researches of these two men crystallized the basic concept and inaugurated a fruitful period of cellular studies. This remains true, although there were errors in their description of some cell processes, which were rather quickly corrected in the half century that followed as the construction and design of the microscope lenses improved and new techniques in the preparation of materials for microscopic study were developed.

In its essential the cell theory is a simple idea, although the cell has been found to be anything but the simple mechanism that was first pictured. It may be summarized as follows: All living things are composed of one or more cells or of cells and their products. The cell is the unit of structure and of function of all plants and animals. The cells of all living things are fundamentally alike in their chemical construction. New cells arise from pre-existing cells by a process of cell division. The cell is the unit of reproduction and development, since every living thing begins life as a single cell, the fertilized egg, and develops from it by cell reproduction and differentiation. The cell serves also as the unit of inheritance of all living things.

Most of these aspects of the cell theory were described by Schwann and Schleiden in a form that proved generally acceptable to biologists. That they placed too much emphasis on the cell wall was revealed by later studies, which concentrated on the living substance within the boundaries of the wall. Dujardin first recognized the importance of this material and called it *sarcode*. Von Mohl, Purkinje, and Schultze replaced this name with *protoplasm*. This dynamic, chemically complex material was to prove to be more than 'the physical basis of life', for it embodied the essence of life itself.

One of the major weaknesses in the theory as stated by Schwann and Schleiden was their description of cell formation. The intricate process of cell division was subsequently explained with particular clarity by Fleming and Strasburger, who revealed that the material of the nucleus (Chromatin) was distributed to the daughter cells of a cell division in a fashion which ensured that each would receive an equal amount of the same material. This finding was later to provide the means of understanding the mechanism of heredity.

The cell proved to be a complex unit, and its chemistry, its metabolism, and even its structure required more and more refined techniques for their elucidation. The science of cytology, as the study of cells is called, continues to develop and is still an important branch of biological research.

Theodor Schwann and Matthias Schleiden can be regarded as collaborators in this significant work. Schwann was a student of Johannes Müller (see p. 221), the great physiologist, marine biologist, and teacher, at Bonn, and followed him to Berlin, where he became his assistant. After the publication of the cell theory, Schwann became professor at the University of Louvain and after nine years moved to the University of Liège. He was known as an outstanding experimenter and demonstrator and an excellent teacher.

Schleiden was a successful lawyer whose interest in science was so compelling that he gave up his law practice and, after graduation in medicine, devoted himself mainly to botany. He stimulated Schwann to the final development and statement of the cell theory.

The two collaborators made a strange pair. Schwann was gentle and kindly and avoided controversy, whereas Schleiden was assured, disputative, and certain to provoke discussion. They complemented one another in this single joint effort and each made a significant contribution to the result.

Schleiden published first, in 1838, and reached two major conclusions. He announced that plants were built up of cells and modifications of cells and that the embryo of a plant arose from a single cell. Schwann did the more comprehensive work and first used the term *cell theory*. He was responsible for the theoretical work which coordinated and synthesized the whole story.

The reading below is taken from *Microscopical Researches into the Accordance in the Structure and Growth of Animals and Plants,* by Schwann, translated by Henry Smith for the Sydenham Society in 1847.

¶ *Introduction*

Although plants present so great a variety of external form, yet they are no less remarkable for the simplicity of their internal structure. This extraordinary diversity in figure is produced solely by different modes of junction of simple elementary structures, which, though they present various modifications, are yet throughout essentially the same, namely, *cells*. The entire class of the cellular plants consists only of cells; many of them are formed solely of homogeneous cells strung together, some of even a single cell. In like manner, the vascular plants, in their earliest condition, consist merely of simple cells; and the pollen granule, which, according to Schleiden's discovery, is the basis of the new plant, is in its essential parts only a cell. In perfectly developed vascular plants the structure is more complex, so that not long since, their elementary tissues were distinguished as cellular and fibrous tissue, and vessels or spiral tubes. Researches on the structure, and particularly on the development of these tissues, have, however, shown that these fibres and spiral tubes are but elongated cells, and the spiral fibres only spiral-shaped depositions upon the internal surface of the cells. Thus the vascular plants consist likewise of cells, some of which only have advanced to a higher degree of development. The lactiferous vessels are the only structures not as yet reduced to cells; but further observations are required with respect to their development. According to Unger ... they in like manner consist of cells, the partition-walls of which become obliterated.

Animals, which present a much greater variety of external form than is found in the vegetable kingdom, exhibit also, and especially the higher classes in the perfectly-developed condition, a much more complex structure in their individual tissues. How broad is the distinction between a muscle and a nerve, between the latter and cellular tissue (which agrees only in name with that of plants), or elastic or horny tissue, and so on. When, however, we turn to the history of the development of these tissues, it appears that all their manifold forms originate likewise only from cells, indeed from cells which are entirely analogous to those of vegetables, and which exhibit the most remarkable accordance with them in some of the vital phenomena which they manifest. *The design of the present treatise is to prove this by a series of observations.*

It is, however, necessary to give some account of the vital phenomena of vegetable cells. Each cell is, within certain limits, an Individual, an independent Whole. The vital phenomena of one are repeated, entirely or in part, in all the rest. These Individuals, however, are not ranged side by side as a mere Aggregate, but so operate together in a manner unknown to us, as to produce a harmonious Whole.

*

I soon conjectured that the cellular formation might be a widely extended, perhaps a universal principle for the formation of organic substances.

*

By still further examination I constantly found this principle of cellular formation more fully realized. The germinal membrane was soon discovered to be composed entirely of cells, and shortly afterwards cell-nuclei, and subsequently also cells, were found in all tissues of the animal body at their origin; so that all tissues consist of cells, or are formed by various modes from cells.

¶ The Cell Theory

When organic nature, animals and plants, is regarded as a Whole, in contradistinction to the inorganic kingdom, we do not find that all organisms and all their separate organs are compact masses, but that they are composed of innumerable small particles of a definite form. These elementary particles, however, are subject to the most extraordinary diversity of figure, especially in animals; in plants they are, for the most part or exclusively, cells. This variety in the elementary parts seemed to hold some relation to their more diversified physiological function in animals, so that it might be established as a principle, that every diversity in the physiological signification of an organ requires a difference in its elementary particles; and, on the contrary, the similarity of two elementary particles seemed to justify the conclusion that they were physiologically similar. It was natural that among the very different forms presented by the elementary particles, there should be some more or less alike, and that they might be divided, according to their similarity of figure, into fibres, which compose the great mass of the bodies of animals, into cells, tubes, globules, etc. The division was, of course, only one of natural history, not expressive of any physiological idea, and just as a primitive muscular fibre, for example, might seem to differ from one of areolar tissue, or all fibres from cells, so would there be in like manner a difference, however gradually marked, between the different kinds of cells. It seemed as if the organism arranged the molecules in the definite forms exhibited by its different elementary particles, in the way required by its physiological function. It might be expected that there would be a definite mode of development for each separate kind of elementary structure, and that it would be similar in those structures which were physiologically identical, and such a mode of development was, indeed, already more or less perfectly known with regard to muscular fibres, blood-corpuscles, the ovum, and epithelium-cells. The only process common to all of them, however, seemed to be the expansion of their elementary particles after they had once assumed their proper form. The manner in which their different elementary particles were first formed appeared to vary very much. In muscular fibres they were globules, which were placed together in rows, and coalesced to form a fibre, whose growth proceeded in the direction of its length. In the blood-corpuscles it was a globule, around which a vesicle was formed, and continued to grow; in the case of the ovum, it was a globule, around which a vesicle was developed and continued to grow, and around this again a second vesicle was formed.

The formative process of the cells of plants was clearly explained by the researches of Schleiden, and appeared to be the same in all vegetable cells. So that when plants were regarded as something special, as quite distinct from the animal kingdom, one universal principle of development was observed in all the elementary particles of the vegetable organism, and physiological deductions might be drawn from it with regard to the independent vitality of the individual cells of plants, etc. But when the elementary particles of animals and plants were considered from a common point, the vegetable cells seemed to be merely a separate species, coördinate with the different species of animal cells, just as the entire class of cells was coördinate with the fibres, etc., and the uniform principle of development in vegetable cells might be explained by the slight physiological difference of their elementary particles.

The object, then, of the present investigation was to show that the mode in which the molecules composing the elementary particles of organisms are combined does not vary according to the physiological signification of those particles, but that they are everywhere arranged according to the same laws; so that whether a muscular fibre, a nerve-tube, an ovum, or a blood-corpuscle is to be formed, a corpuscle of a certain form, subject only to some modifica-ions, a cell-nucleus, is universally generated in the first instance; around this corpuscle a cell is developed, and it is the changes which one or more of these cells undergo that determine the subsequent forms of the elementary particles; in short, that there is one common principle of development for all the elementary particles of organisms.

In order to establish this point it was necessary to trace the progress of development in two given elementary parts, physiologically dissimilar, and to compare them with one another. If these not only completely agreed in growth, but in their mode of generation also, the principle was established that elementary parts, quite distinct in a physiological sense, may be developed according to the same laws. This was the theme of the first section of this work. The course of development of the cells of cartilage and of the cells of the chorda dorsalis was compared with that of vegetable cells. Were the cells of plants developed merely as infinitely minute vesicles which progressively expand, were the circumstances of their development less characteristic than those pointed out by Schleiden, a comparison, in the sense here required, would scarcely have been possible. We endeavoured to prove in the first section that the complicated process of development in the cells of plants recurs in those of cartilage and of the chorda dorsalis. We remarked the similarity in the formation of the cell-nucleus, and of its nucleolus in all its modifications, with the nucleus of vegetable cells, and the pre-existence of the cell-nucleus and the development of the cell around it, the similar situation of the nucleus in relation to the cell, the growth of the cells, and the thickening of their wall during growth, the formation of cells within cells, and the transformation of the cell-contents just as in the cells of plants. Here, then, was a complete accordance in every known stage in the progress of development of two elementary parts which are quite distinct, in a physiological sense, and it was established that the principle of development in two such parts may be the same, and so far as could be ascertained in the cases here compared, it is really the same.

But regarding the subject from this point of view we are compelled to prove the universality of this principle of development, and such was the object of the second section. For so long as we admit that there are elementary parts which originate according to entirely different laws, and between which and the cells which have just been compared as to the principle of their development there is no connexion, we must presume that there may still be some unknown difference in the laws of the formation of the parts just compared, even though they agree in many points. But, on the contrary, the greater the number of physiologically different elementary parts, which, so far as can be known, originate in a similar manner, and the greater the difference of these parts in form and physiological signification, while they agree in the perceptible phenomena of their mode of formation, the more safely may we assume that all elementary parts have one and the same fundamental principle of development. It was, in fact, shown that the elementary parts of most tissues, when traced backwards from their state of complete development to their primary condition, are only developments of cells, which so far as our observations, still incomplete, extend, seemed to be formed in a similar manner to the cells compared in the first section. As might be expected, according to this principle the cells, in their earliest stage, were almost always furnished with the characteristic nuclei, in some the pre-existence of this nucleus, and the formation of the cell around it was proved, and it was then that the cells began to undergo the various modifications, from which the diverse forms of the elementary parts of animals resulted. Thus the apparent difference in the mode of development of muscular fibres and blood-corpuscles, the former originating by the arrangement of globules in rows, the latter by the formation of a vesicle around a globule, was reconciled in the fact that muscular fibres are not elementary parts coordinate with blood-corpuscles, but that the globules composing muscular fibres at first correspond to the blood-corpuscles, and are, like them, vesicles or cells, containing the characteristic cell nucleus, which, like the nucleus of the blood-corpuscles, is probably formed before the cell. The elementary parts of all tissues are formed of cells in an analogous, though very diversified manner, so that it may be asserted, *that there is one universal principle of development for the elementary parts of organisms, however different, and that this principle is the formation of cells.* This is the chief result of the foregoing observations.

The whole of the foregoing investigation has been conducted with the object of exhibiting from observation alone the mode in which the elementary parts of organized bodies are formed. Theoretical views have been either entirely excluded, or where they were required (as in the foregoing retrospect of cell-life), for the purpose of rendering facts more clear, or preventing subsequent repetitions, they have been so presented that it can be easily seen how much is observation and how much argument.

ROSS HARRISON

b. 1871

LIVING NERVE CELLS ARE SUCCESSFULLY
GROWN OUTSIDE THE LIVING BODY

THE cells of multicellular organisms are not independent but function as units of a complex, interdependent body in which the specialized activities of each are essential to the survival of the whole. They are organized into tissues, organs, and systems, each of which performs a specific function for maintaining the organism. One of the problems that long perplexed cytologists was that of maintaining cells of a multicellular organism alive outside the body, so that their functioning and development might be studied more effectively.

Many attempts, including some efforts of Dutrochet, had been made to master the methods and techniques of maintaining single cells outside living bodies, but the problem was not solved with complete reliability until 1907, when Ross Harrison developed the technique for tissue cultures. His methods were subsequently refined, particularly by Alexis Carrel, who succeeded in culturing embryo chick heart tissue without interruption for more than thirty years.

The techniques of successful tissue culture have become an essential tool of research biologists and physicians and have been applied to a host of problems, from the culture of cancer cells to studies on the effects of radiation on living cells. When Harrison published his brilliantly simple techniques in 1907, it was recognized that a new and fascinating field had been opened up. This was effectively demonstrated by the publication in 1953 of *An Index to the Literature of Living Cells Cultivated in Vitro*, which listed more than 15,000 articles.

Harrison's complete paper therefore deserves to be included here as it appeared in the *Proceedings of the Society for Experimental Medicine and Biology*, Vol. 4, 1907. It represents a single facet of the flourishing science of cytology which had its humble origins in the work of Hooke and other pioneers.

Harrison received his training at Johns Hopkins University and did most of his teaching and research at Yale, where he served as professor from 1907 to 1938, when he retired. He continues his work there as professor emeritus. Harrison's contributions have been widely recognized. He has been awarded countless honours by biological societies and universities the world over and has served as advisor, trustee, and counsel to many research foundations. He has edited several biological research journals and has delivered the Croomian lecture of the Royal Society, the Linacre lecture at Cambridge, the Dunham lecture at Harvard, and the Harvey Society lecture.

¶ The Growth of Living Nerve Cells in Vitro

The immediate object of the following experiments was to obtain a method by which the end of a growing nerve could be brought under direct observation while alive, in order that a correct conception might be had regarding what takes place as the fibre extends during embryonic development from the nerve centre out to the periphery.

The method employed was to isolate pieces of embryonic tissue known to give rise to nerve fibres, as for example, the whole or fragments of the medullary tube or ectoderm from the branchial region, and to observe their further development. The pieces were taken from frog embryos about three mm. long, at which stage, i.e. shortly after the closure of the medullary folds, there is no visible differentiation of the nerve elements. After carefully dissecting it out the piece of tissue is removed by a fine pipette to a cover slip upon which is a drop of lymph freshly drawn from one of the lymph sacs of an adult frog. The lymph clots very quickly, holding the tissue in a fixed position. The cover slip is then inverted over a hollow slide and the rim sealed with paraffin. When reasonable aseptic precautions are taken, tissues will live under these conditions for a week and in some cases specimens have been kept alive for nearly four weeks. Such specimens may be readily observed from day to day under highly magnifying powers.

While the cell aggregates, which make up the different organs and organ complexes of the embryo, do not undergo normal transformation in form, owing no doubt to the abnormal conditions of mechanical tension to which they are subjected, nevertheless the individual tissue elements do differentiate characteristically. Groups of epidermis cells round themselves off into little spheres or stretch out into long bands, their cilia remain active for a week or more and a typical cuticular border develops. Masses of cells taken from the myotomes differentiate into muscle fibres showing fibrillae with typical striations. When portions of myotomes are left attached to a piece of the medullary cord the muscle fibres which develop will, after two or three days, exhibit frequent contractions. In pieces of nervous tissue numerous fibres are formed, though owing to the fact that they are developed largely within the mass of transplanted tissue itself, their mode of development cannot always be followed. However, in a large number of cases fibres were observed which left a mass of nerve tissue and extended out into the surrounding lymph clot. It is these structures which concern us at the present time.

In the majority of cases the fibres were not observed until they had almost completed their development, having been found usually two, occasionally three, and once or twice four days after isolation of the tissue. They consist of an almost hyaline protoplasm, entirely devoid of the yolk granules, with which the cell-bodies are gorged.

Within this protoplasm there is no definiteness of structure; though a faint fibrillation may sometimes be observed and faintly defined granules are discernible. The fibres are about $1.5-3\mu$ thick and their contours show here and there irregular varicosities. The most remarkable feature of the fibre is its enlarged end, from which extend numerous fine simple or branched filaments. The end swelling bears a resemblance to certain rhizopods and close observation reveals a continual change in form, especially as regards the origin and branching of the filaments. In fact the changes are so rapid that it is difficult to draw the details accurately. It is clear we have before us a mass of protoplasm undergoing amoeboid movements. If we examine sections of young normal embryos shortly after the first nerves have developed, we find exactly similar structures at the end of the developing nerve fibres. This is especially so in the case of the fibres which are connected with the giant cells described by Rohon and Beard.

Still more instructive are the cases in which the fibre is brought under observation before it has completed its growth. Then it is found that the end is very active and that its movement results in the drawing out and lengthening of the fibre to which it is attached. One fibre was observed to lengthen almost $20\ \mu$ in 25 minutes, another over $25\ \mu$ in 50 minutes. The longest fibres observed were 0.2 mm. in length.

When the placodal thickenings of the branchial region are isolated, similar fibres are formed and in several of these cases they have been seen to arise from individual cells. On the other hand, other tissues of the embryo such as myotomes, yolk endoderm, notochord, and indifferent ectoderm from the abdominal region do not give rise to structures of this kind. There can therefore be no doubt that we are dealing with a specific characteristic of nervous tissue.

It has not yet been found possible to make permanent specimens which show the isolated nerve fibres completely intact. The structures are so delicate that the mere immersion in the preserving fluid is sufficient to cause violent tearing and this very frequently results in the tearing away of the tissue in its entirety from the clot. Nevertheless, sections have been cut of some of the specimens and nerves have been traced from the walls of the medullary tube, but they were in all cases broken off short.

In view of this difficulty an effort, which resulted successfully, was made to obtain permanent specimens in a somewhat different way. A piece of medullary cord about four or five segments long was excised from an embryo and this was replaced by a cylindrical clot of proper length and calibre, which was obtained by allowing blood or lymph of an adult frog to clot in a capillary tube. No difficulty was experienced in healing the clot into the embryo in proper position. After two, three, or four days the specimens were preserved and examined in serial sections. It was found that the funicular fibres from the brain and anterior part of the cord, consisting of naked axones without sheath cells, had grown for a considerable distance into the clot.

These observations show beyond question that the nerve fibre develops by the outflowing of protoplasm from the central cells. This protoplasm retains its amoeboid activity at its distal end, the result being that it is drawn out into a long thread which becomes the axis cylinder. No other cells or living structures take part in this process. The development of the nerve fibre is thus brought about by means of one of the very primitive properties of living protoplasm, amoeboid movement, which, though probably common to some extent to all the cells of the embryo, is especially accentuated in the nerve cells at this period of development.

The possibility becomes apparent of applying the above method to the study of the influences which act upon a growing nerve. While at present it seems certain that the mere outgrowth of the fibres is largely independent of external stimuli, it is of course probable that in the body of the embryo there are many influences which guide the moving end and bring about contact with the proper end structure. The method here employed may be of value in analysing these factors.

═══════

V

THE PROCESSES OF LIFE

STRUCTURE and function are interdependent. Man has been interested in the functioning of his body and of the living things from the earliest days, but the scientific investigation of body processes was impossible without an accurate knowledge of body structure. The monumental studies of human anatomy by Vesalius unquestionably served as the starting point of the revolution in medicine. They were soon followed by one of the earliest and most effective applications of the method of direct observation and experiment to the study of nature: the work of Harvey completed the transition from the ancient and medieval approach to the modern study of the function of living things.

The extent of the revolution in man's concept of body function can be appreciated only with some knowledge of the traditional views which were so abruptly superseded. Medical thought for some two thousand years before Harvey was dominated by the doctrine of the four humours, generally attributed to Polybus of the Hippocratic school (c. 390 B.C.). According to this doctrine, the body is made up of four humours – blood (sanguis), phlegm (pituita), black bile (melancholia), and yellow bile (cholera) – just as the four elements – fire, water, earth, and air – make up non-living matter. The elements and humours were associated, yellow bile corresponding with air, black bile with earth, blood with fire, and phlegm with water. Every element was compounded of a pair of primary qualities: fire combined the qualities heat and dryness, earth cold and dryness, water cold and moisture, and air heat and moisture.

Bodily health depended on the presence of the four

humours in the correct proportions, and diseases arose from an excess of one or another of the humours. Thus diseases were classified as sanguine, choleric, melancholic, or phlegmatic, according to which humour was in excess. Each person had a tendency to one of the four types of disease, and each humour was associated with a special organ of the body – e.g. blood with the liver, or phlegm with the lungs. Many expressions now used to describe temperament or personality – phlegmatic, melancholic, sanguine, or choleric – reveal the strength of this traditional view.

The earliest thinkers, aware of the uniqueness of life, looked for some common principle or quality which separated living from non-living matter. Aristotle found the principle in what was known as *psyche*, a word which has had an interesting development in meaning. Originally, it meant 'breath' and was used as synonymous with life, since breathing is the most obvious sign of life. Later it came to mean life; then the principle or quality of life; and finally soul or spirit. The absence of any experimental basis for concepts dealing with the functions of living things enabled such terms as psyche or humour to acquire a mystical significance which prevented growth and inhibited change.

A later synthesis which had even greater influence on medical thought than Aristotle's was that of Galen, which became the authoritative word on the structure and function of the human body. Galen's ingenious explanation of the functioning of the body and the activities of the circulatory system served medicine until the time of Vesalius and Harvey.

According to Galen, the basic principle of life is a spirit, or *pneuma* (another Greek word used for breath, spirit, etc.), breathed from the general World-Spirit into the lung, from which it passes through a blood vessel (known to us as the pulmonary vein) to the left ventricle of the heart and thence into the blood. But where does the blood originate? The mixture of digested materials in the digestive tract is carried to the liver by the portal vein and changed by the liver into venous blood, imbued with another *pneuma* which is present in all living substance. The blood thus picks up 'natural spirit' in the liver and nutritive material from the intestines and is distributed from the liver by ebbing and flowing through the venous system. One branch vein reaches the right side of the heart, from which some blood comes to the lungs by way of the pulmonary artery. Here impurities are expelled from the body and the blood in the right ventricle is turned back into the venous system.

One of Galen's main points was his belief that there were minute pores by which blood could trickle from the right ventricle into the left ventricle. Although these pores were never demonstrated, the belief persisted until Harvey showed otherwise. In the left ventricle, said Galen, the blood meets the pneuma brought from the outside by the pulmonary vein and is elaborated as the vital spirit, to be carried by arteries to many parts of the body. One of these branch arteries brings blood to the base of the brain, where the blood is infused with a third pneuma, the animal spirit, which is carried by the nerves, believed by Galen to be hollow. Thus three spirits dominate the functioning of the body – the natural spirit, from the outside; the vital spirit, innate in all living substance; and the animal spirit, from the brain.

Galen's ingenious experiments on the functions of the nervous system and his knowledge of the functions of the spinal cord were not improved or extended until the work of Bell, Müller, and Magendie in the nineteenth century. Like Ptolemy in astronomy and Aristotle in physics and philosophy, Galen remained the authority in medicine for more than thirteen hundred years.

Harvey first clearly presented the idea that each organ has a discoverable function related to the functions of all other organs in the body and to the body as a whole.

Using this new approach, Harvey made a discovery which represents the turning point in the history of the study of life functions. The details of Harvey's contribution will be discussed in the introduction to the reading illustrating his work. Its most decisive effect was the complete abandonment of the mystical view, whose vague and almost meaningless terms, such as psyche, pneuma, vital spirit, and others, were replaced by a precise vocabulary based on the concepts of the newer physics and chemistry.

The study of life processes in the spirit of Harvey grew rapidly through the seventeenth and eighteenth centuries and moved along a number of paths which led to the specialization characteristic of modern physiology. During the nineteenth century, these studies were accelerated by the great developments in organic and inorganic chemistry. This continuing story of discovery involves the accomplishments of so many scientists that a mere listing of the notable contributors would fill several pages. In this section we can do no more than indicate a few of the fields of research which were first explored during this period. Malpighi's discovery of the capillaries supplemented Harvey's work and completed the modern account of the circulation of the blood. Van Helmont demonstrated by experiment the role of water in the growth of plants. Hales was a proponent of rigorous quantitative procedures in the investigation of plant and animal functions. Ingenhousz, physician and engineer, was a pioneer in the experimental study of photosynthesis – the basic food-manufacturing process in plants – which is only now beginning to yield some of its secrets. Johannes Müller is regarded as one of the great biologists of all time, largely responsible for determining the general direction of modern experimental work in physiology, by applying chemistry, physics and comparative anatomy to physiological problems. As teacher and writer he influenced many great biologists. Claude Bernard was a master of experimental techniques, a perceptive, highly original investigator who brought his talents to more important themes – especially the metabolism of carbohydrates, endocrine secretions, and the concept of the constant internal environment.

WILLIAM HARVEY
1578–1657

THE CIRCULATION OF THE BLOOD IS
DEMONSTRATED AND PROVED

ALTHOUGH William Harvey was himself a product of the intellectual climate of his time, he was able further to loosen the fetters of that medieval authoritarianism which Copernicus, Galileo, and Vesalius had done so much to remove from the mind of man. By offering an explanation of a body process in physical terms, Harvey initiated the modern science of physiology. His work thus served as a foundation stone of biology and medicine as sciences and was truly revolutionary in its effects.

Harvey studied at Cambridge and then went to practise medicine in London and became associated with St Bartholomew's Hospital. When Harvey began his medical work, the spirit of inquiry was in the air. Gilbert had already published his experiments and observations on magnets and Francis Bacon (who became a patient of Harvey) was advocating the virtues of the inductive method of acquiring scientific knowledge by accumulating observations and testing the results by experiments.

Harvey was elected a Fellow of the Royal College of Physicians and appointed physician first to King James I and then to Charles I, who gave him access to the royal deer parks at Windsor for experimental purposes. It was at this time that Harvey became interested in the problem of the action of the heart and the circulation of the blood. During his investigations Harvey dissected some forty species of animals, many of them cold-blooded, in which the heart beats slowly and can be more readily observed.

Harvey first referred to the circular movement of the blood in his lectures on anatomy delivered at the Royal

College of Physicians from 1615 onwards. He did not publish an account of his theory until 1628 by which time he had accumulated experimental evidence to support it. The book was a small volume of some seventy-eight pages, written in Latin and bearing the title *Exercitatio anatomica de motu cordis et sanguinis in animalibus* ('Anatomical Dissertation Concerning the Motion of the Heart and Blood in Animals').

The argument and demonstration were classic in their simplicity and lacked but one element to complete the account of circulation: Harvey did not demonstrate the existence of capillaries, the observation of which required a better miscroscope than Harvey had at his disposal. Shortly after Harvey's death, Marcello Malpighi was able to complete the story of circulation by observing the capillaries of the lungs.

Harvey's demonstration can be followed easily, and its sequence makes an impressive and convincing scientific proof. Harvey began by observing that when the heart contracted it hardened, and he concluded from this that the heart was a hollow muscle. Every contraction of the heart was accompanied by an expansion of the arteries which could be felt in the pulse, indicating that the arteries expanded because blood was pumped into them by the heart.

The study of the heart revealed valves between the right auricle and right ventricle, and Harvey showed that when the right ventricle contracts the blood must pass via the pulmonary artery to the lungs, since the valves prevent its return to the auricle. When the ventricle relaxes, the blood does not return to it from the pulmonary artery, because the artery has valves which prevent this.

The movement of blood through the left side of the heart is similar to that of the blood entering the left auricle from the pulmonary vein. From the left auricle it moves to the left ventricle, with valves between the auricle and the ventricle preventing the return of blood when the ventricle contracts. The only exit for the blood from the left ventricle is the aorta, the largest artery in the body.

It was at this point in his argument that Harvey made his crucial calculation. Estimating the amount of blood pumped out of the heart by each beat (about 2 ounces) and multiplying this quantity by the number of beats per minute (about seventy-two), he showed that the heart pumps about nine pounds of blood through the whole system in a matter of minutes. He reasoned that the same blood must return to the heart and be pumped around again and again.

After a simple experiment in which he severed an artery and noted that the animal bled to death, Harvey concluded that this happens because the blood that is lost does not reach the veins and thus cannot be returned to the arteries. As he described it: 'I began to think whether there might not be a movement, as it were, in a circle. I saw that the blood, forced by the action of the left ventricle into the arteries, was sent out to the body at large. In like manner the blood forced by the action of the left ventricle into the pulmonary artery is sent out to the lungs ... the blood in animals is impelled in a circle, and is in a state of ceaseless movement.'

Harvey continued his investigations throughout his life. In 1651 he published a treatise on the embryological development of animals entitled *De generatione animalium*, in which he reached some valuable conclusions on animal development and coined a phrase that was to prove to be prophetic: *Ex ovo omnia* (everything develops from the egg). Nothing that Harvey accomplished subsequently had such significance as his study of circulation; in fact, very few discoveries recorded in scientific history equal it and none surpass it. The selection that follows is taken from the English translation from the Latin by Robert Willis in the Everyman Edition.

¶ *Chapter I: The Author's Motives for Writing*

When I first gave my mind to vivisections, as a means of discovering the motions and uses of the heart, and sought to discover these from actual inspection, and not from the writings of others, I found the task so truly arduous, so full of difficulties, that I was almost tempted to think, with Fracastorius, that the motion of the heart was only to be comprehended by God. For I could neither rightly perceive at first when the systole and when the diastole took place, nor when and where dilatation and contraction occurred, by reason of the rapidity of the motion, which in many animals is accomplished in the twinkling of an eye, coming and going like a flash of lightning; so that the systole presented itself to me now from this point, now from that; the diastole the same; and then everything was reversed, the motions occurring, as it seemed, variously and confusedly together. My mind was therefore greatly unsettled, nor did I know what I should myself conclude, nor what believe from others; I was not surprised that Andreas Laurentius should have said that the motion of the heart was as perplexing as the flux and reflux of Euripus had appeared to Aristotle.

At length, and by using greater and daily diligence, having frequent recourse to vivisections, employing a variety of animals for the purpose, and collating numerous observations, I thought that I had attained to the truth, that I should extricate myself and escape from this labyrinth, and that I had discovered what I so much desired, both the motion and the use of the heart and arteries; since which time I have not hesitated to expose my views upon these subjects, not only in private to my friends, but also in public, in my anatomical lectures, after the manner of the Academy of old.

These views, as usual, pleased some more, others less; some chid and calumniated me, and laid it to me as a crime that I had dared to depart from the precepts and opinion of all anatomists; others desired further explanations of the novelties, which they said were both worthy of consideration, and might perchance be found of signal use. At length, yielding to the requests of my friends, that all might be made participators in my labours, and partly moved by the envy of others, who receiving my views with uncandid minds and understanding them indifferently, have essayed to traduce me publicly, I have been moved to commit these things to the press, in order that all may be enabled to form an opinion both of me and my labours. This step I take all the more willingly, seeing that Hieronymus Fabricius of Aquapendente, although he has accurately and learnedly delineated almost every one of the several parts of animals in a special work, has left the heart alone untouched. Finally, if any use or benefit to this department of the republic of letters should accrue from my labours, it will, perhaps, be allowed that I have not lived idly, and, as the old man in the comedy says:

> For never yet has any one attained
> To such perfection, but that time, and place,
> And use, have brought addition to his knowledge;
> Or made correction, or admonished him,
> That he was ignorant of much which he
> Had thought he knew; or led him to reject
> What he had once esteemed of highest price.

So will it, perchance, be found with reference to the heart at this time; or others, at least, starting from hence, the way pointed out to them, advancing under the guidance of a happier genius, may make occasion to proceed more fortunately, and to inquire more accurately.

⁋ Chapter II: Of the Motions of the Heart, as seen in the Dissection of Living Animals

In the first place, then, when the chest of a living animal is laid open and the capsule that immediately surrounds the heart is slit up or removed, the organ is seen now to move, now to be at rest – there is a time when it moves, and a time when it is motionless.

These things are more obvious in the colder animals, such as toads, frogs, serpents, small fishes, crabs, shrimps, snails, and shell-fish. They also become more distinct in warm-blooded animals, such as the dog and hog, if they be attentively noted when the heart begin to flag, to move more slowly, and, as it were, to die: the movements then become slower and rarer, the pauses longer, by which it is made much more easy to perceive and unravel what the motions really are, and how they are performed. In the pause as in death, the heart is soft, flaccid, exhausted, lying, as it were, at rest.

In the motion, and interval in which this is accomplished, three principal circumstances are to be noted:

1. That the heart is erected, and rises upwards to a point, so that at this time it strikes against the breast and the pulse is felt externally.

2. That it is everywhere contracted, but more especially towards the sides, so that it looks narrower, relatively longer, more drawn together. The heart of an eel taken out of the body of the animal and placed upon the table or the hand, shows these particulars; but the same things are manifest in the heart of small fishes and of those colder animals where the organ is more conical or elongated.

3. The heart being grasped in the hand, is felt to become harder during its action. Now this hardness proceeds from tension, precisely as when the forearm is grasped, its tendons are perceived to become tense and resilient when the fingers are moved.

4. It may further be observed in fishes, and the colder-blooded animals, such as frogs, serpents, etc., that the heart, when it moves, becomes of a paler colour, when quiescent of a deeper blood-red colour.

From these particulars it appeared evident to me that the motion of the heart consists in a certain universal tension – both contraction in the line of its fibres, and constriction in every sense. It becomes erect, hard, and of diminished size during its action; the motion is plainly of the same nature as that of the muscles when they contract in the line of their sinews and fibres; for the muscles, when in action, acquire vigour and tenseness, and from soft become hard, prominent, and thickened: in the same manner the heart.

We are therefore authorized to conclude that the heart, at the moment of its action, is at once constricted on all sides, rendered thicker in its parietes and smaller in its ventricles, and so made apt to project or expel its charge of blood. This, indeed, is made sufficiently manifest by the fourth observation preceding, in which we have seen that the heart, by squeezing out the blood it contains becomes paler, and then when it sinks into repose and the ventricle is filled anew with blood, that the deeper crimson colour returns. But no one need remain in doubt of the fact, for if the ventricle be pierced the blood will be seen to be forcibly projected outwards upon each motion or pulsation when the heart is tense.

These things, therefore, happen together or at the same instant: the tension of the heart, the pulse of its apex, which is felt externally by its striking against the chest, the thickening of its parietes, and the forcible expulsion of the blood it contains by the constriction of its ventricles.

Hence the very opposite of the opinions commonly received, appears to be true; inasmuch as it is generally believed that when the heart strikes the breast and the pulse is felt without, the heart is dilated in its ventricles and is filled with blood; but the contrary of this is the fact, and the heart, when it contracts [and the shock is given], is emptied. Whence the motion which is generally regarded as the diastole of the the heart, is in truth its systole. And in like manner the intrinsic motion of the heart is not the diastole but the systole; neither is it in the diastole that the heart grows firm and tense, but in the systole, for then only, when tense, is it moved and made vigorous.

Neither is it by any means to be allowed that the heart only moves in the line of its straight fibres, although the great Vesalius, giving this notion countenance, quotes a bundle of osiers bound into a pyramidal heap in illustration; meaning, that as the apex is approached to the base, so are the sides made to bulge out in the fashion of arches, the cavities to dilate, the ventricles to acquire the form of a cupping-glass and so to suck in the blood. But the true effect of every one of its fibres is to constringe the heart at the same time that they render it tense; and this rather with the effect of thickening and amplifying the walls and substance of the organ than enlarging its ventricles. And, again, as the fibres run from the apex to the base, and draw the apex towards the base, they do not tend to make the walls of the heart bulge out in circles, but rather the contrary; inasmuch as every fibre that is circularly disposed, tends to become straight when it contracts; and is distended laterally and thickened, as in the case of muscular fibres in general, when they contract, that is, when they are shortened longitudinally, as we see them in the bellies of the muscles of the body at large. To all this, let it be added, that not only are the ventricles contracted in virtue of the direction and condensation of their walls, but further, that those fibres, or bands, styled nerves by Aristotle, which are so conspicuous in the ventricles of the larger animals, and contain all the straight fibres, (the parietes of the heart containing only circular ones,) when they contract simultaneously, by an admirable adjustment all the internal surfaces are drawn together, as if with cords, and so is the charge of blood expelled with force.

Neither is it true, as vulgarly believed, that the heart by any dilatation or motion of its own has the power of drawing the blood into the ventricles; for when it acts and becomes tense, the blood is expelled; when it relaxes and sinks together it receives the blood in the manner and wise which will by and by be explained.

¶ *Chapter III: Of the Motion of Arteries, as seen in the Dissection of Living Animals*

In connexion with the motions of the heart these things are further to be observed having reference to the motions and pulses of the arteries:

1. At the moment the heart contracts, and when the breast is struck, when in short the organ is in its state of systole, the arteries are dilated, yield a pulse, and are in the state of diastole. In like manner, when the right ventricle contracts and propels its charge of blood, the arterial vein [the pulmonary artery] is distended at the same time with the other arteries of the body.

2. When the left ventricle ceases to act, to contract, to pulsate, the pulse in the arteries also ceases; further, when this ventricle contracts languidly, the pulse in the arteries is scarcely perceptible. In like manner, the pulse in the right ventricle failing, the pulse in the vena arteriosa [pulmonary artery] ceases also.

3. Further, when an artery is divided or punctured, the blood is seen to be forcibly propelled from the wound at the moment the left ventricle contracts; and, again, when the pulmonary artery is wounded, the blood will be seen spouting forth with violence at the instant when the right ventricle contracts.

So also in fishes, if the vessel which leads from the heart to the gills be divided, at the moment when the heart becomes tense and contracted, at the same moment does the blood flow with force from the divided vessel.

In the same way, finally, when we see the blood in arteriotomy projected now to a greater, now to a less distance, and that the greater jet corresponds to the diastole of the artery and to the time when the heart contracts and strikes the ribs, and is in its state of systole, we understand that the blood is expelled by the same movement.

From these facts it is manifest, in opposition to commonly received opinions, that the diastole of the arteries corresponds with the time of the heart's systole; and that the arteries are filled and distended by the blood forced into them by the contraction of the ventricles; the arteries, therefore, are distended, because they are filled like sacs or bladders, and are not filled because they expand like bellows. It is in virtue of one and the same cause, therefore, that all the arteries of the body pulsate, viz. the contraction of the left ventricle; in the same way as the pulmonary artery pulsates by the contraction of the right ventricle.

Finally, that the pulses of the arteries are due to the impulses of the blood from the left ventricle, may be illustrated by blowing into a glove, when the whole of the fingers will be found to become distended at one and the same time, and in their tension to bear some resemblance to the pulse. For in the ratio of the tension is the pulse of the heart, fuller, stronger, more frequent as that acts more vigorously, still preserving the rhythm and volume and order of the heart's contractions. Nor is it to be expected that because of the motion of the blood, the time at which the contraction of the heart takes place, and that at which the pulse in an artery (especially a distant one) is felt, shall be otherwise than simultaneous: it is here the same as in blowing up a glove or bladder; for in a plenum (as in a drum, a long piece of timber, etc.) the stroke and the motion occur at both extremities at the same time. Aristotle,* too, has said, 'the blood of all animals palpitates within their veins (meaning the arteries,) and by the pulse is sent everywhere simultaneously.' And further,† 'thus do all the veins pulsate together and by successive strokes, because they all depend upon the heart; and, as it is always in motion, so are they likewise always moving together, but by successive movements.' It is well to observe with Galen, in this place, that the old philosophers called the arteries veins.

* *De animalia*, iii, cap. 9.   † *De respiratione*, cap. 20.

I happened upon one occasion to have a particular case under my care, which plainly satisfied me of this truth: A certain person was affected with a large pulsating tumour on the right side of the neck, called an aneurism, just at that part where the artery descends into the axilla, produced by an erosion of the artery itself, and daily increasing in size; this tumour was visibly distended as it received the charge of blood brought to it by the artery, with each stroke of the heart: the connexion of parts was obvious when the body of the patient came to be opened after his death. The pulse in the corresponding arm was small, in consequence of the greater portion of the blood being diverted into the tumour and so intercepted.

Whence it appears that wherever the motion of the blood through the arteries is impeded, whether it be by compression or infarction, or interception, there do the remote divisions of the arteries beat less forcibly, seeing that the pulse of the arteries is nothing more than the impulse or shock of the blood in these vessels.

¶ *Chapter VIII: Of the Quantity of Blood Passing Through the Heart from the Veins to the Arteries*

Thus far I have spoken of the passage of the blood from the veins into the arteries, and of the manner in which it is transmitted and distributed by the action of the heart; points to which some, moved either by the authority of Galen or Columbus, or the reasonings of others, will give in their adhesion. But what remains to be said upon the quantity and source of the blood which thus passes, is of so novel and unheard-of character, that I not only fear injury to myself from the envy of a few, but I tremble lest I have mankind at large for my enemies, so much doth wont and custom, that become as another nature, and doctrine once sown and that hath struck deep root, and respect for antiquity influence all men: Still the die is cast, and my trust is in my love of truth, and the candour that inheres in cultivated minds. And sooth to say, when I surveyed my mass of evidence, whether derived from vivi-sections, and my various reflections on them, or from the ventricles of the heart and the vessels that enter into and issue from them, the symmetry and size of these conduits – for nature doing nothing in vain, would never have given them so large a relative size without a purpose – or from the arrangement and intimate structure of the valves in particular, and of the other parts of the heart in general, with many things besides, I frequently and seriously be-thought me, and long revolved in my mind, what might be the quantity of blood which was transmitted, in how short a time its passage might be effected, and the like; and not finding it possible that this could be supplied by the juices of the ingested aliment without the veins on the one hand becoming drained, and the arteries on the other getting ruptured through the excessive charge of blood, unless the blood should somehow find its way from the arteries into the veins, and so return to the right side of the heart; I began to think whether there might not be as a MOTION, AS IT WERE, IN A CIRCLE. Now this I afterwards found to be true; and I finally saw that the blood, forced by the action of the left ventricle into the arteries, was distributed to the body at large, and its several parts, in the same manner as it is sent through the lungs, impelled by the right ventricle into the pulmonary artery, and that it then passed through the veins and along the vena cava, and so round to the left ventricle in the manner already indi-cated. Which motion we may be allowed to call circular, in the same way as Aristotle says that the air and the rain emulate the circular motion of the superior bodies; for the moist earth, warmed by the sun, evaporates; the vapours drawn upwards are condensed, and descending in the form of rain, moisten the earth again; and by this arrangement are generations of living things produced; and in like manner too are tempests and meteors engendered by the circular motion, and by the approach and recession of the sun.

And so, in all likelihood, does it come to pass in the body, through the motion of the blood; the various parts are nourished, cherished, quickened by the warmer, more perfect, vaporous, spirituous, and, as I may say, alimentive blood; which, on the contrary, in contact with these parts becomes cooled, coagulated, and, so to speak, effete; whence it returns to its sovereign the heart, as if to its source, or to the inmost home of the body, there to recover its state of excellence or perfection. Here it resumes its due fluidity and receives an infusion of natural heat – powerful, fervid, a kind of treasury of life, and is impregnated with spirits, and it might be said with balsam; and thence it is again dispersed; and all this depends on the motion and action of the heart.

The heart, consequently, is the beginning of life; the sun of the microcosm, even as the sun in his turn might well be designated the heart of the world; for it is the heart by whose virtue and pulse the blood is moved, perfected, made apt to nourish, and is preserved from corruption and coagulation; it is the household divinity which, discharging its function, nourishes, cherishes, quickens the whole body, and is indeed the foundation of life, the source of all action. But of these things we shall speak more opportunely when we come to speculate upon the final cause of this motion of the heart.

Hence, since the veins are the conduits and vessels that transport the blood, they are of two kinds, the cava and the aorta; and this not by reason of there being two sides of the body, as Aristotle has it, but because of the difference of office; nor yet, as is commonly said, in consequence of any diversity of structure, for in many animals, as I have said, the vein does not differ from the artery in the thickness of its tunics, but solely in virtue of their several destinies and uses. A vein and an artery, both styled vein by the ancients, and that not undeservedly, as Galen has remarked, because the one, the artery to wit, is the vessel which carries the blood from the heart to the body at large, the other or vein of the present day bringing it back from the general system to the heart; the former is the conduit from, the latter the channel to, the heart; the latter contains the cruder, effete blood, rendered unfit for nutrition; the former transmits the digested, perfect, peculiarly nutritive fluid.

¶ *Chapter XIII: The Third Position is Confirmed; and the Circulation of the Blood is Demonstrated from it*

Thus far have we spoken of the quantity of blood passing through the heart and the lungs in the centre of the body, and in like manner from the arteries into the veins in the peripheral parts and the body at large. We have yet to explain, however, in what manner the blood finds its way back to the heart from the extremities by the veins, and how and in what way these are the only vessels that convey the blood from the external to the central parts; which done, I conceive that the three fundamental propositions laid down for the circulation of the blood will be so plain, so well established, so obviously true, that they may claim general credence. Now the remaining position will be made sufficiently clear from the valves which are found in the cavities of the veins themselves, from the uses of these, and from experiments cognizable by the senses.

The celebrated Hieronymus Fabricius of Aquapendente, a most skilful anatomist, and venerable old man, or, as the learned Riolan will have it, Jacobus Silvius, first gave representations of the valves in the veins, which consist of raised or loose portions of the inner membranes of these vessels, of extreme delicacy, and a sigmoid or semilunar shape. They are situated at different distances from one another, and diversely in different individuals; they are connate at the sides of the veins; they are directed upwards or towards the trunks of the veins; the two – for there are for the most part two together – regard each other, mutually touch, and are so ready to come into contact by their edges, that if anything attempt to pass from the trunks into the branches of the veins, or from the greater vessels into the less, they completely prevent it; they are farther so arranged, that the horns of those that succeed are opposite the middle of the convexity of those that precede, and so on alternately.

The discoverer of these valves did not rightly understand their use, nor have succeeding anatomists added anything to our knowledge: for their office is by no means explained when we are told that it is to hinder the blood, by its weight, from all flowing into inferior parts; for the edges of the valves in the jugular veins hang downwards, and are so contrived that they prevent the blood from rising upwards; the valves, in a word, do not invariably look upwards, but always towards the trunks of the veins, invariably towards the seat of the heart. I, and indeed others, have sometimes found valves in the emulgent veins, and in those of the mesentery, the edges of which were directed towards the vena cava and vena portae. Let it be added that there are no valves in the arteries [save at their roots], and that dogs, oxen, etc., have invariably valves at the divisions of their crural veins, in the veins that meet towards the top of the os sacrum, and in those branches which come from the haunches, in which no such effect of gravity from the erect position was to be apprehended. Neither are there valves in the jugular veins for the purpose of guarding against apoplexy, as some have said; because in sleep the head is more apt to be influenced by the contents of the carotid arteries. Neither are the valves present, in order that the blood may be retained in the divarications or smaller trunks and minuter branches, and not be suffered to flow entirely into the more open and capacious channels; for they occur where there are no divarications; although it must be owned that they are most frequent at the points where branches join. Neither do they exist for the purpose of rendering the current of blood more slow from the centre of the body; for it seems likely that the blood would be disposed to flow with sufficient slowness of its own accord, as it would have to pass from larger into continually smaller vessels, being separated from the mass and fountain-head, and attaining from warmer into colder places.

But the valves are solely made and instituted lest the blood should pass from the greater into the lesser veins, and either rupture them or cause them to become varicose; lest, instead of advancing from the extreme to the central parts of the body, the blood should rather proceed along the veins from the centre to the extremities; but the delicate valves, while they readily open in the right direction, entirely prevent all such contrary motion, being so situated and arranged, that if anything escapes, or is less perfectly obstructed by the cornua of the one above, the fluid passing, as it were, by the chinks between the cornua, it is immediately received on the convexity of the one beneath, which is placed transversely with reference to the former, and so is effectually hindered from getting any farther.

And this I have frequently experienced in my dissections of the veins: if I attempted to pass a probe from the trunk of the veins into one of the smaller branches, whatever care I took I found it impossible to introduce it far any way, by reason of the valves; whilst, on the contrary, it was most easy to push it along in the opposite direction, from without inwards, or from the branches towards the trunks and roots. In many places two valves are so placed and fitted, that when raised they come exactly together in the middle of the vein, and are there united by the contact of their margins; and so accurate is the adaptation, that neither by the eye nor by any other means of examination can the slightest chink along the line of contact be perceived. But if the probe be now introduced from the extreme towards the more central parts, the valves, like the flood-gates of a river, give way, and are most readily pushed aside. The effect of this arrangement plainly is to prevent all motion of the blood from the heart and *vena cava*, whether it be upwards towards the head, or downwards towards the feet, or to either side towards the arms, not a drop can pass; all motion of the blood, beginning in the larger and tending towards the smaller veins, is opposed and resisted by them; whilst the motion that proceeds from the lesser to end in the larger branches is favoured, or, at all events, a free and open passage is left for it.

But that this truth may be made the more apparent, let an arm be tied up above the elbow as if for phlebotomy (A, A, fig. 1).* At intervals in the course of the veins, especially in labouring people and those whose veins are large, certain knots or elevations (B, C, D, E, F) will be perceived, and this not only at the places where a branch is received (E, F), but also where none enters (C, D): these knots or risings are all formed by valves, which thus show themselves externally. And now if you press the blood from the space above one of the valves, from H to O (fig. 2), and keep the point of a finger upon the vein inferiorly, you will see no influx of blood from above; the portion of the vein between the point of the finger and the valve O will be obliterated; yet will the vessel continue sufficiently distended above that valve (O, G). The blood being thus pressed out, and the vein emptied, if you now apply a finger of the other hand upon the distended part of the vein above the valve O (fig. 3), and press downwards, you will find that you cannot force the blood through or beyond the valve; but the greater effort you use, you will only see the portion of vein that is between the finger and the valve become more distended, that portion of the vein which is below the valve remaining all the while empty (H, O, fig. 3).

It would therefore appear that the function of the valves in the veins is the same as that of the three sigmoid valves

* [See Plate 8.]

which we find at the commencement of the aorta and pulmonary artery, viz., to prevent all reflux of the blood that is passing over them.

Farther, the arm being bound as before, and the veins looking full and distended, if you press at one part in the course of a vein with the point of a finger (L, fig. 4), and then with another finger streak the blood upwards beyond the next valve (N), you will perceive that this portion of the vein continues empty (L N), and that the blood cannot retrograde, precisely as we have already seen the case to be in fig. 2; but the finger first applied (H, fig. 2, L, fig. 4), being removed, immediately the vein is filled from below, and the arm becomes as it appears at D C, fig. 1. That the blood in the veins therefore proceeds from inferior or more remote to superior parts, and towards the heart, moving in these vessels in this and not in the contrary direction, appears most obviously. And although in some places the valves, by not acting with such perfect accuracy, or where there is but a single valve, do not seem totally to prevent the passage of the blood from the centre, still the greater number of them plainly do so; and then, where things appear contrived more negligently, this is compensated either by the more frequent occurrence or more perfect action of the succeeding valves or in some other way: the veins, in short, as they are the free and open conduits of the blood returning *to* the heart, so are they effectually prevented from serving as its channels of distribution *from* the heart.

But this other circumstance has to be noted: The arm being bound, and the veins made turgid, and the valves prominent, as before, apply the thumb or finger over a vein in the situation of one of the valves in such a way as to compress it, and prevent any blood from passing upwards from the hand; then, with a finger of the other hand, streak the blood in the vein upwards till it has passed the next valve above, (N, fig. 4) the vessel now remains empty; but the finger at L being removed for an instant, the vein is immediately filled from below; apply the finger again, and having in the same manner streaked the blood upwards, again remove the finger below, and again the vessel becomes distended as before; and this repeat, say a thousand times, in a short space of time. And now compute the quantity of blood which you have thus pressed up beyond the valve, and then multiplying the assumed quantity by one thousand, you will find that so much blood has passed through a certain portion of the vessel; and I do now believe that you will find yourself convinced of the circulation of the blood, and of its rapid motion. But if in this experiment you say that a violence is done to nature, I do not doubt but that, if you proceed in the same way, only taking as great a length of vein possible, and merely remark with what rapidity the blood flows upwards, and fills the vessel from below, you will come to the same conclusion.

¶ *Chapter XIV: Conclusion of the Demonstration of the Circulation*

And now I may be allowed to give in brief my view of the circulation of the blood, and to propose it for general adoption.

Since all things, both argument and ocular demonstration, show that the blood passes through the lungs and heart by the action of the [auricles and] ventricles, and is sent for distribution to all parts of the body, where it makes its way into the veins and pores of the flesh, and then flows by the veins from the circumference on every side to the centre, from the lesser to the greater veins, and is by them finally discharged into the vena cava and right auricle of the heart, and this in such a quantity or in such a flux and reflux thither by the arteries, hither by the veins, as cannot possibly be supplied by the ingesta, and is much greater than can be required for mere purposes of nutrition; it is absolutely necessary to conclude that the blood in the animal body is impelled in a circle, and is in a state of ceaseless motion; that this is the act or function which the heart performs by means of its pulse; and that it is the sole and only end of the motion and contraction of the heart.

MARCELLO MALPIGHI
1628–94

THE DESCRIPTION OF THE CAPILLARIES OF THE LUNGS COMPLETES THE THEORY OF BLOOD CIRCULATION

MARCELLO MALPIGHI, an original and penetrating observer, succeeded in producing an impressive array of discoveries in spite of harassment, dispute, and jealousy which threatened to injure both his good name and his scientific reputation. A family dispute about the boundary lines between his father's property and the land of the Sbaraglia family developed into a feud in which members of the Sbaraglia family and their representatives persecuted Malpighi all his life. He faced these unmerited attacks with dignity and moderation, and he enhanced his reputation by his uncommonly gentle and modest disposition.

Born near Bologna, Malpighi studied at its university, where he received the degree of Doctor of Medicine and later became Professor of Medicine. To escape persecution he moved to Pisa, and here he became an associate of Borelli, a professor of mathematics noted for his application of physics to physiology, especially in the study of movement in animals.

Because the climate of Pisa impaired his health, Malpighi returned to Bologna, and it was there that he made most of his discoveries in physiology, the microscopic anatomy of plants and animals, the anatomy of insects, and the development of animals and plants.

In 1667 he was invited by Henry Oldenburg, secretary of the Royal Society, to become a regular correspondent and a year later he became a fellow. Among his fairly regular communications to the Royal Society was a monograph on the structure and life history of the silkworm (*De bomyce*). He also described accurately the heart, nerve cord, and the spiracles of the bee as well as its metamorphosis.

Malpighi's treatise on the anatomy of plants contained exceptional illustrations of their microscopic structures and showed vascular bundles, medullary rays, wood fibres, and stomata, although his interpretations of these structures were often in error.

Malpighi, who was one of the greatest of the microscopists, used his lenses to study the development of the chick and made a series of ten excellent, accurate drawings of his observations. He made extensive studies of the structure of glands and other tissues, and his name is associated with several structures which he was the first to describe: the Malpighian corpuscles of the kidney; the Malpighian layer of the skin, and the Malpighian tubes of the insect.

His greatest achievement, the discovery of the capillaries of the lung of the frog, completed, as we have seen, the monumental studies of Harvey by showing how blood reaches the veins from the arteries. Leeuwenhoek also observed and described the capillaries, but Malpighi was the first to recognize their importance. As Fraser Harris put it, 'Harvey made the existence of capillaries a logical necessity, Malpighi made it a histological certainty.' In 1691 Malpighi moved to Rome to become physician to Pope Innocent XII, but death came after only three years.

The selection that follows is taken from James Young's translation of *De pulmonibus* in the *Proceedings of the Royal Society of Medicine*, Vol. 23, 1929.

¶ *To that very famous and learned Man Alphonsus Borellius, celebrated Professor of Science at Pisa*

§ *Epistle II. About the Lungs*

There is the difficulty and obscurity to be met with in natural things, that there seems to be something in them that is not to be determined altogether by our senses. And so, steadfastly working with very great labour, we may contemplate Nature showing herself in her beginnings, as it were in a volume elaborated through mysteries. And when we try to unravel the obscure things in the viscera of animals, at length by our efforts, and only with great weariness, we conclude that the truth of our observations is made out. We borrow illumination, as if by degrees, from dissection, sometimes of insects, sometimes of perfect animals. For nature is accustomed to rehearse with certain large, perhaps baser, and all classes of wild [animals], and to place in the imperfect the rudiments of the perfect animals.

And now, most famous man, I will handle the matter more closely: there were two things which, in my epistle about observation on the lungs, I left as doubtful and to be investigated with more exact study.

(1) The first was what may be the network described therein, where certain bladders and sinuses are bound together in a certain way in the lungs.

(2) The other was whether the vessels of the lungs are connected by mutual anastomosis, or gape into the common substance of the lungs and sinuses.

The solution of these problems may prepare the way for greater things and will place the operation of nature more clearly before the eyes. For the unloosing of these knots I have destroyed almost the whole race of frogs, which does not happen in that savage *Batrachomyomachia* of Homer. For in the anatomy of frogs, which, by favour of my very excellent colleague D. Carolo Fracassato, I had set on foot in order to become more certain about the membranous substance of the lungs, it happened to me to see such things that not undeservedly I can better make use of that [saying] of Homer for the present matter – 'I see with my eyes a work trusty and great.' For in this [frog anatomy] owing to the simplicity of the structure, and the almost complete transparency of the vessels which admits the eye into the interior, things are more clearly shown so that they will bring the light to other more obscure matters.

In the frog, therefore, the abdomen being laid open lengthwise, the lungs, adhering on each side to the heart, come forth. They are not slack as in other animals, but remain tense for the animal's requirements. They are nothing more than a membranous bladder, which at first sight seems to be spattered with very small spots, arranged in order after the fashion of the skin of the dogfish – commonly called *Sagrino*. In form and surface protuberances it resembles the cone of a pine; but internally and externally a certain texture of vessels diversely prolonged is connected together, which, by the pulse, by contrary movement, and the insertion of the vein, are pulmonary arteries. In the concave and interior part of this [bladder] it almost fades into an empty space devoted to the reception of air, but it is not everywhere smooth but is interrupted by the occurrence of alveoli. These are produced by membranous walls raised to a little height. They are not all of this shape, but when the walls are produced out in length and width and connected together, the bays [sinuses] are formed almost into hexagons; and bent at the corners of the sinuses the membrane is extended a little as infundibulum is constituted; and thus the lungs of the smaller frogs are fashioned. . . .

*

Observation by means of the microscope will reveal more wonderful things than those viewed in regard to mere structure and connexion: for while the heart is still beating the contrary [i.e., in opposite directions in the different vessels] movement of the blood is observed in the vessels – though with difficulty – so that the circulation of the blood is clearly exposed. This is more clearly recognized in the mesentery and in other great veins contained in the abdomen.

Thus by this impulse the blood is driven in very small [streams] through the arteries like a flood into the several cells, one or other branch clearly passing through or ending there. Thus the blood, much divided, puts off its red colour, and, carried round in a winding way, is poured out on all sides till at length it may reach the walls, the angles, and the absorbing branches of the veins.

The power of the eye could not be extended further in the opened living animal, hence I had believed that this body of the blood breaks into the empty space, and is collected again by a gaping vessel and by the structure of the walls. The tortuous and diffused motion of the blood in divers directions, and its union at a determinate place offered a handle to this. But the dried lung of the frog made my belief dubious. This lung had, by chance, preserved the redness of the blood in (what afterwards proved to be) the smallest vessels, where by means of a more perfect lens, no more there met the eye the points forming the skin called *Sagrino*, but vessels mingled annularly. And, so great is the divarication of these vessels as they go out, here from a vein, there from an artery, that order is no longer preserved, but a network appears made up of the prolongations of both vessels. This network occupies not only the whole floor, but extends to the walls, and is attached to the outgoing vessel, as I could see with greater difficulty but more abundantly in the oblong lung of a tortoise, which is similarly membranous and transparent. Here it was clear to sense that the blood flows away through the tortuous vessels, that it is not poured into spaces but always works through tubules, and is dispersed by the multiplex windings of the vessels. Nor is it a new practice of Nature to join together the extremities of vessels, since the same holds in the intestines and other parts; nay, what seems more wonderful, she joins the upper and the lower ends of veins to one another by visible anastomosis, as the most learned Fallopius has very well observed. . . .

*

From these things, therefore, as to the first problems to be solved, from analogy and the simplicity which nature uses in all her operations, it can be inferred that that network which formerly I believed to be nervous in nature, mingled in the bladders and sinuses, is [really] a vessel carrying the body of blood thither or carrying it away. Also that, although in the lungs of perfect animals the vessels seem sometimes to gape and end in the midst of the network of rings, nevertheless it is likely that, as in the cells of frogs and tortoises, that vessel is prolonged further into very small vessels in the form of a network, and these escape the senses on account of their exquisite smallness.

Also from these things can be solved with the greatest probability the question of the mutual union and anastomosis of the vessels. For if Nature turns the blood about in vessels, and combines the ends of the vessels in a network, it is likely that in other cases an anastomosis joins them; this is clearly recognized in the bladder of frogs swollen with urine, in which the above described motion of the blood is observed through the transparent vessels joined together by anastomosis, and not that those vessels have received that connexion and course which the veins or fibres work out in the leaves of nearly all trees. . . .

I have put these few little observations into a letter that I might increase the things found out about the lungs. If I have set in motion all the points of my observations I have owed the addition to the frog. You will bring out the truth and dignity of these matters by your authority and contrivance. Meantime, apply yourself happily to philosophy, and may you go on to render me altogether happy by increasing a little my very unimportant thoughts of your writings *De animalium motu.*

Farewell!

Bologna, 1661

———

JOHANN BAPTISTA VAN HELMONT
1577–1644

THE ROLE OF WATER IN THE GROWTH OF
PLANTS IS SHOWN BY EXPERIMENT

An important stage in the development of biological thought is represented by the Mechanist school, which maintained that all the phenomena of life could be explained in terms of physics and chemistry. In opposition there arose the vitalists who believed in the existence of some vital force, variously defined and interpreted, not circumscribed by the laws of physical science. The controversy between the mechanists and the vitalists, which reached its climax during the last years of the seventeenth and the first half of the eighteenth century, influenced most biological writing of that period and proved a useful stimulus to investigation.

The French philosopher Descartes (1596–1650) was the originator of the purely mechanistic view of life. Borelli (1608–79), a professor of mathematics at the University of Pisa, through his friendship with the great pathologist Malpighi, became deeply interested in physiology and, applying mathematical principles to philosophical problems, expounded convincingly an explanation of body function in physical terms. From his work developed the Iatrophysical School.

It was soon apparent to some that physics alone was inadequate to explain all the phenomena of life and attempts were made to apply the very primitive chemistry of the period to explain biological activities. This approach to the problem of living things developed, as chemistry grew in stature, into the Iatrochemical School. One of the most successful of the early Iatrochemists was van Helmont, who may be regarded as a pioneer of physiological chemistry. He was born in Brussels and returned there to practise medicine after graduating at the University of Louvain. He later moved to Vilvorde, where he remained until his death. He had married an heiress and was thus able to devote himself to chemical research. His work aroused the suspicions of the Inquisition and he spent two years in prison. His chief work *Ortus medicinae* was published by his son after his death.

Van Helmont applied exact quantitative methods to physiological research and made many careful and accurate observations, including the first grammetric study of the urine. His theoretical concepts in contrast are complex and to expound them he was compelled to coin many new terms. He regarded living activities as chemical processes, dependent particularly on the action of ferments, but these processes were regulated by mystical agencies, the *archaei*. He was in fact endeavouring to reconcile iatrochemistry and vitalism.

The experiment described below demonstrated that water had been transmuted into solid wood by the action of the 'Seedes' in the tree – 'Seede' meaning a kind of ferment. Although van Helmont introduced the word 'gas', he used it in a sense very different from that of our modern concept of a 'completely elastic fluid not liquid or solid at ordinary temperatures'. For him 'gas' was a form of water. He observed various kinds of 'fumes', but apparently did not find any explanation for them other than that – in his terms – they were a stage in the process of converting water into substance and back to water.

This selection is taken from the collected works entitled *Ortus medicinae*, translated by John Chandler in 1662.

¶ *Is Wood Made of Water?*

All earth, clay, and every body that may be touched, is truly and materially the offspring of water onely, and is reduced again into water, by nature and art. . . . Water alwayes remains whole as it is; or without any dividing of the three beginnings, it is transformed and goes into fruits whither the Seedes do call and withdraw it.

For an Element should cease to be a simple body if it is to be separated into anything before or more simple than itself. But nothing in corporeall things is granted to be before, or more simple than an element.

But I have learned by this handicraft-operation, that all Vegetables do immediately and materially proceed out of the Element of water onely. For I took an Earthen vessel in which I put two hundred pounds of Earth that had been dried in a Furnace, which I moystened with Rainwater, and I implanted therein the Trunk or Stem, of a Willow Tree, weighing five pounds; and at length, five years being finished, the Tree sprung from thence did weigh one hundred and sixty-nine pounds, and about three ounces: But I moystened the Earthen vessel with Rainwater, or distilled water (alwayes when there was need) . . . and lest the dust should be co-mingled with the Earth, I covered the lip or mouth of the Vessel, with an Iron Plate covered with Tin, and easily passable with many holes. I computed not the weight of the leaves that fell off, in the four Autumnes. At length, I again dried the Earth of the Vessel, and there were found the same two hundred pound, wanting about two ounces. Therefore one hundred and sixty-four pounds of Wood, Barks, and Roots arose out of water onely. . . . Fire indeed destroyeth simple but it generates nothing. . . . Therefore Wood, since it is wholly of water, the ashes . . . shall be of water.

STEPHEN HALES
1677–1761

THE MOVEMENT OF LIQUIDS IN PLANTS IS STUDIED BY RIGOROUS QUANTITATIVE PROCEDURES

INGENIOUS experimenter, lucid writer, and independent thinker, Stephen Hales was the founder of quantitative physiology and helped to introduce the rigorous methods of physics to the study of biological processes.

Born in Kent, Hales was next to the youngest of eleven children in a family of long and distinguished pedigree. He entered Cambridge to study theology and to prepare for holy orders in the Church of England, but, in the manner of the times, he also read mathematics, physics, and botany. His interest in science became more than superficial, and he was particularly stimulated in the biological sciences by a fellow student, William Stukeley, who was ten years younger than Hales. By a rather strange turn of events, Stukeley, who had been trained in science, gave up medicine and took holy orders, whereas Hales, whose primary responsibility was as a churchman, pursued his scientific avocation with notable results.

In 1709 Hales was appointed vicar of Teddington, and he held the living for fifty years. Unlike many of the clergy of his times, he seems to have been concerned with the problems of the world outside his parish. Apart from his interests in biology, he was a pioneer in prison reform and made improvements in ventilation which were applied to ships, hospitals, and prisons.

In his scientific activities, Hales reflected the influences of Newton in his avoidance of hypotheses and in his search for a mechanical or physical explanation of living phenomena. His most significant work was done in plant physiology and published in 1727 as *Vegetable Staticks*. In these experimental studies Hales developed instruments and procedures for measuring plant processes exactly. He measured the water taken in by the roots and given off by the leaves (transpiration). He also measured the rate of rise of water in plant stems as well as the force now known as root pressure. In a prophetic guess he concluded that plants are nourished by something in the atmosphere, a surmise that was not substantiated for almost a century. He also studied the growth of stems by making marks at different points and observing the differences in the rate of growth in various parts of the stem.

Hales also investigated blood pressure and blood flow, comparing blood pressure with that of sap in plants and measuring the former directly by placing a tube in the vein of a live mammal, such as a horse or a dog, and observing the rise in the level of the blood in the tube. He also calculated the speed of blood movement in veins and capillaries. Most of the experiments on animals were performed before those on plants, but Hales did not publish his results until 1733 in *Haemastaticks*, the pioneer work in quantitative animal physiology.

Hales was a Fellow of the Royal Society and was awarded its Copley medal. He was one of the few foreign members of the French Academy.

The selection, taken from *Vegetable Staticks*, illustrates Hales's approach to biological problems (see Plate 7).

---

§ *The Introduction*

The farther researches we make into this admirable scene of things, the more beauty and harmony we see in them: And the stronger and clearer convictions they give us, of the being, power, and wisdom of the divine Architect, who has made all things concur with a wonderful conformity, in carrying on, by various and innumerable combinations of matter, such a circulation of causes and effects, as was necessary to the great ends of nature.

And since we are assured that the all-wise Creator has observed the most exact proportions, of *number, weight, and measure*, in the make of all things; the most likely way therefore, to get any insight into the nature of those parts of creation; which come within our observation, must in all reason be to number, weigh, and measure. And we have much encouragement to pursue this method of searching into the nature of things, from the great success that has attended any attempts of this kind.

Thus, in relation to those Planets which revolve about our Sun, the great Philosopher of our age * has, by numbering and measuring, discovered the exact proportions that are observed in their periodical revolutions and distances from their common centres of motion and gravity: And that God has not only *comprehended the dust of the earth in a measure, and weighed the mountains in scales, and the hills in a balance* (Isai. xl, 12), but that he also holds the vast revolving Globes, of this our solar system, most exactly poised on their common centre of gravity.

And if we reflect upon the discoveries that have been made in the animal economy, we shall find that the most considerable and rational accounts of it have been chiefly owing to the statical examination of their fluids, viz., by inquiring what quantity of fluids, and solids dissolved into fluids, the animal daily takes in for its support and nourishment: And with what force and different rapidities those fluids are carried about in their proper channels, according to the different secretions that are to be made from them: And in what proportion the recrementitious [excremental] fluid is conveyed away, to make room for fresh supplies; and what portion of this recrement nature

* [Sir Isaac Newton.]

allots to be carried off by the several kinds of emunctories [cleansing organs] and excretory ducts.

And since in vegetables, their growth and the preservation of their vegetable life is promoted and maintained, as in animals, by the very plentiful and regular motion of their fluids, which are the vehicles ordained by nature to carry proper nutriment to every part; it is therefore reasonable to hope that in them also, by the same method of inquiry, considerable discoveries may in time be made, there being in many respects, a great analogy between plants and animals.

§ *Preface*

... I was endeavouring by several ways to stop the bleeding of an old stem of a Vine, which was cut too near the bleeding season, which I feared might kill it. Having, after other means proved ineffectual, tied a piece of bladder over the transverse cut of the Stem I found the force of the Sap did greatly extend the bladder; whence I concluded, that if a long glass tube were fixed there in the same manner as I had before done to the Arteries of several living Animals I should thereby obtain the real ascending force of the Sap in the Stem, which succeeded according to my expectation: and hence it is that I have been insensibly led on to make farther and farther researches by variety of Experiments.

As the Art of Physick [medicine] has of late years been much improved by a greater knowledge of the animal economy; so doubtless a farther insight into the vegetable economy must needs proportionately improve our skill in Agriculture and Gardening, which gives me reason to hope that inquiries of this kind will be acceptable to many who are intent upon improving those innocent, delightful, and beneficial Arts: Since they cannot be insensible that the most rational ground for Success in this laudable Pursuit must arise from a greater insight into the nature of Plants.

Finding by many Experiments in the fifth chapter, that the Air is plentifully inspired by Vegetables, not only at their roots, but also through several parts of their trunks and branches; this put me upon making a more particular inquiry into the nature of the Air, and to discover, if possible, wherein its great importance to the life and support of Vegetables might consist; on which account I was obliged to delay the Publication of the rest of these Experiments, which were read two years since before the Royal Society, till I had made some progress in this inquiry: An account of which I have given in the sixth chapter.

§ *Experiment XLVI*

In *August,* I cut off the bark, for an inch round, of a young thriving Oak-branch, on the North-west side of the tree. The leaves of this and another branch, which had the bark cut at the same time, fell early, viz., about the latter end of *October,* when the leaves of all the other branches of the same tree, except those at the very top of the tree, continued on all the winter.

This is a further proof that less sap goes to branches which have the bark cut off than to others.

The 19th of *April* following, the buds of this branch were five or seven days forwarder than those of other branches of the same tree; the reason of which may probably be because less fresh crude sap coming to this branch than the others, and the perspirations in all branches being, *caeteris paribus* [other things being equal] nearly equal, the lesser quantity of sap in this branch must sooner be inspissated [thickened] into a glutinous substance, fit for new productions, than the sap of other branches that abounded with a greater plenty of fresh thin sap.

The same is the reason why Apples, Pears, and many other fruits, which have some of their great sap-vessels eaten asunder by insects bred in them, are ripe many days before the rest of the fruit on the same trees; as also that fruit which is gathered some time before it is ripe will ripen sooner than if it had hung on the tree, though it will not be so good; because in these cases the worm-eaten fruit is deprived of part of its nourishment, and the green-gathered fruit of all.

And for the same reason some fruits are sooner ripe towards the tops of the trees than the other fruit on the same tree; viz., not only because they are more exposed to the sun; but also, because being at a greater distance from the root, they have somewhat less nourishment.

And this is, doubtless, one reason why plants and fruits are forwarder in dry, sandy, or gravelly soils than in moister soils; viz., not only because those soils are warmer, on account of their dryness; but also, because less plenty of moisture is conveyed up the plants; which plenty of moisture, though it promotes their growth, yet retards their coming to maturity. And for the same reason, the uncovering the roots of trees for some time will make the fruit be considerably the forwarder.

And on the other hand, where trees abound with too great a plenty of fresh-drawn sap, as is the case of trees whose roots are planted too deep in cold, moist earth, as also of too luxuriant Peach and other wall trees; or, which comes almost to the same, where the sap cannot be perspired off in a due proportion; as in orchards, where trees stand too near each other, so as to hinder perspiration, whereby the sap is kept in too thin and crude a state; in all these cases little or no fruit is produced.

Hence also, in moderately dry summers, *caeteris paribus*, there is usually greatest plenty of fruit; because the sap in the bearing twigs and buds is more digested, and brought to a better consistence for shooting out with vigour and firmness than it is in cool moist summers: And this observation has been verified in the years 1723, 1724, and 1725.

But to return to the subject of the motion of the sap: When the sap has first passed thro' that thick and fine strainer, the bark of the root, we then find it in greatest quantities in the most lax part, between the bark and wood, and *that* the same through the whole tree. And if, in the early spring, the Oak and several other trees were to be examined near the top and bottom, when the sap first begins to move, so as to make the bark easily run or peel off, I believe it would be found that the lower bark is first moistened; whereas the bark of the top branches ought first to be moistened, if the sap descends by the bark: As to the Vine, I am pretty well assured that the lower bark is first moistened.

We see in many of the foregoing experiments what quantities of moisture trees do daily imbibe and perspire. Now the celerity of the sap must be very great, if that quantity of moisture must, most of it, ascend to the top of the tree, then descend, and ascend again, before it is carried off by perspiration.

The defect of a circulation in vegetables seems in some measure to be supplied by the much greater quantity of liquor which the vegetable takes in, than the animal, whereby its motion is accelerated; for by Experiment 1, we find the sun-flower, bulk for bulk, imbibes and perspires seventeen times more fresh liquor than a man, every twenty-four hours.

Besides, nature's great aim in vegetables being only that the vegetable life be carried on and maintained, there was no occasion to give its sap the rapid motion which was necessary for the blood of animals.

In animals, it is the heart which sets the blood in motion, and makes it continually circulate, but in vegetables we can discover no other cause of the sap's motion but the strong attraction of the capillary sap-vessels, assisted by the brisk undulations and vibrations caused by the sun's warmth, whereby the sap is carried up to the top of the tallest trees, and is there perspired off through the leaves: But when the surface of the tree is greatly diminished by the loss of its leaves, then also the perspiration and motion of the sap is proportionably diminished, as is

SECVNDA
MVSCVLO.
RVM TA.
BVLA.

Illustration of muscles drawn for Vesalius's anatomy

The Griffin as pictured in *The Book of Beasts*. It has the body parts of a
lion and the wings and beak of an eagle

A drawing by Leeuwenhoek from his letter to the Royal Society of 17 September 1683

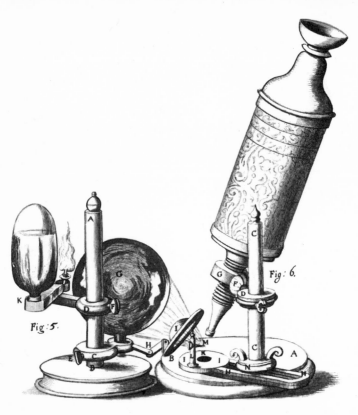

Drawing of Hooke's microscope and the lamp used to illuminate
the objects he viewed

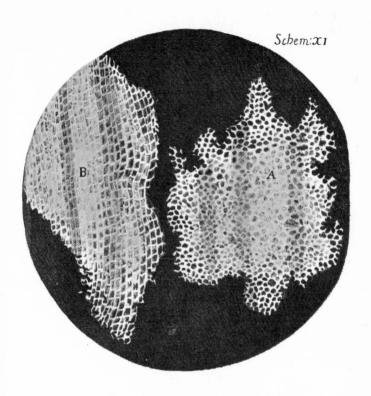

Drawing of cells in cork by Hooke

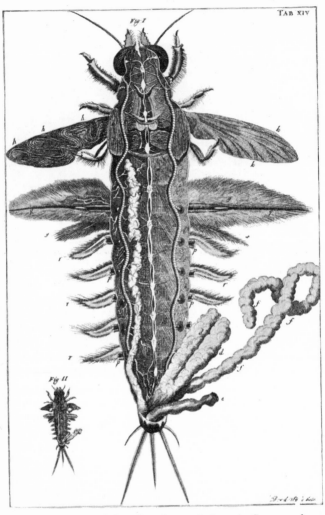

Drawing of detailed dissection of a mayfly larva by Swammerdam

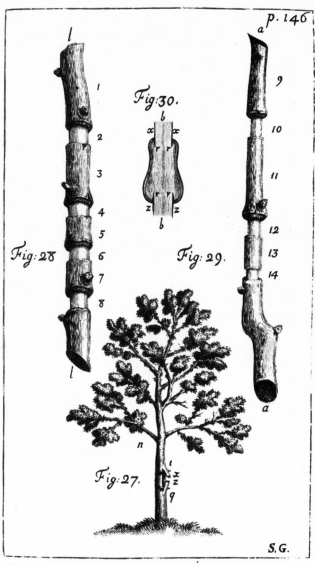

Illustration from Hales's demonstration of the movement of
liquids in plants

7

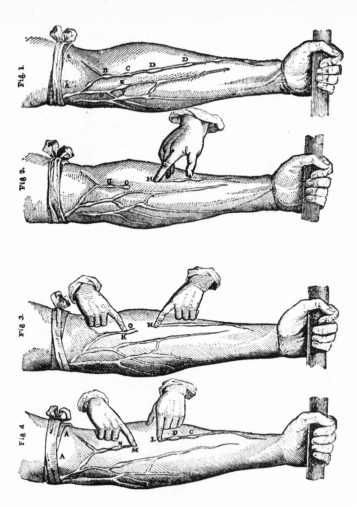

Illustration from Harvey's work in which he demonstrates the
presence of valves in the veins

plain from many of the foregoing experiments: So that the ascending velocity of the sap is principally accelerated by the plentiful perspiration of the leaves, thereby making room for the fine capillary vessels to exert their vastly attracting power, which perspiration is effected by the brisk rarefying vibrations of warmth: A power that does not seem to be any ways well adapted to make the sap descend from the tops of vegetables by different vessels to the root. . . .

The instances of the Jessamine tree and of the Passion tree have been looked upon as strong proofs of the circulation of the sap, because their branches, which were far below the inoculated Bud, were gilded: But we have many visible proofs in the Vine and other bleeding trees of the sap's receding back and pushing forwards alternately at different times of the day and night. And there is great reason to think that the sap of all other trees has such an alternate, receding, and progressive motion, occasioned by the alternacies of day and night, warm and cool, moist and dry.

For the sap in all vegetables does probably recede in some measure from the tops of branches, as the sun leaves them; because its rarefying power then ceasing, the greatly rarefied sap, and air mixt with it, will condense and take up less room than they did, and the dew and rain will then be strongly imbibed by the leaves, as is probable from Exper. 42 and several others; whereby the body and branches of the vegetable, which have been much exhausted by the great evaporation of the day, may at night imbibe sap and dew from the leaves; for by several Experiments in the first chapter, plants were found to increase considerably in weight in dewy and moist nights. And by other experiments on the Vine in the third chapter, it was found that the trunk and branches of Vines were always in an imbibing state, caused by the great perspiration of the leaves, except in the bleeding season; but when at night that perspiring power ceases, then the contrary imbibing power will prevail, and draw the sap and dew from the leaves, as well as moisture from the roots.

And we have further proof of this in Experiment 12, where, by fixing mercurial gages to the stems of several trees which do not bleed, it is found that they are always in a strongly imbibing state, by drawing up the mercury several inches. Whence it is easy to conceive how some of the particles of the gilded Bud in the inoculated Jessamine may be absorbed by it, and thereby communicate their gilding Miasma to the sap of other branches; especially when some months after the inoculation, the stock of the inoculated Jessamine is cut off a little above the Bud; whereby the stock, which was the counteracting part to the stem, being taken away, the stem attracts more vigorously from the Bud.

Another argument for the circulation of the sap, is that some sorts of graffs will infect and canker the stocks they are grafted on. But by Exper. 12, and 37, where mercurial gages were fixed to fresh cut stems of trees, it is evident that those stems were in a strongly imbibing state; and consequently the cankered stocks might very likely draw sap from the graff, as well as the graff alternately from the stock; just in the same manner as leaves and branches do from each other, in the vicissitudes of day and night. And this imbibing power of the stock is so great, where only some of the branches of a tree are grafted, that the remaining branches of the stock will, by their strong attraction, starve those graffs; for which reason it is usual to cut off the greatest part of the branches of the stock, leaving only a few small ones to draw up the sap.

The instance of the Ilex grafted upon the *English* Oak, seems to afford a very considerable argument against a circulation. For, if there were a free uniform circulation of the sap thro' the Oak and Ilex, why should the leaves of the Oak fall in winter, and not those of the Ilex?

Another argument against an uniform circulation of the sap in trees, as in animals, may be drawn from Exper. 37, where it was found by the three mercurial gages fix'd to the same Vine, that while some of its branches changed their state of protruding [discharging] sap into a state of imbibing, others continued protruding sap, one nine, and the other thirteen days longer.

In the second Vol. of Mr *Lowthrop's Abridgment of the Philos. Transact.*, p. 708, is recited an Experiment of Mr *Brotherton's*; viz, A young Hazel, n (Fig. 27) * was cut into the body at x z with a deep gash; the parts of the body below at z, and above at x, were cleft upwards and downwards, and the splinters x z by wedges were kept off from touching each other, or the rest of the body. The following year, the upper splinter x was grown very much, but the lower splinter z did not grow; but the rest of the body grew, as if there had been no gash made: I have not yet succeeded in making this Experiment, the wind having broken at x z all the trees I prepared for it. But if there was a Bud at x which shot out leaves, and none at z, then, by Experiment 41, 'tis plain that those leaves might draw much nourishment through x, and thereby make it grow; and I believe, if, vice versa, there were a leaf-bearing Bud at z, and none at x, that then the splinter z would grow more than x.

The reason of my conjecture I ground upon this Experiment, viz., I chose two thriving shoots of a dwarf *Pear-tree*, l l a a, Fig. 28, 29. At three quarters of an inch distance, I took half an inch breadth of bark off each of them, in several places, viz., 2, 4, 6, 8, and at 10, 12, 14. Every one of the remaining ringlets of bark had a leaf-bearing bud which produced leaves the following summer, except the ringlet 13, which had no such Bud. The ringlet 9 and 11 of a a grew and swelled at their bottoms till *August*, but the ringlet 13 did not increase at all, and in *August* the whole shoot a a withered and died; but the shoot l l lives and thrives well, each of its ringlets swelling much at the bottom: Which swellings at their bottoms must be attri-

* [See Plate 7.]

buted to some other cause than the stoppage of the sap in its return downwards, because in the shoot l l, its return downwards is intercepted three several times by cutting away the bark at 2, 4, 6. The larger and more thriving the leaf-bearing Bud was, and the more leaves it had on it, so much more did the adjoining bark swell at the bottom. . . .

That the sap does not descend between the bark and the wood, as the favourers of a circulation suppose, seems evident from hence; viz, that if the bark be taken off for three or four inches breadth quite round, the bleeding of the tree above that bared place will much abate, which ought to have the contrary effect, by intercepting the course of the refluent sap, if the sap descended by the bark.

But the reason of the abatement of the bleeding in this case may well be accounted for, from the manifest proof we have in these Experiments, that the sap is strongly attracted upwards by the vigorous operation of the perspiring leaves and attracting Capillaries. But when the bark is cut off for some breadth below the bleeding place, then the sap which is between the bark and the wood below that disbarked place is deprived of the strong attracting power of the leaves, etc., and consequently the bleeding wound cannot be supplied so fast with sap as it was before the bark was taken off.

Hence also we have a hint for a probable conjecture why, in the alternately disbarked sticks, l l a a, Fig. 28, 29, the bark swelled more at the upper part of the disbarked places than at the lower; viz., because those lower parts were thereby deprived of the plenty of nourishment which was brought to the upper parts of those disbarked places by the strong attraction of the leaves on the Buds 7, etc., of which we have a further confirmation in the ringlet of bark, No. 13, Fig. 29, which ringlet did not swell or grow at either end, being not only deprived of the attraction of the superior leaves, by the bark placed No. 12, but also without any leaf-bud of its own, whose branching sap-vessels, being like those of other leaf-buds rooted downwards in the wood, might thence draw sap, for the nourishment of itself and the adjoining bark, No. 13. But had these rooting sap-vessels run upwards, instead of downwards, 'tis probable that in that case the upper part of each ringlet of bark, and not the lower, would have swelled, by having nourishment thereby brought to it from the inmost wood.

We may hence also see the reason why, when a tree is unfruitful, it is brought to bear fruit by the taking ringlets of bark off from its branches; viz., because thereby a less quantity of sap arising, it is better digested and prepared for the nourishment of the fruit; which, from the greater quantity of oil that is usually found in the seeds and their containing vessels than in other parts of plants, shows that more sulphur and air is requisite for their production than there is for the production of wood and leaves.

But the most considerable objection against this progressive motion of the sap, without a circulation, arises from hence, viz., that it is too precipitate a course for a due digestion of the sap, in order to nutrition. Whereas in animals nature has provided that many parts of the blood shall run a long course, before they are either applied to nutrition, or discharged from the animal.

But when we consider that the great work of nutrition, in vegetables as well as in animals (I mean, after the nutriment is got into the veins and arteries of animals), is chiefly carried on in the fine capillary vessels, where nature selects and combines, as shall best suit her different purposes, the several mutually attracting nutritious particles, which were hitherto kept disjoined by the motion of their fluid vehicle; we shall find that nature has made an abundant provision for this work in the structure of vegetables; all whose composition is made up of nothing else but innumerable fine capillary vessels, and glandulous portions or vesicles.

Upon the whole, I think we have, from these experiments and observations, sufficient ground to believe that there is no circulation of the sap in vegetables; notwithstanding many ingenious persons have been induced to think there was, from several curious observations and experiments, which evidently prove that the sap does in some measure recede from the top towards the lower parts of plants, whence they were with good probability of reason induced to think that the sap circulated.

The likeliest method effectually and convincingly to determine this difficulty, whether the sap circulates or not, would be by ocular inspection, if that could be attained. And I see no reason we have to despair of it, since by the great quantities imbibed and perspired, we have good ground to think that the progressive motion of the sap is considerable in the largest sap-vessels of the transparent stems of leaves. And if our eyes, assisted with microscopes, could come at this desirable sight, I make no doubt but that we should see the sap, which was progressive in the heat of the day, would on the coming of the cool evening and the falling dew, be retrograde in the same vessels.

JAN INGENHOUSZ

1730–99

THE PROCESS OF PHOTOSYNTHESIS IN GREEN PLANTS IS DESCRIBED IN A SERIES OF EXPERIMENTS

PHOTOSYNTHESIS is the process, fundamental to the life of all the higher plants, and indirectly to all animal life, by which, with sunlight as the source of energy, simple organic substances are built up into complex organic compounds. The significance of the experiments of Jan Ingenhousz was not appreciated either by himself or by his contemporaries, but they form the foundation of the modern study of photosynthesis, which is still far from being fully understood.

Before Ingenhousz, important contributions to our knowledge of the vital processes of plants had been made by Johann Baptista van Helmont who related the increase in weight of a plant to the water it absorbed, and by John Priestley. In *Experiments and Observations on Different Kinds of Air*, published in 1774, Priestley showed that green plants give off the gas which we now know as oxygen and that this gas is essential for animal life.

Ingenhousz was born at Breda, in Holland, and studied medicine at Leyden, Louvain, Paris, and Edinburgh, receiving his degree from Louvain. He was a good linguist and later published writings in French, English, and Dutch. He became an expert in smallpox inoculation and later was appointed physician to the Austrian Court and the Empress Maria Theresa.

During a leave of absence from his medical duties in the summer of 1778, Ingenhousz visited England, where he performed a series of some five hundred experiments in three months. The results were published the following year as *Experiments on Vegetables, Discovering Their Great Power of Purifying the Common Air in the Sunshine, and of Injuring it in the Shade and at Night*, from which the readings below were taken.

Ingenhousz showed that the green parts of plants perform the process we now know as photosynthesis. He had, in fact, observed chlorophyll, though he did not name or define it. He showed that green plants give off oxygen in the presence of sunlight and carbon dioxide in the shade and at night. He explained his observations in terms of the phlogiston theory, but later he adapted his interpretation of his results to Lavoisier's discoveries and to the newer chemistry.

In 1782 Senebier added another step to the understanding of photosynthesis when he showed that the green plants fix free carbon dioxide of the atmosphere. De Saussure, in 1804, confirmed the work of Ingenhousz and performed a series of rigorous quantitative experiments using the newer chemistry and physics. Since then chemists and biochemists have narrowed the problem down to the biosynthesis within the cell of the green plant and the manner in which light energizes the process.

═══════

I was not long engaged in this inquiry before I saw a most important scene opened to my view: I observed, *that plants not only have a faculty to correct bad air in six or ten days, by growing in it, as the experiments of Dr Priestley indicate, but that they perform this important office in a compleat manner in a few hours; that this wonderful operation is by no means owing to the vegetation of the plant, but to the influence of the light of the sun upon the plant. I found that plants have, moreover, a most surprising faculty of elaborating the air which they contain, and undoubtedly absorb continually from the common atmosphere, into real and fine dephlogisticated air* [oxygen]; *that they pour down continually, if I may so*

*express myself, a shower of this depurated air, which,
diffusing itself through the common mass of the atmosphere, contributes to render it more fit for animal life;
that this operation is far from being carried on constantly,
but begins only after the sun has for some time made his
appearance above the horizon, and has, by his influence,
prepared the plants to begin anew their beneficial operation upon the air, and thus upon the animal creation,
which was stopped during the darkness of the night; that
this operation of the plants is more or less brisk in proportion to the clearness of the day, and the exposition of the
plants more or less adapted to receive the direct influence
of that great luminary; that plants shaded by high build-
ings, or growing under a dark shade of other plants, do not
perform this office, but, on the contrary, throw out an air
hurtful to animals, and even contaminate the air which
surrounds them; that this operation of plants diminishes
towards the close of the day, and ceases entirely at sun-set,
except in a few plants, which continue this duty somewhat longer than others; that this office is not performed
by the whole plant, but only by the leaves and the green
stalks that support them; that acrid, ill-scented, and even
the most poisonous plants perform this office in common
with the mildest and the most salutary; that the most
part of leaves pour out the greatest quantity of this
dephlogisticated air from their under-surface, principally
those of lofty trees; that young leaves, not yet come to their
full perfection, yield dephlogisticated air less in quantity,
and of an inferior quality, than what is produced by full-
grown and old leaves; that some plants elaborate dephlogisticated air better than others; that some of the
aquatic plants seem to excell in this operation; that all
plants contaminate the surrounding air by night, and
even in the day-time in shaded places; that, however, some
of those which are inferior to none in yielding beneficial
air in the sunshine, surpass others in the power of infecting the circumambient air in the dark, even to such a*

degree, that in a few hours they render a great body of good air so noxious, that an animal placed in it loses its life in a few seconds; that all flowers render the surrounding air highly noxious, equally by night and by day; that the roots removed from the ground do the same, some few, however, excepted; but that in general fruits have the same deleterious quality at all times, though principally in the dark, and many to such an astonishing degree, that even some of those fruits which are the most delicious, as, for instance, peaches, contaminate so much the common air as would endanger us to lose our lives, if we were shut up in a room in which a great deal of such fruits are stored up; that the sun by itself has no power to mend air without the concurrence of plants, but on the contrary is apt to contaminate it.

These are some of the secret operations of plants I discovered in my retirement, of which I will endeavour to give some account in the following pages; submitting, however, to the judgement of the candid reader the consequences, which I thought might fairly be deduced from the facts I am to relate. . . .

All plants possess a power of correcting, in a few hours, foul air unfit for respiration; but only in clear daylight, or in the sunshine.

This remarkable property of plants is indeed very great; for in a few hours, nay even sometimes in an hour and a half, they purify so much a body of air quite unfit for respiration, as to be equal in goodness to atmospheric air. They will even do it when they are enclosed in a glass vessel, without any water. One leaf of a vine, shut up in an ounce phial, full of air fouled by breathing so that a candle could not burn in it, restored this air to the goodness of common air in the space of an hour and a half. But plants enjoy this privilege only in the day-time, and when they grow in unshaded places.

This power of plants extends itself even to the worst of all airs, in which an animal finds his destruction in a moment; such as is pure inflammable and highly phlogisti-cated air, which is little or scarcely at all diminishable by nitrous air. I observed some difference in various kinds of plants in this respect, and found that water-plants seem to possess this quality in a greater degree than others. The willow tree and the *persicaria urens* were found eminent in producing this effect; and may it not be provi-dentially ordained it should be so, as those plants grow better in marshy, low grounds, and even in stagnated waters, whose bottoms are generally muddy, and yield a great deal of inflammable air, which may be collected at the surface of the water by stirring up the ground, and may be kindled by throwing a burning paper upon the water, which is an amusing experiment by night? Plants, however, want longer time to correct this kind of air, at least that which is extracted from metals by vitriolic acid.

*

This work is a part of the result of above 500 experiments, all of which were made in less than three months, having begun them in June and finished them in the beginning of September, working from morning till night.

§ SECTION VIII: *Experiments Showing that Plants Have a Remarkable Power To Correct Bad Air in the Day*

56. A sprig of *peppermint* put in a jar full of air fouled by breathing (so as to extinguish a candle), and exposed to the sun, had corrected this air in three hours so far that a candle could burn in it.

57. A sprig of *nettle* was put in a jar full of air fouled by breathing so as to extinguish a candle; it was placed in a room during the whole night; next morning the air was found as bad as before. The jar was put at nine in the morning in the sunshine; in the space of two hours the air was so much corrected, that it was found to be nearly as good as common air.

§ SECTION XIX: *Experiments Showing that the Sun by Itself, Without the Assistance of Plants, Does not Improve Air, but Renders It Rather Worse*

124. Two jars, half full of air taken from the atmosphere at the same time, and half full of pump water, were left by themselves during four hours, the one exposed to a bright sunshine, the other placed within the house, only two steps from a door opening in the garden.

The air kept in the house gave, in six different trials, constantly the appearance of being better than that of the jar placed in the sun. One measure of the air kept within doors with one of nitrous air occupied $1.06\frac{1}{2}$ whereas that exposed to the sun occupied $1.08\frac{1}{2}$.

I must acknowledge, however, that this experiment ought to be repeated more than once, to put the fact out of any doubt. I made it the very last day of my stay in the country and thus had no time to repeat it.

JOHANNES MÜLLER
1801–58

THE FUNCTION OF THE SPINAL NERVES OF A FROG IS DEMONSTRATED

JOHANNES MÜLLER, regarded as one of the greatest of all biologists, made important contributions to physiology, embryology, anatomy, and marine biology. He introduced comparative physiology and showed a remarkable facility in the application of the methods of chemistry, physics, and psychology to the analysis of physiological problems. His great skill as an investigator was equalled, if not surpassed, by his effectiveness as a teacher. His students make up a veritable galaxy of nineteenth-century biologists.

Müller was born in Coblenz where his father was a shoemaker, and studied medicine at Bonn. After three years of further study in Berlin, he returned to Bonn as professor and later succeeded his mentor at Berlin as professor of anatomy and physiology, a position he retained for the rest of an active life.

He made many contributions on the physiology and anatomy of sight, hearing, and the other senses. He developed the theory of 'specific nerve energies', in which he held that the nerves which serve each sense organ determine the nature of the sensation registered, regardless of the mode of stimulation of the nerve. His *Handbook of Physiology* brought together in a definitive way all useful knowledge on the subject with much new material from his own investigations and those of his students. His many anatomical investigations included one on the structure of the lancelet, or amphioxus, and another on the hagfish, a primitive group of fish. He also verified Aristotle's description of live bearing of young in the shark.

As an embryologist Müller studied the life histories of

many marine invertebrates and was the first to describe the free-swimming larval stages of starfish and other echinoderms, tracing the complex development of these forms into mature adulthood. He made many other field observations of marine life, both on the shore and in the open sea.

Although he used the methods of chemistry and physics, Müller felt that there is in the living organism something unique which transcends its mechanism – a vital principle beyond analysis and measurement. This vitalism led Müller to believe that it was impossible to measure the velocity of a nerve impulse. This measurement was made by one of Müller's own pupils, Hermann Helmholtz, ten years later.

The reading below illustrates Müller's experimental approach in demonstrating the function of spinal nerves. It is taken from the English translation of his *Elements of Physiology*, by William Baly, published in 1837.

═══

¶ *Of the Sensitive and Motor Roots of the Spinal Nerves*

The fact that the same nerves supply the body with sensitive and motor power, and that one of these functions of a nerve may, in consequence of paralysis, be lost while the other is preserved, is one of the most important in physiology. Sir Charles Bell first conceived the ingenious idea that the posterior roots of the spinal nerves, which have upon them a ganglion, are the source of sensation; the anterior roots, of motion; and that the primitive fibres of these roots after their union are mixed, and thus distributed for the supply of the skin and muscles. This view he proposed in 1811, in a treatise entitled 'An Idea of a New Anatomy of the Brain, Submitted for the Observation of the Author's Friends'. Eleven years later, the same theory was advanced by M. Magendie, who, however, has the merit of having first subjected it to the test of experiment in the case of the spinal nerves. M. Magendie maintained, as the result of his experiments, that division of the posterior roots of the nerves deprived the corresponding parts of the body of sensation only, while division of the anterior roots deprived them of motion. M. Magendie's results were only approximative. ... Great, therefore, as was the interest which Sir C. Bell's theory, thus newly illustrated by M. Magendie's experiments, excited, a satisfactory confirmation of the results was still wanting. ...

*

The happy thought at length occurred to me of performing the experiment on frogs. These animals are very tenacious of life, and long survive the opening of the vertebral canal. In them, also, the nerves retain their excitability for a very considerable time, and the large roots of the nerves of the posterior extremities run a long distance within the cavity of the spine before uniting. The result was most satisfactory. The experiments are so easily performed, so certain, and conclusive, that every one can now very readily convince himself of one of the most important truths of physiology.

To lay open the spine, I make use of a small pair of bone-nippers, which cut sharply at the edge and points. The operation is completed in a few minutes, without any injury to the spinal cord. The frogs remain quite lively, and leap about as before. As soon as the spinal canal and the membranes are laid open, the thick posterior roots of the nerves, given off to the lower extremities, come to view. They should be carefully raised with a cataract needle, without including any of the anterior roots, and cut off close to the spinal cord. The end of one of the posterior roots is now seized with a pair of forceps, and the root itself irritated repeatedly with the point of the needle; but not the slightest contraction of the muscles of the posterior extremities ever ensues. The same experiment may be repeated on the very large posterior roots of the nerves of the anterior extremities, and the same result will be obtained.

If, now, one of the anterior roots of the nerves of the lower extremity, which are equally as large as the posterior, is now raised with the needle out of the vertebral canal, it is found that the slightest touch of these anterior roots excites the most powerful contractions of the whole limb. Having cut them through at their insertion into the cord, the extremity of one is seized with the forceps, and the needle used to irritate it as in the case of the posterior root. And each time that the point of the needle is applied, most distinct twitchings of the muscles take place.

These experiments may be repeated on a large number of frogs, and they will most convincingly prove that *it is quite impossible to excite muscular contractions in frogs by irritating mechanically the posterior roots of the spinal nerves; and that, on the other hand, the slightest irritation of the anterior roots immediately gives rise to very strong actions of the muscles....*

*

The foregoing experiments leave no doubt as to the correctness of Sir C. Bell's theory.

I may further remark that the section of the posterior roots, in dividing them from the spinal cord, is frequently attended with very distinct manifestations in the anterior part of the body that pain is suffered.

CLAUDE BERNARD
1813–78

SOME GENERAL PRINCIPLES OF EXPERIMENTATION IN MEDICINE ARE SET FORTH

CLAUDE BERNARD, born in the village of Saint-Julien, where his father was a wine grower, worked first as a pharmacist. He was greatly attracted by the theatre and wrote a comedy *La Rose du Rome*, which had sufficient success to encourage him to write a full-length tragedy. A distinguished critic to whom he showed his manuscript recognized his considerable literary talent but advised him to study medicine to provide financial security and to devote his leisure to his literary pursuits. He graduated in medicine in Paris and then worked for Magendie, a brilliant experimentalist.

Bernard equalled or excelled Magendie as an investigator and possessed, which his master did not, a remarkable ability for fruitful generalization and synthesis. He was able to coordinate the results of contemporary research and with rare philosophical insight to establish principles of scientific investigation and to expound them, in his *Introduction to the Study of Experimental Medicine* (1865), in lucid and attractive language.

His experiments were brilliantly conceived and carefully planned. Perhaps his most important discovery was that of the formation of glycogen by the liver. The capacity of the body to build up and not merely to break down complex substances had not previously been appreciated. He also carried out valuable experiments in digestion, investigating particularly the role of the pancreatic juice. Further work established the foundations of our knowledge of the sympathetic nervous system which plays a large part in the involuntary functions of the body, including the regulation of blood flow.

The most outstanding of his general concepts was that of the *'milieu intérieur'* or internal environment, and his hypothesis that the complex functions of different organs were very closely interrelated and were directed towards maintaining the constancy of conditions in the internal environment. He suggested the existence of internal secretions, the further study of which has developed into the science of endocrinology.

The passages which follow are taken from H. C. Greene's translation of *An Introduction to the Study of Experimental Medicine.*

—————

¶ Examples of Experimental Physiological Investigation

In scientific investigations, various circumstances may serve as starting-points for research; I will reduce all these varieties, however, to two chief types:

1. Where the starting-point for experimental research is an observation;

2. Where the starting-point for experimental research is a hypothesis or a theory.

§ I. Where the Starting Point for Experimental Research is an Observation

Experimental ideas are often born by chance, with the help of some casual observation. Nothing is more common; and this is really the simplest way of beginning a piece of scientific work. We take a walk, so to speak, in the realm of science, and we pursue what happens to present itself to our eyes. Bacon compares scientific investigation with hunting; the observations that present themselves are the game. Keeping the same simile, we may add that, if the game presents itself when we are looking for it, it may also present itself when we are not looking for it, or when we are looking for game of another kind. I shall cite an example in which these two cases presented themselves in succession.

First example. – One day, rabbits from the market were brought into my laboratory. They were put on the table where they urinated, and I happened to observe that their urine was clear and acid. This fact struck me, because rabbits, which are herbivora, generally have turbid and alkaline urine; while on the other hand carnivora, as we know, have clear and acid urine. This observation of acidity in the rabbits' urine gave me an idea that these animals must be in the nutritional condition of carnivora. I assumed that they had probably not eaten for a long time, and they had been transformed, by fasting, into veritable carnivorous animals, living on their own blood. Nothing was easier than to verify this preconceived idea or hypothesis by experiment. I gave the rabbits grass to eat; and a few hours later, their urine became turbid and alkaline. I then subjected them to fasting and after twenty-four hours or thirty-six hours at most, their urine again became clear and strongly acid; then after eating grass, their urine became alkaline again, etc. I repeated this very simple experiment a great many times, and always with the same result. I then repeated it on a horse, a herbivorous animal which also has turbid and alkaline urine. I found that fasting, as in rabbits, produced prompt acidity of the urine, with such an increase in urea, that it spontaneously crystallizes at times in the cooled urine. As a result of my experiments, I thus reached the general proposition which then was still unknown, to wit, that all fasting animals feed on meat, so that herbivora then have urine like that of carnivora.

We are here dealing with a very simple, particular fact which allows us easily to follow the evolution of experimental reasoning. When we see a phenomenon which we are not in the habit of seeing, we must always ask ourselves what it is connected with, or putting it differently, what is its proximate cause; the answer or the idea, which presents itself to the mind, must then be submitted to experiment. When I saw the rabbits' acid urine, I instinctively asked myself what could be its cause. The experimental idea consisted in the connexion, which my mind spontaneously made, between acidity of the rabbits' urine, and the state of fasting which I considered equivalent to a true flesh-eater's diet. The inductive reasoning which I implicitly went through was the following syllogism: the urine of carnivora is acid; now the rabbits before me have acid urine; therefore they are carnivora, i.e., fasting. This remained to be established by experiment.

But to prove that my fasting rabbits were really carnivorous, a counterproof was required. A carnivorous rabbit had to be experimentally produced by feeding it with meat, so as to see if its urine would then be clear, as it was during fasting. So I had rabbits fed on cold boiled beef (which they eat very nicely when they are given nothing else). My expectation was again verified, and, as long as the animal diet was continued, the rabbits kept their clear and acid urine.

To complete my experiment, I made an autopsy on my animals, to see if meat was digested in the same way in rabbits as in carnivora. I found, in fact, all the phenomena of an excellent digestion in their intestinal reactions, and I noted that all the chyliferous vessels were gorged with very abundant white, milky chyle, just as in carnivora. But apropos of these autopsies which confirmed my ideas on meat digestion in rabbits, lo and behold a fact presented itself which I had not remotely thought of, but which became, as we shall see, my starting-point in a new piece of work.

Second example (sequel to the last). – In sacrificing the rabbits which I had fed on the meat, I happened to notice that the white and milky lymphatics were first visible in the small intestine at the lower part of the duodenum, about thirty centimetres below the pylorus. This fact caught my attention because in dogs they are first visible much higher in the duodenum just below the pylorus. On examining more closely, I noted that this peculiarity in rabbits coincided with the position of the pancreatic duct which was inserted very low and near the exact place where the lymphatics began to contain a chyle made white and milky by emulsion of fatty nutritive materials.

Chance observation of this fact evoked the idea which brought to birth the thought in my mind, that pancreatic juice might well cause the emulsion of fatty materials and consequently their absorption by the lymphatic vessels. Instinctively again, I made the following syllogism: the white chyle is due to emulsion of the fat; now in rabbits white chyle is formed at the level where pancreatic juice is poured into the intestine; therefore it is pancreatic juice that makes the emulsion of fat and forms the white chyle. This had to be decided by experiment.

In view of this preconceived idea I imagined and at once performed a suitable experiment to verify the truth or falsity of my suppositions. The experiment consisted in trying the properties of pancreatic juice directly on neutral fats. But pancreatic juice does not spontaneously flow outside of the body, like saliva, for instance, or urine; its secretory organ is, on the contrary, lodged deep in the abdominal cavity. I was therefore forced to use the method of experimentation to secure the pancreatic fluid from living animals in suitable physiological conditions and in sufficient quantity. Only then could I carry out my experiment, that is to say, control my preconceived idea; and the experiment proved that my idea was correct. In fact pancreatic juice obtained in suitable conditions from dogs, rabbits, and various other animals, and mixed with oil or melted fat, always instantly emulsified, and later split these fatty bodies into fatty acids, glycerine, etc., by means of a specific ferment.

I shall not follow these experiments further, having

explained them at length in a special work. I wish here to show merely how an accidental first observation of the acidity of rabbits' urine suggested to me the idea of making experiments on them with carnivorous feeding, and how later, in continuing these experiments, I brought to light, without seeing it, another observation concerning the peculiar arrangement of the junction of the pancreatic duct in rabbits. This second observation gave me, in turn, the idea of experimenting on the behaviour of pancreatic juice.

From the above examples we see how chance observation of a fact or phenomenon brings to birth, by anticipation, a preconceived idea or hypothesis about the probable cause of the phenomenon observed; how the preconceived idea begets reasoning which results in the experiment which verifies it; how, in one case, we had to have recourse to experimentation, i.e. to the use of more or less complicated operative processes, etc., to work out the verification. In the last example, experiment played a double role; it first judged and confirmed the provisions of the reasoning which it had begotten; but what is more, it produced a fresh observation. We may therefore call this observation an observation produced or begotten by experiment. This proves that, as we said, all the results of an experiment must be observed, both those connected with the preconceived idea and those without any relation to it. If we saw only facts connected with our preconceived idea, we should often cut ourselves off from making discoveries. For it often happens that an unsuccessful experiment may produce an excellent observation, as the following example will prove. . . .

§*II. When the Starting Point of Experimental Research is a Hypothesis or a Theory*

We have already said and we shall see further on, that in noting an observation we must never go beyond facts. But in making an experiment, it is different. I wish to show that hypotheses are indispensable, and that they are useful, therefore, precisely because they lead us outside of facts and carry science forward. The object of hypotheses is not only to make us try new experiments; they also often make us discover new facts which we should not have perceived without them. In the preceding examples, we saw that we can start from a particular fact and rise one by one to more general ideas, i.e. to a theory. But we have just seen, we can also sometimes start with a hypothesis deduced from a theory. Though we are dealing in this case with reasoning logically deduced from a theory, we have a hypothesis that must still be verified by experiment. Indeed, theories are only an assembling of the earlier facts, on which our hypothesis rests, and cannot be used to demonstrate it experimentally. We said that, in this instance, we must not submit to the yoke of theories, and that keeping our mental independence is the best way to discover the truth. This is proved by the following examples.

First example. – In 1843, in one of my first pieces of work, I undertook to study what becomes of different alimentary substances in nutrition. As I said before, I began with sugar, a definite substance that is easier than any other to recognize and follow in the bodily economy. With this in view, I injected solutions of cane-sugar into the blood of animals, and I noted that even when injected in weak doses the sugar passed into the urine. I recognized later that, by changing or transforming sugar, the gastric juice made it capable of assimilation, i.e., of destruction in the blood.

Thereupon I wished to learn in what organ the nutritive sugar disappeared, and I conceived the hypothesis that sugar introduced into the blood through nutrition might be destroyed in the lungs or in the general capillaries. The theory, indeed, which then prevailed and which was naturally my proper starting-point, assumed that the sugar present in animals came exclusively from foods, and that it was destroyed in animal organisms by the phenomena of combustion, i.e., of respiration. Thus sugar had gained the name of respiratory nutriment. But I was immediately led to see that the theory about the origin of sugar in animals, which served me as a starting-point, was false. As a result of the experiments which I shall describe further on, I was not indeed led to find an organ for destroying sugar, but, on the contrary, I discovered an organ for making it, and I found that all animal blood contains sugar even when they do not eat it. So I noted a new fact, unforeseen in theory, which men had not noticed, doubtless because they were under the influence of contrary theories which they had too confidently accepted. I therefore abandoned my hypothesis on the spot, so as to pursue the unexpected result which has since become the fertile origin of a new path for investigation and a mine of discoveries that is not yet exhausted.

In these researches I followed the principles of the experimental method that we have established, i.e., that, in the presence of a well-noted, new fact which contradicts a theory, instead of keeping the theory and abandoning the fact, I should keep and study the fact, and I hastened to give up the theory, thus conforming to the precept which we proposed in the second chapter: 'When we meet a fact which contradicts a prevailing theory, we must accept the fact and abandon the theory, even when the theory is supported by great names and generally accepted.'

We must therefore distinguish, as we said, between principles and theories, and never believe absolutely in the latter. We had a theory here which assumed that the vegetable kingdom alone had the power of creating the individual compounds which the animal kingdom is supposed to destroy. According to this theory, established and supported by the most illustrious chemists of our day, animals were incapable of producing sugar in their organisms. If I had believed in this theory absolutely, I should have had to conclude that my experiment was vitiated by some inaccuracy; and less wary experimenters than I might have condemned it at once, and might not have tarried longer at an observation which could be theoretically suspected of including sources of error, since it showed sugar in the blood of animals on a diet that lacked starchy or sugary materials. But instead of being concerned about the theory, I concerned myself only with the fact whose reality I was trying to establish. By new experiments and by means of suitable counterproofs, I was thus led to confirm my first observation and to find that the liver is the organ in which animal sugar is formed in certain given circumstances, to spread later into the whole blood supply and into the tissues and fluids.

Animal glycogenesis which I thus discovered, i.e., the power of producing sugar, possessed by animals as well as vegetables, is now an acquired fact of science; but we have not yet fixed on a plausible accounting for the phenomenon. The fresh facts which I made known are the source of numerous studies and many varied theories in apparent contradiction with each other and with my own. When entering on new ground we must not be afraid to express even risky ideas so as to stimulate research in all directions. As Priestley put it, we must not remain inactive through false modesty based on fear of being mistaken. So I made more or less hypothetical theories of glycogenesis; after mine came others; my theories, like other men's, will live the allotted life of necessarily very partial and temporary theories at the opening of a new series of investigations; they will be replaced later by others, embodying a more advanced stage of the question, and so on. Theories are like a stairway; by climbing, science widens its horizon more and more, because theories embody and necessarily include proportionately more facts as they advance. Progress is achieved by exchanging our theories for new ones which go further than the old, until we find one based on a larger number of facts. In the case which now concerns us, the question is not one of condemning the old to the advantage of a more recent theory. What is important is having opened a new road; for well-observed facts, though brought to light by passing theories, will never die; they are the material on which alone the house of science will at last be built, when it has facts enough and has gone sufficiently deep into the analysis of phenomena to know their law or their causation.

To sum up, theories are only hypotheses, verified by more or less numerous facts. Those verified by the most facts are the best; but even then they are never final, never to be absolutely believed. We have seen in the preceding examples that if we had had complete confidence in the prevailing theory of the destruction of sugar in animals, and if we had only had its confirmation in view, we should probably not have found the road to the new facts which we met. It is true that a hypothesis based on a theory produced the experiment; but as soon as the results of the experiment appeared, theory and hypothesis had to disappear, for the experimental facts were now just an observation, to be made without any preconceived idea.

In sciences as complex and as little developed as physiology, the great principle is therefore to give little heed to hypotheses or theories and always to keep an eye alert to observe everything that appears in every aspect of an experiment. An apparently accidental and inexplicable circumstance may occasion the discovery of an important new fact, as we shall see in the continuation of the example just noted.

VI

THE DEVELOPMENT AND
EVOLUTION OF LIFE

MAN has long speculated on his origins and on the origins of the many kinds of life around him. Primitive man and the peoples of the earlier civilizations, wondering whence, how, and why he came to be, formulated many theories some of which exerted a profound influence on the development of philosophical and religious thought. To the inquiring mind these theories afforded little satisfaction as they failed to provide a rational explanation based on observed facts.

The idea of the evolution of organic life occurred quite early in Greek philosophy and reappeared from time to time through the Middle Ages. Some of the more influential of these philosophical speculations appeared in the works of Aristotle and Thomas Aquinas; but in these writings, and in many others, there were no efforts to support the theory by evidence, nor were the many observable facts which demanded explanation examined systematically. For most people in the Western world, the story of creation as related in the book of Genesis provided an adequate answer to their questions. According to this doctrine, held by both scientists and churchmen as late as the early years of the nineteenth century, man, as well as all animals and plants, had been created a few thousand years ago and had remained unchanged ever since. As Lamarck expressed it: 'Nature (or its Author) in creating animals has foreseen all possible sorts of circumstances in which they would be destined to live, and has given to each species a constant organization, as well as a form determined and invariable in its parts, which forces each species to live in the places and climates where it is found, and there to preserve the habits which we know belong to it.'

Observant men had noted quite early that there were on earth many distinctly different types of plants and animals. They observed that many animals resembled one another in basic structure, and they assumed that these were probably related. This was true of plants as well. The individual type of living thing was the species, but its scientific significance was not established until the late seventeenth and early eighteenth centuries.

There were a number of efforts to explain the relationship between species of similar structure; one attempt, made by the Greeks, arranged all living things in a kind of ladder of life with man at the top. One such ladder was described by Aristotle, who did not, however, suggest any formal scheme of classification.

The modern system of classification and nomenclature of plants and animals was developed by Linnaeus, who succeeded in classifying every known animal and plant and assigning it to a position in his system. He grouped the animals and plants in *classes, orders, genera,* and *species,* each of these categories being a division whose members were more or less closely related. The class was the largest grouping, and its members were less closely related than the members of an order; they in turn had less in common than the members of the same genus. There have been many modifications of Linnaeus's scheme; for example, further categories such as the *phylum* and the *family* have been added. The feature of his plan which remained unchanged was the binomial system of naming each distinct type of plant and animal by reference to its *genus* and its species.

Although Linnaeus must have observed variations in living things, he was convinced that the species of animals and plants were immutable and that 'there are as many species as God created in the beginning'. This doctrine was not at all satisfying to Lamarck, the French naturalist, who himself had made extensive systematic studies of life forms. Lamarck, the first to attempt a comprehensive theory of evolution, suggested that the vast variety of living things evolved from simpler types. He is a significant figure in the history of the theory of evolution because he accepted the idea as a basic premise; yet he gave an unsatisfactory explanation of the adaptation of animals to the environment by the development of new structures or by atrophy of existing ones. He erroneously maintained that such changes were passed on to the descendants.

Lamarck had little influence on his contemporaries, mainly because his views were opposed strenuously by Georges Cuvier (1769–1832), the most powerful scientific figure in France, if not in Europe, at the time. Cuvier strongly supported the doctrine of special creation, to which he added the theory of catastrophism, which held that the earth had been the scene of a number of violent cataclysms, each of which wiped out all life, and that new life was created following each of these upheavals. Each cataclysm buries the plants and animals of the preceding era, accounting for the fossils of many extinct species with which Cuvier was familiar.

Charles Lyell (1797–1875), the English geologist, found many inconsistencies in Lamarck's arguments. He was especially disturbed by Lamarck's assumption that species were continuously changing, a view which conflicted with the Linnaean concept of the species as being remarkably constant in their characteristics. Lyell thought that Lamarck had not proved that changes were actually taking place.

Lyell's work, in fact, prepared the way for Darwin. His most compelling contribution was the idea of uniformitarianism as an answer to Cuvier's catastrophism, his argument being that the forces shaping the surface of the earth (wind, glacier, wave, and earthquake) operate in the present as in the past and that these forces continue to produce their effects over long periods of time.

It was at this time that Charles Darwin set out on his famous voyage in the *Beagle* in 1831, the year before

Cuvier's death. This voyage was not only the turning-point in Darwin's life; it marked the beginning of the greatest revolution in man's conception of the living universe and his position in it.

On returning to England, Darwin set himself the task of proving or disproving the fact of evolution of species. For twenty-two years he gathered evidence in almost fantastic detail and reflected on it. He would not have published his theory when he did had not Alfred Russel Wallace come upon the basic explanation independently and communicated his ideas to Darwin. That these two great men agreed to make a joint announcement, in July 1858, reflects great credit on both and in no way lessens the greater importance of Darwin's work.

On Darwin's more detailed exposition, published the following year, Henry Fairfield Osborn has commented that 'the demonstration of evolution as a universal law of living nature is the greatest intellectual achievement of the nineteenth century. Evolution has outgrown the rank of a theory, for it has won a place in natural law beside Newton's law of gravitation, and in one sense holds a still higher rank, because evolution is the universal master, while gravitation is among its agents.'

In what lay the importance of Darwin's theory? Darwin's conclusions must be examined from two points of view. The first contribution was to establish beyond dispute the fact of evolution. The conclusiveness of his argument swept away all opposition, and there is no scientist today who questions the doctrine. The overwhelming evidence which Darwin marshalled from all the biological disciplines to support his case must be examined in detail to be fully appreciated.

Darwin's second contribution was his suggestion of the mechanism by which evolution is brought about – the concept of natural selection. It is here that modern biologists have taken issue with Darwin. His arguments were presented in the context of the biological knowledge of his time, and some of the factors operating in natural selection, and on which Darwin based his case, proved unreliable – especially his notion of the mechanics of inheritance.

Darwin stressed the importance of small variations as the material out of which new species are originated. Unfortunately, he knew nothing of Mendel's experimental demonstration of the mode of inheritance of discrete variations – facts which would have greatly strengthened this aspect of his argument. The rediscovery of Mendel's publication in 1900 initiated modern work in genetics and ultimately led to the discovery of the gene, the mechanism of life's reproductive continuity. Mendelian genetics alone does not provide the explanation of the development of new types. It is here that DeVries's discovery of mutations, the spontaneous alteration of the hereditary material, provides additional and perhaps conclusive support for the origin of new characters with adaptive advantages in the struggle for existence.

The modern extension of the work of Mendel and DeVries has yielded the 'adequate and critical view of genetic phenomena' and has completed the Darwinian revolution. It has thrown light not only on the origin of man but also on his destiny.

LINNAEUS
1707–78

THE BINOMIAL SYSTEM OF NAMING PLANTS AND ANIMALS IS ESTABLISHED IN ITS MODERN FORM

FROM time to time during the development of science there has emerged a man whose work has served to coordinate and to set a standard of reference for the contributions of others. The latter may have had considerable intrinsic merits but their real significance is revealed only in the light of the works of the greater man. Among such men can be numbered Ptolemy, Roger Bacon, Francis Bacon, Galileo, and Newton. Although more such personalities emerge as science advances there are few who dominate their period and their field.

Linnaeus (born Carl Linné) was such a man; his contribution – the classification of all plants, minerals, and animals known to man. His work, the subject of a lifetime of tremendous enthusiasm, was based on foundations laid before he was twenty-eight years old. Few men have published a definitive study at so early an age and seen it accepted as a standard work of reference. Linnaeus was not to know that the same work would stand, in many respects, as an effective guide to procedure for two centuries after his death.

Linnaeus was probably inspired by the work of such men as John Ray (1627–1705), the 'father of English natural history', Joseph Tournefort (1656–1708), professor at the Jardin des Plantes in Paris, and Augustus Rivinus (1652–1723). All of these had attempted to classify the subjects of natural history, but they were as much concerned with the specimens they collected as with their classification, and it was left to Linnaeus to pursue the latter as an end in itself.

Though he was an arrogant man who wrote as if he had been personally present at the Creation (cf. A. R. Hall, *The Scientific Revolution*, London (Longmans), 1954, p. 293), he attracted co-workers from all over the world; with these he conducted a vast correspondence, encouraging field work on a systematic basis, itself no mean contribution to scientific development. One of his pupils, for example, accompanied Captain Cook, the eighteenth-century explorer of the Pacific Islands.

That the time was ripe for an efficient classifier is evident from the enormously accelerating rate of discovery of new plants and animals. It is said that whereas 6,000 plants had been recognized by the year 1600, in the next century some 12,000 more were discovered. Some earlier works on the structure of flowers led Linnaeus to the idea of classification by reference to the stamens (the pollen-bearing male organs in a flower) and the pistil (the female part). Observation of these characteristics provided the first basis for classification: the class being based on the number of stamens; the order on the number of pistils. These, as Linnaeus pointed out, were arbitrary features; his further classifications, into *genera* and *species*, were based on more natural distinctions. Names of plants could be determined by the last two factors; hence the binomial system of nomenclature, which, soon after it was published, became generally adopted. Thus, in the binomial system every species is identified by its genus and species name, such as *Felis leo* for the lion or *Homo sapiens* for man.

Inevitably Linnaeus was confronted by the problem of the origin of the species he observed. His original view was that they represented an unchanged and unchanging continuity, derived from the original creation. Hence new species could not arise. He seems to have questioned his views on this in later life, but the doctrine of immutability remained the subject of controversy for some time.

Linnaeus's library and collection of specimens, which he had intended to be preserved in Sweden, were sold by his widow to an Englishman, James Edward Smith, an early patron of Linnaeus. They have remained in London in the custody of the Linnaean Society (founded by Smith in 1788), which became an important scientific body in the field which Linnaeus had so dynamically inaugurated.

The first of the two readings below is taken from the translation by W. Turton in 1806 of the last edition of *Systema naturae* (1788); the second is from the translation by Sir A. Hort of *Critica botanica* for the Ray Society in 1938.

─────

¶ *Introduction*

Man, when he enters the world, is naturally led to inquire who he is; whence he comes; whither he is going; for what purpose he is created; and by whose benevolence he is preserved. He finds himself descended from the remotest creation; journeying to a life of perfection and happiness; and led by his endowments to a contemplation of the works of nature.

Like other animals who enjoy life, sensation, and perception; who seek for food, amusements, and rest, and who prepare habitations convenient for their kind, he is curious and inquisitive; but, above all other animals, he is noble in his nature, in as much as, by the powers of his mind, he is able to reason justly upon whatever discovers itself to his senses; and to look, with reverence and wonder, upon the works of Him who created all things.

That existence is surely contemptible, which regards only the gratification of instinctive wants, and the preservation of a body made to perish. It is therefore the business of a thinking being, to look forward to the purposes of all things; and to remember that the end of creation is, that God may be glorified in all his works.

Hence it is of importance that we should study the

works of nature, than which, what can be more useful, what more interesting? For, however large a portion of them lies open to our present view; a still greater part is yet unknown and undiscovered.

All things are not within the immediate reach of human capacity. Many have been made known to us, of which those who went before us were ignorant; many we have heard of, but know not what they are; and many must remain for the diligence of future ages.

It is the exclusive property of man, to contemplate and to reason on the great book of nature. She gradually unfolds herself to him who, with patience and perseverance, will search into her mysteries; and when the memory of the present and of past generations shall be entirely obliterated, he shall enjoy the high privilege of living in the minds of his successors, as he has been advanced in the dignity of his nature, by the labours of those who went before him.

The UNIVERSE comprehends whatever exists; whatever can come to our knowledge by the agency of our senses. The *Stars*, the *Elements*, and this our *Globe*.

The STARS are bodies remote, lucid, revolving in perpetual motion. They shine, either by their own proper light, as the *Sun*, and the remoter *fixed Stars*; or are *Planets* receiving light from others. Of these the primary planets are solar; *Saturn, Jupiter, Mars*, the *Earth, Venus, Mercury*, and *Georgium Sidus**: the secondary are those subservient to, and rolling round the primary, as the *Moon* round the earth.

The ELEMENTS are bodies simple, constituting the atmosphere of, and probably filling the spaces between the stars.

Fire;	lucid,	resilient,	warm,	evolant,	vivifying.
Air;	transparent,	elastic,	dry,	encircling,	generating.
Water;	diaphanous,	fluid,	moist,	gliding,	conceiving.
Earth;	opaque,	fixed,	cold,	quiescent,	sterile.

* [The original name of Uranus.]

The EARTH is a planetary sphere, turning round its own axis, once in twenty-four hours, and round the sun once a year; surrounded by an *atmosphere* of elements, and covered by a stupendous crust of *natural bodies*, which are the objects of our studies. It is terraqueous; having the depressed parts covered with waters; the elevated parts gradually dilated into dry and habitable continents. The *land* is moistened by *vapours*, which, rising from the waters, are collected into *clouds*: these are deposited upon the tops of mountains; form small *streams*, which unite into *rivulets*, and reunite into those ever-flowing *rivers*, which pervading the thirsty earth, and affording moisture to the productions growing for the support of her living inhabitants, are at last returned into their parent *sea*.

The study of natural history, simple, beautiful, and instructive, consists in the collection, arrangement, and exhibition of the various productions of the earth.

These are divided into the three grand kingdoms of nature, whose boundaries meet together in the Zoophytes.

MINERALS inhabit the interior parts of the earth in rude and shapeless masses, are generated by salts, mixed together promiscuously, and shaped fortuitously.

They are bodies *concrete*, without life or sensation.

VEGETABLES clothe the surface with verdure, imbibe nourishment through bibulous roots, breathe by quivering leaves, celebrate their nuptials in a genial metamorphosis, and continue their kind by the dispersion of seed within prescribed limits.

They are bodies *organized*, and have *life* and not sensation.

ANIMALS adorn the exterior parts of the earth, respire, and generate eggs; are impelled to action by hunger, congeneric affections, and pain; and by preying on other animals and vegetables, restrain within proper proportion the numbers of both.

They are bodies *organized*, and have *life, sensation*, and the power of locomotion.

MAN, the last and best of created works, formed after the image of his Maker, endowed with a portion of intellectual divinity, the governor and subjugator of all other beings, is, by his wisdom alone, able to form just conclusions from such things as present themselves to his senses, which can only consist of bodies merely natural. Hence the first step of wisdom is to know these bodies; and to be able, by those marks imprinted on them by nature, to distinguish them from each other, and to affix to every object its proper name.

These are the elements of all science; this is the great alphabet of nature: for if the name be lost, the knowledge of the object is lost also; and without these, the student will seek in vain for the means to investigate the hidden treasures of nature.

METHOD, the soul of Science, indicates that every natural body may, by inspection, be known by its own peculiar name; and this name points out whatever the industry of man has been able to discover concerning it: so that amidst the greatest apparent confusion, the greatest order is visible.

SYSTEM is conveniently divided into five branches, each subordinate to the other: *class, order, genus, species*, and *variety*, with their names and characters. For he must first know the name who is willing to investigate the object.

The science of nature supposes an exact knowledge of the nomenclature, and a systematic arrangement of all natural bodies. In this arrangement, the *classes* and *orders* are arbitrary; the *genera* and *species* are natural. All true knowledge refers to the species, all solid knowledge to the genus.

Of these three grand divisions the *animal* kingdom ranks highest in comparative estimation, next the *vegetable*, and the last and lowest is the *mineral* kingdom. ANIMALS enjoy *sensation* by means of a living organization, animated by a medullary substance; *perception* by nerves; and *motion* by the exertion of the will.

They have *members* for the different purposes of life; *organs* for their different senses; and *faculties* or powers for the application of their different perceptions.

They all originate from an *egg*.

Their external and internal structure; their comparative anatomy, habits, instincts, and various relations to each other, are detailed in authors who professedly treat on these subjects.

The natural *division* of animals is into six *classes*, formed from their internal structure.

Heart with 2 auricles, 2 ventricles;	viviparous	MAMMALIA	1
blood warm, red	oviparous	BIRDS	2
Heart with 1 auricle, 1 ventricle;	lungs voluntary	AMPHIBIA	3
blood cold, red	external gills	FISHES	4
Heart with 1 auricle, ventricle 0;	have antennae	INSECTS	5
sanies cold, white	have tentacula	WORMS	6

I. MAMMALIA. *Lungs* respire alternately; *jaws* incumbent, covered; *teeth* usually within; *teats* lactiferous; *organs* of sense, tongue, nostrils, eyes, ears, and papillae of the skin; *covering*, hair, which is scanty in warm climates, and hardly any on aquatics; *supporters*, 4 feet, except in aquatics; and in most a *tail*: *walk* on the *earth*, and *speak*.

II. BIRDS. *Lungs* respire alternately; *jaws* incumbent, naked, extended, without teeth; *eggs* covered with a calcareous shell; *organs* of sense, tongue, nostrils, eyes, and ears without auricles; *covering*, incumbent, imbricate feathers; *supporters*, feet 2, wings 2; and a heart-shaped rump; *fly* in the *air*, and *sing*.

III. AMPHIBIA. *Jaws* incumbent; *penis* (frequently) double; *eggs* (usually) membranaceous; *organs* of sense, tongue, nostrils, eyes, ears; *covering*, a naked skin; *supporters* various, in some 0; *creep* in *warm* places and *hiss*.

IV. FISHES. *Jaws* incumbent; *penis* (usually) 0; *eggs* without white; *organs* of sense, tongue, nostrils? eyes, ears; *covering*, imbricate scales; *supporters*, fins; *swim* in the *water*, and *smack*.

V. INSECTS. *Spiracles*, lateral pores; *jaws* lateral; *organs* of sense, tongue, eyes, antennae on the head, brain 0, ears 0, nostrils 0; *covering*, a bony coat of mail; *supporters*, feet, and in some, wings; *skip* on *dry* ground, and *buzz*.

VI. WORMS. *Spiracles*, obscure; *jaws*, various; frequently *hermaphrodites*; organs of sense tentacula, (generally) eyes, brain 0, ears 0, nostrils 0; *covering*, calcareous or 0, except spines; *supporters*, feet 0, fins 0; *crawl* in *moist* places, and are *mute*.

¶ *Introduction. To the foremost botanist of this age Jo. Jac. Dillenius Doctor of Medicine Sherardian Professor of Botany in the University of Oxford, Fellow of the Imperial Academy of Natural Sciences, and of the Royal Society. Carolus Linnaeus gives greeting*

How great a burden has been laid on the shoulders of botanists by disagreement in names, which is the first step toward barbarism, none should know better than you, most illustrious sir, who are today putting the final touches to Sherard's eagerly awaited *Phytopinax*. Name changes have, however, hitherto been unavoidable among botanists, so long as no laws had been adopted by which names could be judged. Botanists live in a free state, and for them no eternal law can be prescribed unless it be adopted by the citizens both present and future, and indeed unless it be none other than a law that can be shown by argument and example to be so faultless and indispensable that none better can be devised. Before botany can have such laws as I conceive and desire, the various citizens must advance their own arguments, and then let posterity decide on the best.

In publishing my observations concerning names I set your illustrious name at the head of my little book, that I may not be overwhelmed by the criticisms of malicious persons, who are more anxious to find some way of ridiculing the opinions of others than to make any original contribution to science themselves; for the world today recognizes none greater than you. You know how great a price mankind has always set upon the pleasing of great men: for me, not to displease you means no less. At the same time I thank you, as far as may be done here, for the great kindness with which you never failed to surround me while I pursued the arts at Oxford. It was due to you that I wrote much on the theory of botany, when I myself, properly conscious of how lightly I was laden, should long ago have taken in my sails. It was you, lastly, who, accustomed to weighing everything in the scales of sane reason and principle, opened to me the path which, albeit with hesitant steps, I now seek to tread. Graciously receive, therefore, this offering from your devoted disciple. Farewell, noble sir, and as the unshakable pivot of our science may you long be spared.

CLIFFORTIAN MUSEUM

1737, June 22

¶ Preface

What difficulty has been caused to botanists from the revival of the sciences down to the present day by the invention of new names is known to everyone who has handled the subject; accordingly, when at the beginning of the last century the invasion of barbarism threatened by the vast horde of names in use was stemmed by C. Bauhin, by the general consent of botanists anyone who should in future dare to introduce new names was stigmatized with a black mark, and this was well advised, since, in the circumstances, the stage of learning which the science had at that time reached did not make it possible to frame better names.

When at length the commonwealth of botany had been brought by Morison under an ordered constitution, and an eternal law, taken from nature's book, had been promulgated any who should offend against or transgress this law were branded as ignoramuses. No exception was then allowed: all specific names which did not suit the genus in question were to be banned by an inexorable decree of fate. Alas! What widespread wild confusion ensued toward the end of the last century, while the citizens of the commonwealth of botany were distracted by internal strife beneath the triumvirate of Ray, Tournefort, and Rivinus; Tournefort and Rivinus bestowing different names on each genus and the genera being distributed in one way by the one, and in another by the other. At length Tournefort obtained the victory in regard to genera, and, peace being restored, the world of botanists from that time forward fought shy of the making of any more new names.

However, citizens of the commonwealth never ceased to bring in every day new supplies from foreign lands, to distinguish them as they arrived with more suitable names, to restore what was lacking to repair previous disasters, to become wiser and devise better counsels, and to provide for the general well-being of the commonwealth, though not one of them took upon himself to introduce a complete reformation of its constitution (for Vaillant died just as he began to do so) or to bestow new names. Nevertheless by slow and almost imperceptible steps from Tournefort's time down to the present day more new names have crept in than were ever bestowed at the bidding of any dictator; this is obvious if one brings into comparison the new names of Feuillée, Commelin, Boerhaave, Vaillant, Pontedera, Dillenius, Ruppius, Scheuchzer, Knaut, Montius, Heucher, Buxbaum, Michelli, Kramer, Burman, et cetera. An inevitable necessity compels men to run on rocks which they have not learned to avoid; sound reason enjoins that they should refuse the road by which it is unsafe to travel; and so also it is fated that botanists should impose wrong names, so long as the science remains an untilled field, so long as laws and rules have not been framed on which they [can] erect as on firm foundations the science of botany; and so the aforesaid botanists have, under pressure of necessity, corrected most wisely the faulty names given by their predecessors.

As I turn over the laborious works of the authorities I observe them busied all day long with discovering plants, describing them, drawing them, bringing them under genera and classes; I find, however, among them few philosophers, and hardly any who have attempted to develop nomenclature, one of the two foundations of botany, though that a name should remain unshaken is quite as essential as attention to genera. That they can find no rules given by the ancients for the bestowal of names, no demonstrations or settled principles, is the complaint of novices, and equally of men practised in the science. For any rules of nomenclature which botanists have brought in from time to time are too specialized for any certain conclusion to be drawn from them. Again there is so much disagreement between the authorities that the reader can hardly determine to which in preference to the others he should give his allegiance, since satisfactory principles are not everywhere to be seen. Wherefore it is not surprising if, when the novice has developed into a mature botanist, appearing the while to have done all that was possible, he in his work makes mistakes over nomenclature and so comes to burden botany with wrong names.

Wherefore we can never hope for a lasting peace and better times till botanists come to an agreement among themselves about the fixed laws in accordance with which judgement can be pronounced on names, that is to say, good names can be absolutely distinguished from bad ones, the good ones maintained and the bad ones banished without any exception, so that botany firmly built on immovable principles may remain a fortress inviolable and unshaken.

Before botanists can admit such laws it is necessary that someone among them should take upon himself to offer proposals to be examined by other botanists, so that if they are good they may be confirmed, if unsound they may be convicted of unsoundness and abandoned, while something better is put in their place. But, so long as botanists refuse to make this beginning, so long also will they remain in doubt and uncertainty, and false names will accumulate every day to burden botany. Now as hitherto no one has thought fit to undertake this self-denying task, I have determined to make the attempt; for if a citizen in a free commonwealth may speak his mind it will be at least allowable for me to state my principles among botanists! I have not reached such an extreme of hardihood as to believe that all my reasoning is so firmly based but that someone else may propound reasoning much more mature; still, mine will be true until some other principles are shown to be truer. To you, my dearly beloved botanists, I submit my rules, the rules which I have laid down for myself, and in accordance with which I intend to walk. If they seem to you worthy, let them be used by you also; if not, please propound something better!

JEAN LAMARCK

1744–1829

THE INHERITANCE OF CHARACTERISTICS
ACQUIRED BY USE AND DISUSE IS UTILIZED TO
EXPLAIN THE EVOLUTION OF LIFE

THE work of Lamarck received little recognition in his lifetime and his successors, including Charles Darwin, regarded it with ridicule or contempt. The revaluation of the contributions of the earlier evolutionary theorists and systematists, occasioned partly by the celebration of Darwin's centenary, has accorded a far greater measure of appreciation to the genius of Lamarck and has established the validity of many of his opinions. The long period of neglect which his writings suffered and the disrespect with which his doctrines were greeted may in some measure be attributed to his personal eccentricities and his unattractive literary style.

After serving in the Army he entered medicine when his health failed, but soon became interested in meteorology and then in botany. At the age of forty-four, he was appointed to a chair of zoology. His own experience in both botany and zoology impressed upon him the need to study living things as a whole and he coined the word 'biology'. His studies and classification of fossils led his thoughts to the effect of environment upon development. At the age of fifty, Lamarck began the study of Invertebrates about which he previously knew very little. After nine years of work he provided a classification which, with a few changes, is still used today. Not only did he place the invertebrates in groups but he also arranged them in such a way that it was possible to show their evolution from one into the other. True, his theory of evolution is not accepted today, but Lamarck was thinking in a way which very few before him ever attempted and on a subject about which very little was known. In Lamarck's time so little was known about the invertebrates that some scientists grouped snakes and crocodiles with the insects. The work Lamarck did in the field of invertebrate zoology alone should have made him famous.

In 1809, there appeared his most important work, *Zoological Philosophy*. In it he tried to show that various parts of the body appeared because they were necessary, or disappeared because of disuse when variations in the environment caused a change in habit. He believed these body changes were inherited by the offspring and that, if this process continued for a long time, new species would eventually be produced. Hence Lamarck thought that it ought to be possible to arrange all living things in a branching series showing some species gradually changing into others.

Unfortunately, he chose poor examples to illustrate his ideas, and he never attempted to show how one species might gradually change into another on the basis of the inheritance of acquired characters. His ideas were not accepted, nor have other, more recent theories which have been proposed to explain how new species arose. At this time, also, Lamarck's contemporary, the renowned Cuvier, proposed his own theory of evolution. It was inferior to Lamarck's, but such was Cuvier's fame that Lamarck's ideas were ignored and remained so for many years.

Lamarckism fitted into the general theories of human perfectibility that were prevalent during the nineteenth century. Improvement of the environment of an individual would lead, inevitably, to the improvement of the species. Towards the end of the century, however, August Weismann (1834–1914) studied experimentally the nature of the reproductive cell and came to the conclusion that it was not affected by environment. He argued that the continuity of life was contained in these cells, as distinct from the body, so that, notwithstanding any changes produced in the body by environment, what happened to the succeeding generation was determined by the reproductive cell, itself unaffected by the body change. The work of Hugo DeVries and Gregor Mendel confirmed the view that Lamarck's ideas were misleading. They served, however, to prepare the ground for the concept of evolution, soon to be introduced by Charles Darwin.

———

¶ *Chapter 3: Of Species Among Living Bodies*

It is not a futile purpose to decide definitely what we mean by the so-called *species* among living bodies, and to inquire if it is true that species are of absolute constancy, as old as nature, and have all existed from the beginning just as we see them today; or if, as a result of changes in their environment, albeit extremely slow, they have not in course of time changed their characters and shape. . . .

Let us first see what is meant by the name of species.

Any collection of like individuals which were produced by others similar to themselves is called a species.

This definition is exact; for every individual possessing life always resembles very closely those from which it sprang; but to this definition is added the allegation that the individuals composing a species never vary in their specific characters, and consequently that species have an absolute constancy in nature.

It is just this allegation that I propose to attack, since clear proofs drawn from observation show that it is ill-founded.

The almost universally received belief is that living bodies constitute species distinguished from one another by unchangeable characteristics, and that the existence of these species is as old as nature herself. This belief became established at a time when no sufficient observations had been taken, and when natural science was still almost negligible. It is continually being discredited for those who have seen much, who have long watched nature, and who have consulted with profit the rich collections of our museums.

Moreover, all those who are much preoccupied with the study of natural history, know that naturalists now find it extremely difficult to decide what objects should be regarded as species.

They are in fact not aware that species have really only a constancy relative to the duration of the conditions in which are placed the individuals composing it; nor that some of these individuals have varied, and constitute races which shade gradually into some other neighbouring species.

Hence naturalists come to arbitrary decisions about individuals observed in various countries and diverse conditions, sometimes calling them varieties and sometimes species. The work connected with the determination of species therefore becomes daily more defective, that is to say, more complicated and confused. . . .

Let me repeat that the richer our collections grow, the more proofs do we find that everything is more or less merged into everything else, that noticeable differences disappear, and that nature usually leaves us nothing but minute, nay puerile, details on which to found our distinctions. . . .

It is only those who have long and diligently studied the question of species and who have examined rich collections, that are in a position to know to what extent species among living bodies merge into one another. And no one else can know that species only appear to be isolated, because others are lacking which are close to them but have not yet been collected.

I do not mean that existing animals form a very simple series, regularly graded throughout; but I do mean that they form a branching series, irregularly graded and free from discontinuity, or at least once free from it. . . .

I ask, where is the experienced zoologist or botanist who is not convinced of the truth of what I state? ...

¶ *Chapter 7: Of the Influence of the Environment on the Activities and Habits of Animals, and the Influence of the Activities and Habits of these Living Bodies in Modifying their Organization and Structure*

We are not here concerned with an argument, but with the examination of a positive fact. ... This fact consists in the influence that is exerted by the environment on the various living bodies exposed to it. ...

The influence of the environment as a matter of fact is in all times and places operative on living bodies; but what makes this influence difficult to perceive is that its effects only become perceptible or recognizable (especially in animals) after long period of time. ...

I must now explain what I mean by this statement: *the environment affects the shape and organization of animals*, that is to say that when the environment becomes very different, it produces in course of time corresponding modifications in the shape and organization of animals.

It is true if this statement were to be taken literally, I should be convicted of an error; for, whatever the environment may do, it does not work any direct modification whatever in the shape and organization of animals. But great alterations in the environment of animals lead to great alterations in their needs, and these alterations in their needs necessarily lead to others in their activities. Now if the new needs become permanent, the animals then adopt new habits which last as long as the needs that evoked them. This is easy to demonstrate, and indeed requires no amplification.

It is then obvious that a great and permanent alteration

in the environment of any race of animals induces new habits in these animals.

Now, if a new environment, which has become permanent for some race of animals, induces new habits in these animals, that is to say, leads them into new activities which become habitual, the result will be the use of some one part in preference to some other part, and in some cases the total disuse of some part no longer necessary.

Nothing of all this can be considered as hypothesis or private opinion; on the contrary, they are truths which, in order to be made clear, only require attention and the observation of facts.

We shall shortly see by the citation of known facts in evidence, in the first place, that new needs which establish a necessity for some part really bring about the existence of the part, as a result of efforts; and that subsequently its continued use gradually strengthens, develops, and finally greatly enlarges it; in the second place, we shall see that in some cases, when the new environment and the new needs have together destroyed the utility of some part, the total disuse of that part has resulted in its gradually ceasing to share in the development of the other parts of the animal; it shrinks and wastes little by little, and ultimately, when there has been total disuse for a long period, the part in question ends by disappearing. All this is positive; I propose to furnish the most convincing proofs of it.

In plants, where there are no activities and consequently no habits, properly so-called, great changes of environment none the less lead to great differences in the development of their parts; so that these differences cause the origin and development of some, and the shrinkage and disappearance of others. But all this is here brought about by the changes sustained in the nutrition of the plant, in its absorption and transpiration, in the quantity of caloric [heat], light, air, and moisture that it habitually receives; lastly in the dominance that some of the various vital movements acquire over others.

Among individuals of the same species, some of which are continually well fed and in an environment favourable to their development, while others are in an opposite environment, there arises a difference in the state of the individuals which gradually becomes very remarkable. How many examples I might cite both in animals and plants which bear out the truth of this principle! ...

Suppose, for instance, that a seed of one of the meadow grasses ... is transported to an elevated place on a dry, barren, and stony plot much exposed to the winds, and is there left to germinate; if the plant can live in such a place, it will always be badly nourished, and if the individuals reproduced from it continue to exist in this bad environment, there will result a race fundamentally different from that which lives in the meadows and from which it originated. The individuals of this new race will have small and meagre parts; some of their organs will have developed more than others, and will then be of unusual proportions. ...

What nature does in the course of long periods we do every day when we suddenly change the environment in which some species of living plant is situated.

Every botanist knows that plants which are transported from their native places to gardens for purposes of cultivation, gradually undergo changes which ultimately make them unrecognizable. Many plants, by nature hairy, become glabrous or nearly so; a number of those which used to lie and creep in the ground, became erect; others lose their thorns or excrescences; others again whose stem was perennial and woody in their native hot climates, become herbaceous in our own climates and some of them become annuals; lastly, the size of their parts itself undergoes very considerable changes. These effects of alterations of environment are so widely recognized, that botanists do not like to describe garden plants unless they have been recently brought into cultivation. ...

Where in nature do we find our cabbages, lettuces, etc.,

in the same state as in our kitchen gardens? and is not the case the same with regard to many animals which have been altered or greatly modified by domestication? ...

But instead of being contented with generalities which might be considered hypothetical, let us investigate the facts directly, and consider the effects in animals of the use or disuse of their organs on these same organs, in accordance with the habits that each race has been forced to contract. ...

The permanent disuse of an organ, arising from a change of habits, causes a gradual shrinkage and ultimately the disappearance and even extinction of that organ. ...

The vertebrates, whose plan of organization is almost the same throughout ... have their jaws armed with teeth; some of them, however, whose environment has induced the habit of swallowing the objects they feed on without any preliminary mastication, are so affected that their teeth do not develop. The teeth then remain hidden in the bony framework of the jaws, without being able to appear outside; or indeed they actually become extinct down to their last rudiments.

In the right-whale, which was supposed to be completely destitute of teeth, M. Geoffroy has nevertheless discovered teeth concealed in the jaws of the foetus of this animal. The professor has moreover discovered in birds the groove in which the teeth should be placed, though they are no longer to be found there.

Even in the class of mammals, comprising the most perfect animals, where the vertebrate plan of organization is carried to its highest completion, not only is the right-whale devoid of teeth, but the ant-eater is also to be found in the same condition, since it has acquired a habit of carrying out no mastication, and has long preserved this habit in its race.

Eyes in the head are characteristic of a great number of different animals, and essentially constitute a part of the plan of organization of the vertebrates.

Yet the mole, whose habits require a very small use of sight, has only minute and hardly visible eyes, because it uses that organ so little....

The *Proteus*, an aquatic reptile allied to the salamanders, and living in deep dark caves under the water, has only vestiges of the organ of sight, vestiges which are covered up and hidden....

It was part of the plan of organization of the reptiles, as of other vertebrates, to have four legs in dependence on their skeleton. Snakes ought consequently to have four legs....

Snakes, however, have adopted the habit of crawling on the ground and hiding in the grass; so that their body, as a result of continually repeated efforts at elongation for the purpose of passing through narrow spaces, has acquired a considerable length, quite out of proportion to its size. Now, legs would have been quite useless to these animals and consequently unused. Long legs would have interfered with their need of crawling, and very short legs would have been incapable of moving their body, since they could only have had four. The disuse of these parts thus became permanent in the various races of these animals, and resulted in the complete disappearance of these same parts, although legs really belong to the plan of organization of the animals of this class....

It is known that great drinkers, or those who are addicted to drunkenness, take very little solid food, and eat hardly anything; since the drink which they consume so copiously and frequently is sufficient to feed them.

Now since fluid foods, especially spirits, do not long remain either in the stomach or intestine, the stomach and the rest of the intestinal canal lose among drinkers the habit of being distended, just as among sedentary persons, who are continually engaged on mental work and are accustomed to take very little food; for in their case also the stomach slowly shrinks and the intestine shortens....

Compare two men of equal ages, one of whom has contracted the habit of eating very little, since his habitual studies and mental work have made digestion difficult, while the other habitually takes much exercise, is often out-of-doors, and eats well; the stomach of the first will have very little capacity left and will be filled up by a very small quantity of food, while that of the second will have preserved and even increased its capacity.

Here then is an organ which undergoes profound modification in size and capacity, purely on account of a change of habits during the life of the individual.

The frequent use of any organ, when confirmed by habit, increases the functions of that organ, leads to its development, and endows it with a size and power that it does not possess in animals which exercise it less.

We have seen that the disuse of any organ modifies, reduces, and finally extinguishes it. I shall now prove that the constant use of any organ, accompanied by efforts to get the most out of it, strengthens and enlarges that organ, or creates new ones to carry on the functions that have become necessary.

The bird which is drawn to the water by its need of finding there the prey on which it lives, separates the digits of its feet in trying to strike the water and move about on the surface. The skin which unites these digits at their base acquires the habit of being stretched by these continually repeated separations of the digits; thus in course of time there are formed large webs which unite the digits of ducks, geese, etc., as we actually find them. In the same way efforts to swim, that is to push against the water so as to move about in it, have stretched the membranes between the digits of frog, sea-tortoises, the otter, beaver, etc.

On the other hand, a bird which is accustomed to perch on trees and which springs from individuals all of whom had acquired this habit, necessarily has longer digits on its feet and differently shaped from those of the aquatic animals that I have just named. Its claws in time become lengthened, sharpened, and curved into hooks, to clasp the branches on which the animal so often rests.

We find in the same way that the bird of the waterside which does not like swimming and is yet in need of going to the water's edge to secure its prey, is continually liable to sink in the mud. Now this bird tries to act in such a way that its body should not be immersed in the liquid, and hence makes its best efforts to stretch and lengthen its legs. The long-established habit acquired by this bird and all its race of continually stretching and lengthening its legs, results in the individuals of this race becoming raised as though on stilts, and gradually obtaining long, bare legs, denuded of feathers up to the thighs and often higher still.

We note again that this same bird wants to fish without wetting its body, and is thus obliged to make continual efforts to lengthen its neck. Now these habitual efforts in this individual and its race must have resulted in course of time in a remarkable lengthening, as indeed we actually find in the long necks of all water-side birds.

If some swimming birds like the swan and goose have short legs and yet a very long neck, the reason is that these birds while moving about on the water acquire the habit of plunging their head as deeply as they can into it in order to get the aquatic larvae and various animals on which they feed; whereas they make no effort to lengthen their legs.

If an animal, for the satisfaction of its needs, makes repeated efforts to lengthen its tongue, it will acquire a considerable length (ant-eater, green-woodpecker); if it requires to seize anything with this same organ, its tongue will then divide and become forked. Proofs of my statement are found in humming-birds which use their tongues for grasping things, and in lizards and snakes which use theirs to palpate and identify objects in front of them. . . .

Nothing is more remarkable than the effect of habit in herbivorous mammals.

A quadruped, whose environment and consequent needs have for long past inculcated the habit of browsing on grass, does nothing but walk about on the ground; and for the greater part of its life is obliged to stand on its four feet, generally making only few or moderate movements. The large portion of each day that this kind of animal has to pass in filling itself with the kind of food that it cares for, has the result that it moves but little and only uses its feet for support in walking or running on the ground, and never for holding on, or climbing trees. . . .

The habit of standing on their four feet during the greater part of the day, for the purpose of browsing, has brought into existence a thick horn which invests the extremity of their digits; and since these digits have no exercise and are never moved and serve no other purpose than that of support like the rest of the foot, most of them have become shortened, dwindled and, finally, even disappeared. . . .

Nevertheless some of these herbivorous animals, especially the ruminants, are incessantly exposed to the attacks of carnivorous animals in the desert countries that they inhabit, and they can only find safety in headlong flight. Necessity has in these cases forced them to exert themselves in swift running, and from this habit their body has become more slender and their legs much finer; instances are furnished by the antelopes, gazelles, etc. . . .

It is interesting to observe the result of habit in the peculiar shape and size of the giraffe: this animal, the largest of the mammals, is known to live in the interior of Africa in places where the soil is nearly always arid and barren, so that it is obliged to browse on the leaves of trees and to make constant efforts to reach them. From this habit long maintained in all its race, it has resulted that the animal's fore-legs have become longer than its hind legs, and that its neck is lengthened to such a degree that the giraffe, without standing up on its hind legs, attains a height of six metres (nearly twenty feet). . . .

The effect of habit is quite as remarkable in the carnivorous mammals as in the herbivore but it exhibits results of a different kind.

Those carnivores, for instance, which have become accustomed to climbing, or to scratching the ground for digging holes, or to tearing their prey, have been under the necessity of using the digits of their feet: now this habit has promoted the separation of their digits, and given rise to the formation of the claws with which they are armed....

Can there be any more striking instance than that which we find in the kangaroo? This animal, which carries its young in a pouch under the abdomen, has acquired the habit of standing upright, so as to rest only on its hind legs and tail; and of moving only by means of a succession of leaps, during which it maintains its erect attitude in order not to disturb its young. And the following is the result:

1. Its fore-legs, which it uses very little and on which it supports itself for a moment on abandoning its erect attitude, have never acquired a development proportional to that of the other parts, and have remained meagre, very short, and with very little strength.

2. The hind legs, on the contrary, which are almost continually in action either for supporting the whole body or for making leaps, have acquired a great development and become very large and strong.

3. Lastly, the tail, which is in this case much used for supporting the animal and carrying out its chief movements, has acquired an extremely remarkable thickness and strength at its base....

I shall show in Part 2, that when the will guides an animal to any action, the organs which have to carry out that action are immediately stimulated to it by the influx of subtle fluids (the nervous fluid), which becomes the determining factor of the movements required. This fact is verified by many observations, and cannot now be called in question....

Now every change that is wrought in an organ through a habit of frequently using it, is subsequently preserved by reproduction, if it is common to the individuals who unite together in fertilization for the propagation of their species. Such a change is thus handed on to all succeeding individuals in the same environment, without their having to acquire it in the same way that it was actually created. . . .

Everything then combines to prove my statement, namely: that it is not the shape either of the body or its parts which give rise to the habits of animals and their mode of life; but that it is, on the contrary, the habits, mode of life, and all the other influences of the environment which have in course of time built up the shape of the body and of the parts of animals. With new shapes, new faculties have been acquired, and little by little nature has succeeded in fashioning animals such as we actually see them.

Can there be any more important conclusion in the range of natural history, or any to which more attention should be paid than that which I have just set forth?

———

CHARLES DARWIN
1809–82

THE THEORY OF NATURAL SELECTION IS
ADVANCED AS THE BASIS OF EVOLUTION

DARWIN was the son of a country doctor. His grand-parents were distinguished figures of the eighteenth century. Erasmus Darwin, a naturalist and a poet, perceived that what the farmer was doing in selecting and crossing his stock had important scientific significance and wrote on evolution. Charles Darwin's maternal grandfather was Josiah Wedgwood, the virtual founder of the Staffordshire potteries and a pioneer in factory organization and industrial design.

Certainly this was a case of environment and heredity favourable to real accomplishment, but Darwin made several false starts before he found his vocation. At Cambridge he first studied for the church, and in his autobiography he wrote, 'Considering how fiercely I have been attacked by the Orthodox, it seems ludicrous that I once intended to be a clergyman.' He became deeply interested in botany and geology and after taking his degree in 1831 he took a position as naturalist on H.M.S. *Beagle*, a survey ship. He sailed in 1831, and five years later returned after having circumnavigated the globe. His *A Naturalist's Voyage* described this long experience, but the implications of what he had observed did not fully affect him until he took up, for pleasure, Thomas R. Malthus's *Essay on the Principles of Population*. Malthus, an English clergyman, had come to the conclusion that the rate of growth of the world's population was outstripping the capacity of the land to provide the food necessary to subsistence and that only recurring famine, pestilence, or wars would tend to keep down the number of inhabitants. Darwin realized that, if Malthus were right, then only the fittest would survive such scourges.

During the voyage, Darwin observed carefully the rock formations and the past and present organisms of the places he visited. He noticed fossils which resembled organisms still in existence, the replacement of species by closely related ones as he travelled southward, and the slight differences among animals from islands situated close to each other. He learned, for example, that the giant tortoises which lived on each of the Galapagos Islands varied sufficiently for it to be possible to tell from which island they came. When Darwin thought about this later, he wondered why, if each organism had been created at the same time, there were so many living things with such slight variations.

From this slim hypothesis, Darwin built up his notes. In 1837, he began to collect facts dealing with the origin of species, and he kept this up for the next twenty years. By 1844, he had decided that Linnaeus had been wrong in his view that species are immutable. The race is capable of modification as the result of the success of qualities favourable to the struggle for survival. Slowly the unfavourable qualities would be eliminated as the stock improved, by the process of natural selection. This led to the theory of organic evolution, described in the following selection.

It should be noted here that, although Mendel's work had already begun, it was unknown to Darwin and was to remain buried in an obscure periodical until the end of the century. As in other cases, the story might have been different had the two men collaborated. Darwin's experiments and observations were conducted over a long period and provided a good precedent for other work, but, unfortunately, most of his followers pursued the philosophical line rather than the experimental. For some Darwinism became almost a religion, nourished by continuous and sometimes violent controversy. But Darwin's thesis as to the possibility of biological change, along with the enormous collection of facts supporting it, provided the scientific world with a concept which has retained its usefulness until today as the cornerstone of biological thought.

One of Darwin's early supporters (along with Charles Lyell, the great geologist, and Thomas Henry Huxley) was Asa Grey (1810–88), a distinguished American naturalist. Darwin's letter to Gray explaining the ideas on which he had been working since his voyage in the *Beagle* helped to establish Darwin's claim to priority. He had delayed publication of his ideas, against the advice of his friends. In 1858 he received a letter from Alfred Russel Wallace (1823–1913), another naturalist, who had explored the Amazon and the East Indian Archipelago. Writing from Indonesia, Wallace stated that, as the result of reading Malthus, he had conceived the idea of the theory of evolution. This strange coincidence was handled by the method of simultaneous presentation to the Linnaean Society and, although the two men differed in their treatment of the theory, there was a mutual respect which advanced the cause of science.

Darwin did not stop with the completion of his great work. If anything, he worked even harder, though he was often ill. Among his other works are *The Descent of Man*, in which he tried to show that man and apes had a common ancestry, and many books on plants. The most important of the latter concerned problems of plant fertilization. He died in 1882 and was buried in Westminster Abbey near the tomb of Sir Isaac Newton. Perhaps Darwin's outstanding characteristic is best described in his own words: 'I have worked as hard and as well as I could, and no man can do more than this.'

The reading below has been taken from the introduction and Chapter 15 of the sixth edition of *The Origin of Species*, published in 1872.

¶ *Introduction*

When on board H.M.S. *Beagle*, as naturalist, I was much struck with certain facts in the distribution of the organic beings inhabiting South America, and in the geological relations of the present to the past inhabitants of that continent. These facts, as will be seen in the latter chapters of this volume, seemed to throw some light on the origin of species – that mystery of mysteries, as it has been called by one of our greatest philosophers. On my return home, it occurred to me, in 1837, that something might perhaps be made out on this question by patiently accumulating and reflecting on all sorts of facts which could possibly have any bearing on it. After five years' work I allowed myself to speculate on the subject, and drew up some short notes; these I enlarged in 1844 into a sketch of the conclusions, which then seemed to me probable: from that period to the present day I have steadily pursued the same object. I hope that I may be excused for entering on these personal details, as I give them to show that I have not been hasty in coming to a decision.

My work is now (1859) nearly finished; but as it will take me many more years to complete it, and as my health is far from strong, I have been urged to publish this abstract. I have more especially been induced to do this, as Mr Wallace, who is now studying the natural history of the Malay Archipelago, has arrived at almost exactly the same general conclusions that I have on the origin of species. In 1858 he sent me a memoir on this subject, with a request that I would forward it to Sir Charles Lyell, who sent it to the Linnean Society, and it is published in the third volume of the Journal of that Society. Sir C. Lyell and Dr Hooker, who both knew of my work – the latter having read my sketch of 1844 – honoured me by thinking it advisable to publish, with Mr Wallace's excellent memoir, some brief extracts from my manuscripts.

This abstract, which I now publish, must necessarily be

imperfect. I cannot here give references and authorities for my several statements; and I must trust to the reader reposing some confidence in my accuracy. No doubt errors may have crept in, though I hope I have always been cautious in trusting to good authorities alone. I can here give only the general conclusions at which I have arrived, with a few facts in illustration, but which I hope, in most cases will suffice. No one can feel more sensible than I do of the necessity of hereafter publishing in detail all the facts, with references, on which my conclusions have been grounded; and I hope in a future work to do this. For I am well aware that scarcely a single point is discussed in this volume on which facts cannot be adduced, often apparently leading to conclusions directly opposite to those at which I have arrived. A fair result can be obtained only by fully stating and balancing the facts and arguments on both sides of each question; and this is here impossible.

I much regret that want of space prevents my having the satisfaction of acknowledging the generous assistance which I have received from very many naturalists, some of them personally unknown to me. I cannot, however, let this opportunity pass without expressing my deep obligations to Dr Hooker, who for the last fifteen years, has aided me in every possible way by his large stores of knowledge and his excellent judgement.

In considering the origin of species, it is quite conceivable that a naturalist, reflecting on the mutual affinities of organic beings, on their embryological relations, their geographical distribution, geological succession, and other such facts, might come to the conclusion that species had not been independently created, but had descended, like varieties, from other species. Nevertheless, such a conclusion, even if well founded, would be unsatisfactory, until it could be shown how the innumerable species inhabiting this world have been modified, so as to acquire that perfection of structure and coadaptation which justly excites our admiration. Naturalists continually refer to external conditions, such as climate, food, etc., as the only possible cause of variation. In one limited sense, as we shall hereafter see, this may be true; but it is preposterous to attribute to mere external conditions the structure; for instance, of the woodpecker, with its feet, tail, beak, and tongue, so admirably adapted to catch insects under the bark of trees. In the case of the mistletoe, which draws its nourishment from certain trees, which has seeds that must be transported by certain birds, and which has flowers with separate sexes absolutely requiring the agency of certain insects to bring pollen from one flower to the other, it is equally preposterous to account for the structure of this parasite, with its relations to several distinct organic beings, by the effects of external conditions, or of habit, or of the volition of the plant itself.

It is, therefore, of the highest importance to gain a clear insight into the means of modification and coadaptation. At the commencement of my observations it seemed to me probable that a careful study of domesticated animals and of cultivated plants would offer the best chance of making out this obscure problem. Nor have I been disappointed; in this and in all other perplexing cases I have invariably found that our knowledge, imperfect though it be, of variation under domestication, afforded the best and safest clue. I may venture to express my conviction of the high value of such studies, although they have been very commonly neglected by naturalists.

From these considerations, I shall devote the first chapter of this abstract to variation under domestication. We shall thus see that a large amount of hereditary modification is at least possible; and, what is equally or more important, we shall see how great is the power of man in accumulating by his selection successive slight variations. I will then pass on to the variability of species in a state of nature; but I shall, unfortunately, be compelled to treat this subject far too briefly, as it can be treated properly only by giving long catalogues of facts. We shall, however, be enabled to discuss what circumstances are most favourable to variation. In the next chapter the struggle for existence among all organic beings throughout the world, which inevitably follows from the high geometrical ratio of their increase, will be considered. This is the doctrine of Malthus, applied to the whole animal and vegetable kingdoms. As many more individuals of each species are born than can possibly survive; and as, consequently, there is a frequently recurring struggle for existence, it follows that any being, if it vary however slightly in any manner profitable to itself, under the complex and sometimes varying conditions of life, will have a better chance of surviving, and thus be *naturally selected*. From the strong principle of inheritance, any selected variety will tend to propagate its new and modified form.

This fundamental subject of natural selection will be treated at some length in the fourth chapter; and we shall then see how natural selection almost inevitably causes much extinction of the less improved forms of life, and leads to what I have called divergence of character. In the next chapter I shall discuss the complex and little known laws of variation. In the five succeeding chapters, the most apparent and gravest difficulties in accepting the theory will be given: namely, first, the difficulties of transitions, or how a simple being or a simple organ can be changed and perfected into a highly developed being or into an elaborately constructed organ; secondly, the subject of instinct, or the mental powers of animals; thirdly, hybridism, or the infertility of species and the fertility of varieties when intercrossed; and fourthly, the imperfection of the geological record. In the next chapter I shall consider the geological succession of organic beings throughout time; in the twelfth and thirteenth, their geographical distribution throughout space; in the fourteenth, their classification or mutual affinities, both when mature and in an embryonic condition. In the last chapter I shall give a brief recapitulation of the whole work, and a few concluding remarks.

No one ought to feel surprise at much remaining as yet unexplained in regard to the origin of species and varieties, if he make due allowance for our profound ignorance in regard to the mutual relations of the many beings which live around us. Who can explain why one species ranges widely and is very numerous, and why another allied species has a narrow range and is rare? Yet these relations are of the highest importance, for they determine the present welfare and, as I believe, the future success and modification of every inhabitant of this world. Still less do we know of the mutual relations of the innumerable inhabitants of the world during the many past geological epochs in its history. Although much remains obscure, and will long remain obscure, I can entertain no doubt, after the most deliberate study and dispassionate judgement of which I am capable, that the view which most naturalists until recently entertained, and which I formerly entertained – namely, that each species has been independently created – is erroneous. I am fully convinced that species are not immutable; but that those belonging to what are called the same genera are lineal descendants of some other and generally extinct species, in the same manner as the acknowledged varieties of any one species are the descendants of that species. Furthermore, I am convinced that natural selection has been the most important, but not the exclusive, means of modification.

¶ Chapter XV: Recapitulation and Conclusion

Recapitulation of the objections to the theory of Natural Selection – Recapitulation of the general and special circumsances in its favour – Causes of the general belief in the immutability of species – How far the theory of Natural Selection may be extended – Effects of its adoption on the study of Natural History – Concluding remarks.

As this whole volume is one long argument, it may be convenient to the reader to have the leading facts and inferences briefly recapitulated.

That many and serious objections may be advanced against the theory of descent with modification through variation and natural selection, I do not deny. I have endeavoured to give to them their full force. Nothing at first can appear more difficult to believe than that the more complex organs and instincts have been perfected, not by means superior to, though analogous with, human reason, but by the accumulation of innumerable slight variations, each good for the individual possessor. Nevertheless, this difficulty, though appearing to our imagination insuperably great, cannot be considered real if we admit the following propositions, namely, that all parts of the organization and instincts offer, at least, individual differences – that there is a struggle for existence leading to the preservation of profitable deviations of structure or instinct – and, lastly, that gradations in the state of perfection of each organ may have existed, each good of its kind. The truth of these propositions cannot, I think, be disputed.

It is, no doubt, extremely difficult even to conjecture by what gradations many structures have been perfected, more especially among broken and failing groups of organic beings, which have suffered much extinction; but we see so many strange gradations in nature, that we ought to be extremely cautious in saying that any organ or instinct, or any whole structure, could not have arrived at its present state by many graduated steps. There are, it must be admitted, cases of special difficulty opposed to the theory of natural selection: and one of the most curious of these is the existence in the same community of two or three defined castes of workers or sterile female ants; but I have attempted to show how these difficulties can be mastered.

With respect to the almost universal sterility of species

when first crossed, which forms so remarkable a contrast with the almost universal fertility of varieties when crossed, I must refer the reader to the recapitulation of the facts given at the end of the ninth chapter, which seem to me conclusively to show that this sterility is no more a special endowment than is the incapacity of two distinct kinds of trees to be grafted together; but that it is incidental on differences confined to the reproductive systems of the intercrossed species. We see the truth of this conclusion in the vast difference in the results of crossing the same two species reciprocally – that is, when one species is first used as the father and then as the mother. Analogy from the consideration of dimorphic and trimorphic plants clearly leads to the same conclusion, for when the forms are illegitimately united, they yield few or no seed, and their offspring are more or less sterile; and these forms belong to the same undoubted species, and differ from each other in no respect except in their reproductive organs and functions.

Although the fertility of varieties when intercrossed, and of their mongrel offspring, has been asserted by so many authors to be universal, this cannot be considered as quite correct after the facts given on the high authority of Gärtner and Kölreuter. Most of the varieties which have been experimented on have been produced under domestication; and as domestication (I do not mean mere confinement) almost certainly tends to eliminate that sterility which, judging from analogy, would have affected the parent-species if intercrossed, we ought not to expect that domestication would likewise induce sterility in their modified descendants when crossed. This elimination of sterility apparently follows from the same cause which allows our domestic animals to breed freely under diversified circumstances; and this again apparently follows from their having been gradually accustomed to frequent changes in their conditions of life.

A double and parallel series of facts seems to throw

much light on the sterility of species, when first crossed, and of their hybrid offspring. On the one side, there is good reason to believe that slight changes in the conditions of life give vigour and fertility to all organic beings. We know also that a cross between the distinct individuals of the same variety, and between distinct varieties, increases the number of their offspring, and certainly gives to them increased size and vigour. This is chiefly owing to the forms which are crossed having been exposed to somewhat different conditions of life; for I have ascertained by a laborious series of experiments that if all the individuals of the same variety be subjected during several generations to the same conditions, the good derived from crossing is often much diminished or wholly disappears. This is one side of the case. On the other side, we know that species which have long been exposed to nearly uniform conditions, when they are subjected under confinement to new and greatly changed conditions, either perish, or if they survive, are rendered sterile, though retaining perfect health. This does not occur, or only in a very slight degree, with our domesticated productions, which have long been exposed to fluctuating conditions. Hence when we find that hybrids produced by a cross between two distinct species are few in number, owing to their perishing soon after conception or at a very early age, or if surviving that they are rendered more or less sterile, it seems highly probable that this result is due to their having been in fact subjected to a great change in their conditions of life, from being compounded of two distinct organizations. He who will explain in a definite manner why, for instance, an elephant or a fox will not breed under confinement in its native country, whilst the domestic pig or dog breed freely under the most diversified conditions, will at the same time be able to give a definite answer to the question why two distinct species, when crossed, as well as their hybrid offspring, are generally rendered more or less sterile, while two domesticated varieties when crossed, and their mongrel offspring, are perfectly fertile.

Turning to geographical distribution, the difficulties encountered on the theory of descent with modification are serious enough. All the individuals of the same species, and all the species of the same genus, or even higher group, are descended from common parents; and therefore, in however distant and isolated parts of the world they may now be found, they must in the course of successive generations have travelled from some one point to all the others. We are often wholly unable even to conjecture how this could have been effected. Yet, as we have reason to believe that some species have retained the same specific form for very long periods of time, immensely long as measured by years, too much stress ought not to be laid on the occasional wide diffusion of the same species; for during very long periods there will always have been a good chance for wide migration by many means. A broken or interrupted range may often be accounted for by the extinction of the species in the intermediate regions. It cannot be denied that we are as yet very ignorant as to the full extent of the various climatical and geographical changes which have affected the earth during modern periods; and such changes will often have facilitated migration. As an example, I have attempted to show how potent has been the influence of the Glacial period on the distribution of the same and of allied species throughout the world. We are as yet profoundly ignorant of the many occasional means of transport. With respect to distinct species of the same genus, inhabiting distant and isolated regions, as the process of modification has necessarily been slow, all the means of migration will have been possible during a very long period; and consequently the difficulty of the wide diffusion of the species of the same genus is in some degree lessened.

As according to the theory of natural selection an interminable number of intermediate forms must have existed,

linking together all the species in each group by gradations as fine as our existing varieties, it may be asked, Why
do we not see these linking forms all around us? Why are
not all organic beings blended together in an inextricable
chaos? With respect to existing forms, we should remember that we have no right to expect (excepting in rare
cases) to discover *directly* connecting links between them,
but only between each and some extinct and supplanted
form. Even on a wide area, which has during a long period
remained continuous, and of which the climatic and other
conditions of life change insensibly in proceeding from a
district occupied by one species into another district
occupied by a closely allied species, we have no just right
to expect often to find intermediate varieties in the intermediate zones. For we have reason to believe that only a
few species of a genus ever undergo change; the other
species becoming utterly extinct and leaving no modified
progeny. Of the species which do change, only a few within
the same country change at the same time; and all modifications are slowly effected. I have also shown that the
intermediate varieties which probably at first existed in
the intermediate zones, would be liable to be supplanted
by the allied forms on either hand; for the latter, from
existing in greater numbers, would generally be modified
and improved at a quicker rate than the intermediate
varieties, which existed in lesser numbers; so that the intermediate varieties would, in the long run, be supplanted
and exterminated.

On this doctrine of the extermination of an infinitude
of connecting links, between the living and extinct inhabitants of the world, and at each successive period between the extinct and still older species, why is not every
geological formation charged with such links? Why does
not every collection of fossil remains afford plain evidence
of the gradation and mutation of the forms of life?
Although geological research has undoubtedly revealed
the former existence of many links, bringing numerous

forms of life much closer together, it does not yield the infinitely many fine gradations between past and present species required on the theory, and this is the most obvious of the many objections which may be urged against it. Why, again, do whole groups of allied species appear, though this appearance is often false, to have come in suddenly on the successive geological stages? Although we now know that organic beings appeared on this globe, at a period incalculably remote, long before the lowest bed of the Cambrian system was deposited, why do we not find beneath this system great piles of strata stored with the remains of the progenitors of the Cambrian fossils? For on the theory, such strata must somewhere have been deposited at these ancient and utterly unknown epochs of the world's history.

I can answer these questions and objections only on the supposition that the geological record is far more imperfect than most geologists believe. The number of specimens in all our museums is absolutely as nothing compared with the countless generations of countless species which have certainly existed. The parent form of any two or more species would not be in all its characters directly intermediate between its modified offspring, any more than the rock-pigeon is directly intermediate in crop and tail between its descendants, the pouter and fantail pigeons. We should not be able to recognize a species as the parent of another and modified species, if we were to examine the two ever so closely, unless we possessed most of the intermediate links; and owing to the imperfection of the geological record, we have no just right to expect to find so many links. If two or three, or even more linking forms were discovered, they would simply be ranked by many naturalists as so many new species, more especially if found in different geological substages, let their differences be ever so slight. Numerous existing doubtful forms could be named which are probably varieties; but who will pretend that in future ages so many fossil links will be discovered, that naturalists will be able to decide whether or not these doubtful forms ought to be called varieties? Only a small portion of the world has been geologically explored. Only organic beings of certain classes can be preserved in a fossil condition, at least in any great number. Many species when once formed never undergo any further change but become extinct without leaving modified descendants; and the periods during which species have undergone modification, though long as measured by years, have probably been short in comparison with the periods during which they retained the same form. It is the dominant and widely ranging species which vary most frequently and vary most, and varieties are often at first local – both causes rendering the discovery of intermediate links in any one formation less likely. Local varieties will not spread into other and distant regions until they are considerably modified and improved; and when they have spread, and are discovered in a geological formation, they appear as if suddenly created there, and will be simply classed as new species. Most formations have been intermittent in their accumulation, and their duration has probably been shorter than the average duration of specific forms. Successive formations are in most cases separated from each other by blank intervals of time of great length, for fossiliferous formations thick enough to resist future degradation can, as a general rule, be accumulated only where much sediment is deposited on the subsiding bed of the sea. During the alternate periods of elevation and of stationary level the record will generally be blank. During these latter periods there will probably be more variability in the forms of life; during periods of subsidence, more extinction.

With respect to the absence of strata rich in fossils beneath the Cambrian formation, I can recur only to the hypothesis given in the tenth chapter; namely, that though our continents and oceans have endured for an enormous period in nearly their present relative positions, we have no reason to assume that this has always been the case: consequently formations much older than any now known may lie buried beneath the great oceans. With respect to the lapse of time not having been sufficient since our planet was consolidated for the assumed amount of organic change, and this objection, as urged by Sir William Thompson, is probably one of the gravest as yet advanced, I can only say, firstly, that we do not know at what rate species change, as measured by years, and secondly, that many philosophers are not as yet willing to admit that we know enough of the constitution of the universe and of the interior of our globe to speculate with safety on its past duration.

That the geological record is imperfect all will admit; but that it is imperfect to the degree required by our theory, few will be inclined to admit. If we look to long enough intervals of time, geology plainly declares that species have all changed; and they have changed in the manner required by the theory, for they have changed slowly and in a graduated manner. We clearly see this in the fossil remains from consecutive formations invariably being much more closely related to each other than are the fossils from widely separated formations.

Such is the sum of the several chief objections and difficulties which may be justly urged against the theory; and I have now briefly recapitulated the answers and explanations which, as far as I can see, may be given. I have felt these difficulties far too heavily during many years to doubt their weight. But it deserves especial notice that the more important objections relate to questions on which we are confessedly ignorant; nor do we know how ignorant we are. We do not know all the possible transitional gradations between the simplest and the most perfect organs; it cannot be pretended that we know all the varied means of Distribution during the long lapse of years, or that we know how imperfect is the Geological Record. Serious as these several objections are, in my judgement they are by no means sufficient to overthrow the theory of descent with subsequent modification.

Now let us turn to the other side of the argument. Under domestication we see much variability, caused, or at least excited, by changed conditions of life; but often in so obscure a manner, that we are tempted to consider the variations as spontaneous. Variability is governed by many complex laws, by correlated growth, compensation, the increased use and disuse of parts, and the definite action of the surrounding conditions. There is much difficulty in ascertaining how largely our domestic productions have been modified; but we may safely infer that the amount has been large, and that modifications can be inherited for long periods. As long as the conditions of life remain the same, we have reason to believe that a modification, which has already been inherited for many generations, may continue to be inherited for an almost infinite number of generations. On the other hand we have evidence that variability, when it has once come into play, does not cease under domestication for a very long period; nor do we know that it ever ceases, for new varieties are still occasionally produced by our oldest domesticated productions.

Variability is not actually caused by man; he only unintentionally exposes organic beings to new conditions of life and then nature acts on the organization and causes it to vary. But man can and does select the variations given by him by nature, and thus accumulates them in any desired manner. He thus adapts animals and plants for his own benefit or pleasure. He may do this methodically, or he made do it unconsciously by preserving the individuals most useful or pleasing to him without any intention of altering the breed. It is certain that he can largely influence the character of a breed by selecting, in each successive generation, individual differences so slight as to be inappreciable except by an educated eye. This unconscious process of selection has been the great agency in the formation of the most distinct and useful domestic breeds. That many breeds produced by man have to a large extent the character of natural species, is shown by the inextricable doubts whether many of them are varieties or aboriginally distinct species.

There is no reason why the principles which have acted so efficiently under domestication should not have acted under nature. In the survival of favoured individuals and races, during the constantly recurrent Struggle for Existence, we see a powerful and ever-acting form of Selection. The struggle for existence inevitably follows from the high geometrical ratio of increase which is common to all organic beings. This high rate of increase is proved by calculation – by the rapid increase of many animals and plants during a succession of peculiar seasons, and when naturalized in new countries. More individuals are born than can possibly survive. A grain in the balance may determine which individuals shall live and which shall die – which variety or species shall increase in number, and which shall decrease; or finally become extinct. As the individuals of the same species come in all respects into the closest competition with each other, the struggle will generally be most severe between them; it will be almost equally severe between the varieties of the same species, and next in severity between the species of the same genus. On the other hand the struggle will often be severe between beings remote in the scale of nature. The slightest advantage in certain individuals, at any age or during any season, over those with which they come into competition, or better adaptation in however slight a degree to the surrounding physical conditions, will, in the long run, turn the balance.

With animals having separated sexes, there will be in most cases a struggle between the males for the possession of the females. The most vigorous males, or those which have most successfully struggled with their conditions of life, will generally leave most progeny. But success will often depend on the males having special weapons or means of defence or charms; and a slight advantage will lead to victory.

As geology plainly proclaims that each land has undergone great physical changes, we might have expected to find that organic beings have varied under nature, in the same way as they have varied under domestication. And if there has been any variability under nature, it would be an unaccountable fact if natural selection had not come into play. It has often been asserted, but the assertion is incapable of proof, that the amount of variation under nature is a strictly limited quantity. Man, though acting on external characters alone and often capriciously, can produce within a short period a great result by adding up mere individual differences in his domestic productions; and every one admits that species present individual differences. But, beside such differences, all naturalists admit that natural varieties exist, which are considered sufficiently distinct to be worthy of record in systematic works. No one has drawn any clear distinction between individual differences and slight varieties; or between more plainly marked varieties and subspecies and species. On separate continents, and on different parts of the same continent, when divided by barriers of any kind, and on outlying islands, what a multitude of forms exist, which some experienced naturalists rank as varieties, others as geographical races or subspecies, and others as distinct, though closely allied species!

If, then, animals and plants do vary, let it be ever so slightly or slowly, why should not variations or individual differences, which are in any way beneficial, be preserved and accumulated through natural selection, or the survival of the fittest? If man can by patience select variations useful to him, why, under changing and complex conditions of life, should not variations useful to nature's living products often arise and be preserved or selected? What limit can be put to this power, acting during long ages and rigidly scrutinizing the whole constitution, structure, and habits of each creature, favouring the good and rejecting the bad? I can see no limit to the power, in slowly and beautifully adapting each form to the most complex relations of life. The theory of natural selection, even if we look no further than this, seems to be in the highest degree probable. I have already recapitulated, as fairly as I could, the opposed difficulties and objections: now let us turn to the special facts and arguments in favour of the theory.

On the view that species are only strongly marked and permanent varieties, and that each species first existed as a variety, we can see why it is that no line of demarcation can be drawn between species, commonly supposed to have been produced by special acts of creation, and varieties which are acknowledged to have been produced by secondary laws. On this same view we can understand how it is that in a region where many species of a genus have been produced, and where they now flourish, these same species should present many varieties; for where the manufactory of species has been active, we might expect, as a general rule, to find it still in action; and this is the case if varieties be incipient species. Moreover, the species of the larger genera, which afford the greater number of varieties or incipient species, retain to a certain degree the character of varieties; for they differ from each other by a less amount of difference than do the species of smaller genera. The closely allied species also of a larger genera apparently have restricted ranges, and in their affinities they are clustered in little groups round other species – in both respects resembling varieties. These are strange relations on the view that each species was independently created, but are intelligible if each existed first as a variety.

As each species tends by its geometrical rate of reproduction to increase inordinately in number; and as the modified descendants of each species will be enabled to increase by as much as they become more diversified in habits and structure, so as to be able to seize on many and widely different places in the economy of nature, there will be a constant tendency in natural selection to preserve the most divergent offspring of any one species. Hence, during a long-continued course of modification, the slight differences characteristic of varieties of the same species, tend to be augmented into the greater differences characteristic of the species of the same genus. New and improved varieties will inevitably supplant and exterminate the older, less improved, and intermediate varieties; and thus species are rendered to a large extent defined and distinct objects. Dominant species belonging to the larger groups within each class tend to give birth to new and dominant forms; so that each large group tends to become still larger, and at the same time more divergent in character. But as all groups cannot thus go on increasing in size, for the world would not hold them, the more dominant groups beat the less dominant. This tendency in the large groups to go on increasing in size and diverging in character, together with the inevitable contingency of much extinction, explains the arrangement of all the forms of life in groups subordinate to groups, all within a few great classes, which has prevailed throughout all time. This grand fact of the grouping of all organic beings under what is called the Natural System, is utterly inexplicable on the theory of creation.

As natural selection acts solely by accumulating slight, successive, favourable variations, it can produce no great or sudden modifications; it can act only by short and slow steps. Hence, the canon of 'Natura non facit saltum,' which every fresh addition to our knowledge tends to confirm, is on this theory intelligible. We can see why throughout nature the same general end is gained by an almost infinite diversity of means, for every peculiarity when once acquired is long inherited, and structures already modified in many different ways have to be adapted for the same general purpose. We can, in short, see why nature is prodigal in variety, though niggard in innovation. But why this should be a law of nature if each species has been independently created no man can explain.

*

As natural selection acts by competition, it adapts and improves the inhabitants of each country only in relation to their coinhabitants; so that we need feel no surprise at the species of any one country, although on the ordinary view supposed to have been created and specially adapted for that country, being beaten and supplanted by the naturalized productions from another land. Nor ought we to marvel if all the contrivances in nature be not, as far as we can judge, absolutely perfect, as in the case even of the human eye; or if some of them be abhorrent to our ideas of fitness. We need not marvel at the sting of the bee, when used against an enemy, causing the bee's own death; at drones being produced in such great numbers for one single act, and being then slaughtered by their sterile sisters; at the astonishing waste of pollen by our fir-trees; at the instinctive hatred of the queen-bee for her own fertile daughters; at *ichneumonidae* feeding within the living bodies of caterpillars; or at other such cases. The wonder, indeed, is, on the theory of natural selection, that more cases of the want of absolute perfection have not been detected.

The complex and little known laws governing the production of varieties are the same, as far as we can judge, with the laws which have governed the production of distinct species. In both cases physical conditions seem to have produced some direct and definite effect, but how much we cannot say. Thus, when varieties enter any new station, they occasionally assume some of the characters proper to the species of that station. With both varieties and species, use and disuse seem to have produced a considerable effect; for it is impossible to resist this conclusion when we look, for instance, at the logger-headed duck, which has wings incapable of flight, in nearly the same condition as in the domestic duck; or when we look at the burrowing tucu-tucu, which is occasionally blind, and then at certain moles, which are habitually blind and have their eyes covered with skin; or when we look at the blind animals inhabiting the dark caves of America and Europe. With varieties and species, correlated variation seems to have played an important part, so that when one part has been modified other parts have been necessarily modified. With both varieties and species, reversions to long-lost character occasionally occur. How inexplicable on the theory of creation is the occasional appearance of stripes on the shoulders and legs of the several species of the horse-genus and of their hybrids! How simply is this fact explained if we believe that these species are all descended from a striped progenitor, in the same manner as the several domestic breeds of the pigeon are descended from the blue and barred rock-pigeon!

*

If we admit that the geological record is imperfect to an extreme degree, then the facts, which the record does give, strongly support the theory of descent with modification. New species have come on the stage slowly and at successive intervals; and the amount of change, after equal intervals of time, is widely different in different groups. The extinction of species and of whole groups of species, which has played so conspicuous a part in the history of the organic world, almost inevitably follows from the principle of natural selection; for old forms are supplanted by new and improved forms. Neither single species nor groups of species reappear when the chain of ordinary generation is once broken. The gradual diffusion of dominant forms, with the slow modification of their descendants, causes the forms of life, after long intervals of time, to appear as if they had changed simultaneously throughout the world. The fact of the fossil remains of each formation being in some degree intermediate in character between the fossils in the formations above and below, is simply explained by their intermediate position in the chain of descent. The grand fact that all extinct beings can be classed with all recent beings, naturally follows from the living and the extinct being the offspring of common parents. As species have generally diverged in character during their long course of descent and modification, we can understand why it is that the more ancient forms, or early progenitors of each group, so often occupy a position in some degree intermediate between existing groups. Recent forms are generally looked upon as being, on the whole, higher in the scale of organization than ancient forms; and they must be higher, in so far as the later and more improved forms have conquered the older and less improved forms in the struggle for life; they have also generally had their organs more specialized for different functions. This fact is perfectly compatible with numerous beings still retaining simple and but little improved structures, fitted for simple conditions of life; it is likewise compatible with some forms having retrograded in organization, by having become at each stage of descent better fitted for new and degraded habits of life. Lastly, the wonderful law of the long endurance of allied forms on the same continent – of marsupials in Australia, of edentata in America, and other such cases – is intelligible, for within the same country the existing and the extinct will be closely allied by descent.

The fact, as we have seen, that all past and present organic beings can be arranged within a few great classes, in groups subordinate to groups, and with the extinct groups often falling in between the recent groups, is intelligible on the theory of natural selection with its contingencies of extinction and divergence of character. On these same principles we see how it is that the mutual affinities of the forms within each class are so complex and circuitous. We see why certain characters are far more serviceable than others for classification; why adaptive characters, though of paramount importance to the beings, are of hardly any importance in classification; why characters derived from rudimentary parts, though of no service to the beings, are often of high classificatory value; and why embryological characters are often the most valuable of all. The real affinities of all organic beings in contradistinction to their adaptive resemblances, are due to inheritance or community of descent. The Natural System is a genealogical arrangement, with the acquired grades of difference, marked by the terms, varieties, species, genera, families, etc.; and we have to discover the lines of descent by the most permanent characters, whatever they may be, and of however slight vital importance.

The similar framework of bones in the hand of a man, wing of a bat, fin of the porpoise, and leg of the horse – the same number of vertebrae forming the neck of the giraffe and of the elephant – and innumerable other such facts, at once explain themselves on the theory of descent with slow and slight successive modifications. The similarity of pattern in the wing and in the leg of a bat, though used for such different purpose – in the jaws and legs of a crab – in the petals, stamens, and pistils of a flower, is likewise, to a large extent, intelligible on the view of the gradual modification of parts or organs, which were aboriginally alike in an early progenitor in each of these classes. On the principle of successive variations not always supervening at an early age, and being inherited at a corresponding not early period of life, we clearly see why the embryos of mammals, birds, reptiles, and fishes should be so closely similar, and so unlike the adult forms. We may cease marvelling at the embryo of an air-breathing mammal or bird having branchial slits and arteries running in loops, like those of a fish which has to breathe the air dissolved in water by the aid of well-developed branchiae.

*

I have now recapitulated the facts and considerations which have thoroughly convinced me that species have been modified, during a long course of descent. This has been effected chiefly through the natural selection of numerous successive, slight, favourable variations; aided in an important manner by the inherited effects of the use and disuse of parts; and in an unimportant manner, that is, in relation to adaptive structures, whether past or present, by the direct action of external conditions, and by variations which seem to us in our ignorance to arise spontaneously. It appears that I formerly underrated the frequency and value of these latter forms of variation, as leading to permanent modifications of structure independently of natural selection. But as my conclusions have lately been much misrepresented, and it has been stated that I attributed the modification of species exclusively to natural selection, I may be permitted to remark that in the first edition of this work, and subsequently, I placed in a most conspicuous position – namely, at the close of the Introduction – the following words: 'I am convinced that natural selection has been the main but not the exclusive means of modification.' This has been of no avail. Great is the power of steady misrepresentation; but the history of science shows that fortunately this power does not long endure.

GREGOR MENDEL

1822–84

THE FUNDAMENTAL LAWS OF INHERITANCE
ARE ESTABLISHED BY EXPERIMENTS
WITH GARDEN PEAS

GREGOR MENDEL was born Johann Mendel, of peasant ancestry in Moravia, now one of the provinces of Czechoslovakia. After simple early instruction by an uncle, Mendel attracted the attention of the clergy and, at the age of twenty-one, became a monk in the monastery of Brünn. At his ordination, he took the name of Gregor, by which he has been known since.

Mendel attended the University of Vienna from 1851 to 1853, where he studied mathematics and physics, and then became a teacher of science at the local secondary school (gymnasium). He continued to teach until 1868, when he was made abbot of the monastery, a position of such responsibility that he did no further teaching and gave up all research as well. It is interesting to speculate on what might have happened had the scientific world responded to Mendel's two publications which led ultimately to the foundation of the science of genetics. Mendel was discouraged by the almost complete indifference of the scientific community to his work. It must, indeed, have been a prime factor in his failure to continue his experimental studies.

For a period of about eight years, from 1858 to 1866, Mendel conducted his famous breeding experiments on the common garden pea for his long and meticulous studies. His first paper was published in 1866 in the *Proceedings of the Natural History Society of Brünn*, the obscurity of which publication may account for the indifference with which the paper was received. It would have been of particular interest to Darwin, a weak link in whose work was his explanation of the manner in which characteristics of living things are passed on from the parent to the offspring. One scientist of some reputation, Carl Nägeli, a botanist, was aware of the publication, but he was unimpressed. Mendel was far in advance of all his contemporaries, many of whom were then studying problems of hybridization and inheritance. But no one paid attention to Mendel's work.

Thirty-four years later, in 1900, in one of those strange coincidences that occasionally occur in the history of science, three men (H. DeVries in Holland, C. Correns in Germany, and E. Tschermak in Austria) independently of one another rediscovered Mendel's work and repeated the experiments. They completely confirmed Mendel's findings and so inaugurated the science of genetics, which was to become one of the most dynamic of all the biological sciences.

Although many investigators before Mendel had done experimental work on hybridization, he was the first to systematize the results of crosses and to discover their statistical relationships. These results and Mendel's explanation of them have come to be known as Mendel's Laws, and they have not been essentially altered since, although they have been supplemented and extended as the range of genetic studies has expanded.

That Mendel succeeded where so many before him had failed to recognize the processes of inheritance is a consequence of his method. He simplified the problem and did not permit other factors in the results to confuse him. Thus, when he was observing the inheritance of height in the garden pea, he disregarded the other characteristics, such as flower and seed, which might complicate the analysis of the results.

The great importance of Mendel's discoveries, apart from the precision and rigour of the proof, came from his emphasis on discontinuous variations in living things rather than on the small variations which were stressed by Darwin and which Darwin felt were the material out of which new varieties were developed. The great amount of genetic experimentation since 1900 has emphasized the validity of Mendel's approach. One of the major discoveries was the work of Hugo DeVries, which will constitute the next reading in this section.

The application of mathematics to the field of biology opened up a new area of research particularly exploited by Thomas Hunt Morgan (1866–1945) and his co-workers, whose studies of the genetics of the fruit fly, *Drosophila*, established the modern approach to genetics. One of the major results of experimentation on *Drosophila* was the recognition of the gene as the hereditary unit (Mendel's factor) and the chromosome as the physical structure in the cell nucleus which carried the genes.

The processes of mitosis (nuclear division) and meiosis (reduction division) were discovered for both plants and animals, and it was found that the chromosomes were distributed in a manner which made Mendel's summaries even more remarkable for their prescience.

The selection that follows is taken from the translation of Mendel's original paper made for the Royal Horticultural Society of London with some editing by Professor W. Bateson.

¶ Introductory Remarks

Experience of artificial fertilization, such as is effected with ornamental plants in order to obtain new variations in colour, has led to the experiments which will here be discussed. The striking regularity with which the same hybrid forms always reappeared whenever fertilization took place between the same species induced further experiments to be undertaken, the object of which was to follow up the developments of the hybrids in their progeny.

To this object numerous careful observers, such as Kölreuter, Gärtner, Herbert, Lecoq, Wichura, and others, have devoted a part of their lives with inexhaustible perserverance. Gärtner especially, in his work *Die Bastarderzeugung im Pflanzenreiche* (The Production of Hybrids in the Vegetable Kingdom), has recorded very valuable observations; and quite recently Wichura published the results of some profound investigations into the hybrids of the Willow. That, so far, no generally applicable law governing the formation and development of hybrids has been successfully formulated can hardly be wondered at by anyone who is acquainted with the extent of the task, and can appreciate the difficulties with which experiments of this class have to contend. A final decision can only be arrived at when we shall have before us the results of detailed experiments made on plants belonging to the most diverse orders.

Those who survey the work done in this department will arrive at the conviction that among all the numerous experiments made, not one has been carried out to such an extent and in such a way as to make it possible to determine the number of different forms under which the offspring of hybrids appear, or to arrange these forms with certainty according to their separate generations, or definitely to ascertain their statistical relations.*

It requires indeed some courage to undertake a labour of such far-reaching extent; this appears, however, to be the only right way by which we can finally reach the solution of a question the importance of which cannot be overestimated in connexion with the history of the evolution of organic forms.

The paper now presented records the results of such a detailed experiment. This experiment was practically confined to a small plant group, and is now, after eight years'

* [It is to the clear conception of these three primary necessities that the whole success of Mendel's work is due. So far as I know this conception was absolutely new in his day.]

pursuit, concluded in all essentials. Whether the plan upon which the separate experiments were conducted and carried out was the best suited to attain the desired end is left to the friendly decision of the reader.

§ *Selection of the Experimental Plants*

The value and utility of any experiment are determined by the fitness of the material to the purpose for which it is used, and thus in the case before us it cannot be immaterial what plants are subjected to experiment and in what manner such experiments are conducted.

The selection of the plant group which shall serve for experiments of this kind must be made with all possible care if it be desired to avoid from the outset every risk of questionable results.

The experimental plants must necessarily –

1. Possess constant differentiating characters.

2. The hybrids of such plants must, during the flowering period, be protected from the influence of all foreign pollen, or be easily capable of such protection.

The hybrids and their offspring should suffer no marked disturbance in their fertility in the successive generations.

Accidental impregnation by foreign pollen, if it occurred during the experiments and were not recognized, would lead to entirely erroneous conclusions. Reduced fertility or entire sterility of certain forms, such as occurs in the offspring of many hybrids, would render the experiments very difficult or entirely frustrate them. In order to discover the relations in which the hybrid forms stand towards each other and also towards their progenitors it appears to be necessary that all members of the series developed in each successive generation should be, *without exception*, subjected to observation.

At the very outset special attention was devoted to the *Leguminosae* on account of their peculiar floral structure. Experiments which were made with several members of this family led to the result that the genus *Pisum* was found to possess the necessary qualifications.

Some thoroughly distinct forms of this genus possess characters which are constant, and easily and certainly recognizable, and when their hybrids are mutually crossed they yield perfectly fertile progeny. Furthermore, a disturbance through foreign pollen cannot easily occur, since the fertilizing organs are closely packed inside the keel and the anther bursts within the bud, so that the stigma becomes covered with pollen even before the flower opens. This circumstance is of special importance. As additional advantages worth mentioning, there may be cited the easy culture of these plants in the open ground and in pots, and also their relatively short period of growth. Artificial fertilization is certainly a somewhat elaborate process, but nearly always succeeds. For this purpose the bud is opened before it is perfectly developed, the keel is removed, and each stamen carefully extracted by means of forceps, after which the stigma can at once be dusted over with the foreign pollen.

In all, thirty-four more or less distinct varieties of Peas were obtained from several seedsmen and subjected to a two years' trial. In the case of one variety there were noticed, among a larger number of plants all alike, a few forms which were markedly different. These however, did not vary in the following year, and agreed entirely with another variety obtained from the same seedsman; the seeds were therefore doubtless merely accidentally mixed. All the other varieties yielded perfectly constant and similar offspring; at any rate, no essential difference was observed during two trial years. For fertilization twenty-two of these were selected and cultivated during the whole period of the experiments. They remained constant without any exception.

Their systematic classification is difficult and uncertain. If we adopt the strictest definition of a species, according to which only those individuals belong to a species which under precisely the same circumstances display precisely similar characters, no two of these varieties could be referred to one species. According to the opinion of experts, however, the majority belong to the species *Pisum sativum*; while the rest are regarded and classed, some as subspecies of *P. sativum*, and some as independent species, such as *P. quadratum*, *P. saccharatum*, and *P. umbellatum*. The positions, however, which may be assigned to them in a classificatory system are quite immaterial for the purposes of the experiments in question. It has so far been found to be just as impossible to draw a sharp line between the hybrids of species and varieties as between species and varieties themselves.

§ *Division and Arrangement of the Experiments*

If two plants which differ constantly in one or several characters be crossed, numerous experiments have demonstrated that the common characters are transmitted unchanged to the hybrids and their progeny; but each pair of differentiating characters, on the other hand, unite in the hybrid to form a new character, which in the progeny of the hybrid is usually variable. The object of the experiment was to observe these variations in the case of each pair of differentiating characters, and to deduce the law according to which they appear in the successive generations. The experiment resolves itself therefore into just as many separate experiments as there are constantly differentiating characters presented in the experimental plants.

The various forms of Peas selected for crossing showed differences in the length and colour of the stem; in the size and form of the leaves; in the position, colour, and size of the flowers; in the length of the flower stalk; in the colour, form, and size of the pods; in the form and size of the seeds; and in the colour of the seed-coats and of the albumen [cotyledons]. Some of the characters noted do not permit of a sharp and certain separation, since the difference is of a 'more or less' nature, which is often difficult to define. Such characters could not be utilized for the separate experiments; these could only be applied to characters which stand out clearly and definitely in the plants. Lastly, the result must show whether they, in their entirety, observe a regular behaviour in their hybrid unions, and whether from these facts any conclusion can be come to regarding those characters which possess a subordinate significance in the type.

The characters which were selected for experiment relate:

1. To the *difference in the form of the ripe seeds*. These are either round or roundish, the depressions, if any, occur on the surface, being always only shallow; or they are irregularly angular and deeply wrinkled (*P. quadratum*).

2. To the *difference in the colour of the seed albumen* (endosperm).* The albumen of the ripe seeds is either pale yellow, bright yellow and orange coloured, or it possesses a more or less intense green tint. This difference of colour is easily seen in the seeds as [=if] their coats are transparent.

3. To the *difference in the colour of the seed-coat*. This is either white, with which character white flowers are constantly correlated; or it is grey, grey-brown, leather-brown, with or without violet spotting, in which case the colour of the standards is violet, that of the wings purple, and the stem in the axils of the leaves is of a reddish tint. The grey seed-coats become dark brown in boiling water.

4. To the *difference in the form of the ripe pods*. These are either simply inflated, not contracted in places; or they are deeply constricted between the seeds and more or less wrinkled (*P. saccharatum*).

5. To the *difference in the colour of the unripe pods*. They are either light to dark green, or vividly yellow, in

* [Mendel uses the terms 'albumen' and 'endosperm' somewhat loosely to denote the cotyledons, containing food-material, within the seed.]

which colouring the stalks, leaf-veins, and calyx partici-
pate.*

6. To the *difference in the position of the flowers*. They
are either axial, that is, distributed along the main stem;
or they are terminal, that is, bunched at the top of the
stem and arranged almost in a false umbel; in this case the
upper part of the stem is more or less widened in section
(*P. umbellatum*).†

7. To the *difference in the length of the stem*. The
length of the stem ‡ is very various in some forms; it is,
however, a constant character for each, in so far that
healthy plants, grown in the same soil, are only subject
to unimportant variations in this character.

In experiments with this character, in order to be able
to discriminate with certainty, the long axis of 6 to 7 ft
was always crossed with the short one of $\frac{3}{4}$ ft to $1\frac{1}{2}$ ft.

Each two of the differentiating characters enumerated
above were united by cross-fertilization. There were made
for the

1st trial	60	fertilizations on	15	plants.
2nd „	58	„	„	10	„
3rd „	35	„	„	10	„
4th „	40	„	„	10	„
5th „	23	„	„	5	„
6th „	34	„	„	10	„
7th „	37	„	„	10	„

From a larger number of plants of the same variety

* One species possesses a beautifully brownish-red coloured pod,
which when ripening turns to violet and blue. Trials with this character were only begun last year. [Of these further experiments it seems no
account was published. Correns has since worked with such a variety.]

† [This is often called the Mummy Pea. It shows slight fasciation.
The form I know has white standard and salmon-red wings.]

‡ [In my account of these experiments (*R.H.S. Journal*, vol xxv, p.
54) I misunderstood this paragraph and took 'axis' to mean the *floral*
axis, instead of the main axis of the plant. The unit of measurement,
being indicated in the original by a dash ('), I carelessly took to have
been an *inch*, but the translation here given is evidently correct.]

only the most vigorous were chosen for fertilization. Weakly plants always afford uncertain results, because even in the first generation of hybrids, and still more so in the subsequent ones, many of the offspring either entirely fail to flower or only form a few and inferior seeds.

Furthermore, in all the experiments reciprocal crossings were effected in such a way that each of the two varieties which in one set of fertilization served as seed-bearer, in the other set was used as the pollen plant.

The plants were grown in garden beds, a few also in pots, and were maintained in their naturally upright position by means of sticks, branches of trees, and strings stretched between. For each experiment a number of pot plants were placed during the blooming period in a greenhouse, to serve as control plants for the main experiment in the open as regards possible disturbance by insects. Among the insects* which visit Peas the beetle *Bruchus pisi* might be detrimental to the experiments should it appear in numbers. The female of this species is known to lay the eggs in the flower, and in so doing opens the keel; upon the tarsi of one specimen, which was caught in a flower, some pollen grains could clearly be seen under a lens. Mention must also be made of a circumstance which possibly might lead to the introduction of foreign pollen. It occurs, for instance, in some rare cases that certain parts of an otherwise quite normally developed flower wither, resulting in a partial exposure of the fertilizing organs. A defective development of the keel has also been observed, owing to which the stigma and anthers remained partially uncovered.† It also sometimes happens that the pollen does not reach full perfection. In this event there occurs a gradual lengthening of the pistil during the blooming period, until the stigmatic tip protrudes at the point of the

* [It is somewhat surprising that no mention is made of Thrips, which swarm in Pea flowers. I had come to the conclusion that this is a real source of error and I see Laxton held the same opinion.]

† [This also happens in Sweet Peas.]

keel. This remarkable appearance has also been observed in hybrids of *Phaseolus* and *Lathyrus*.

The risk of false impregnation by foreign pollen is, however, a very slight one with *Pisum*, and is quite incapable of disturbing the general result. Among more than 10,000 plants which were carefully examined there were only a few cases where an indubitable false impregnation had occurred. Since in the greenhouse such a case was never remarked, it may well be supposed that *Bruchus pisi*, and possibly also the described abnormalities in the floral structure, were to blame.

§ [F₁] *The Forms of the Hybrids* *

Experiments which in previous years were made with ornamental plants have already afforded evidence that the hybrids, as a rule, are not exactly intermediate between the parental species. With some of the more striking characters, those, for instance, which relate to the form and size of the leaves, the pubescence of the several parts, etc., the intermediate, indeed, is nearly always to be seen; in other cases, however, one of the two parental characters is so preponderant that it is difficult, or quite impossible, to detect the other in the hybrid.

This is precisely the case with the Pea hybrids. In the case of each of the seven crosses the hybrid-character resembles † that of one of the parental forms so closely that the other either escapes observation completely or cannot be detected with certainty. This circumstance is of great importance in the determination and classification of the forms under which the offspring of the hybrids appear. Henceforth in this paper those characters which

* [Mendel throughout speaks of his cross-bred Peas as 'hybrids', a term which many restrict to the offspring of two distinct *species*. He, as he explains, held this to be only a question of degree.]

† [Note that Mendel, with true penetration, avoids speaking of the hybrid-character as 'transmitted' by either parent, thus escaping the error pervading the older views of heredity.]

are transmitted entire, or almost unchanged in the hybridization, and therefore in themselves constitute the characters of the hybrid, are termed the *dominant*, and those which become latent in the process *recessive*. The expression 'recessive' has been chosen because the characters thereby designated withdraw or entirely disappear in the hybrids, but nevertheless reappear unchanged in their progeny, as will be demonstrated later on.

It was furthermore shown by the whole of the experiments that it is perfectly immaterial whether the dominant character belongs to the seed-bearer or to the pollen-parent; the form of the hybrid remains identical in both cases. This interesting fact was also emphasized by Gärtner, with the remark that even the most practised expert is not in a position to determine in a hybrid which of the two parental species was the seed or the pollen plant.

Of the differentiating characters which were used in the experiments the following are dominant:

1. The round or roundish form of the seed with or without shallow depressions.

2. The yellow colouring of the seed albumen [cotyledons].

3. The grey, grey-brown, or leather-brown colour of the seed-coat, in association with violet-red blossoms and reddish spots in the leaf axils.

4. The simply inflated form of the pod.

5. The green colouring of the unripe pod in association with the same colour in the stems, the leaf-veins, and the calyx.

6. The distribution of the flowers along the stem.

7. The greater length of stem.

With regard to this last character it must be stated that the longer of the two parental stems is usually exceeded by the hybrid, a fact which is possibly only attributable to the greater luxuriance which appears in all parts of plants when stems of very different length are crossed. Thus, for instance, in repeated experiments, stems of 1 ft and 6 ft in length yielded without exception hybrids which varied in length between 6 ft and $7\frac{1}{2}$ ft.

The hybrid seeds in the experiments with seed-coat are often more spotted, and the spots sometimes coalesce into small bluish-violet patches. The spotting also frequently appears even when it is absent as a parental character.*

The hybrid forms of the seed-shape and of the albumen [colour] are developed immediately after the artificial fertilization by the mere influence of the foreign pollen. They can, therefore, be observed even in the first year of experiment, whilst all the other characters naturally only appear in the following year in such plants as have been raised from the crossed seed.

§ [F_2] *The Generation [Bred] from the Hybrids*

In this generation there reappear, together with the dominant characters, also the recessive ones with their peculiarities fully developed, and this occurs in the indefinitely expressed average proportion of three to one, so that among each four plants of this generation three display the dominant character and one the recessive. This relates without exception to all the characters which were investigated in the experiments. The angular wrinkled form of the seed, the green colour of the albumen, the white colour of the seed-coats and the flowers, the constrictions of the pods, the yellow colour of the unripe pod, of the stalk, of the calyx, and of the leaf venation, the umbel-like form of the inflorescence, and the dwarfed stem, all reappear in the numerical proportion given, without any essential alteration. *Transitional forms were not observed in any experiment.*

Since the hybrids resulting from reciprocal crosses are formed alike and present no appreciable difference in their subsequent development, consequently the results [of the reciprocal crosses] can be reckoned together in each experiment. The relative numbers which were obtained for each pair of differentiating characters are as follows:

* [This refers to the coats of the seeds borne by F_1 plants.]

Expt 1. Form of seed – From 253 hybrids 7,324 seeds were obtained in the second trial year. Among them were 5,474 round or roundish ones and 1,850 angular wrinkled ones. Therefrom the ratio 2·96 to 1 is deduced.

Expt 2. Colour of albumen – 258 plants yielded 8,023 seeds, 6,022 yellow, and 2,001 green; their ratio, therefore, is as 3·01 to 1.

In these two experiments each pod yielded usually both kinds of seeds. In well-developed pods which contained on the average six to nine seeds, it often happened that all the seeds were round (Expt 1) or all yellow (Expt 2); on the other hand there were never observd more than five wrinkled or five green ones in one pod. It appears to make no difference whether the pods are developed early or later in the hybrid or whether they spring from the main axis or from a lateral one. In some few plants only a few seeds developed in the first formed pods, and these possessed exclusively one of the two characters, but in the subsequently developed pods the normal proportions were maintained nevertheless.

As in separate pods, so did the distribution of the characters vary in separate plants. By way of illustration the first ten individuals from both series of experiments may serve.

	EXPERIMENT 1		EXPERIMENT 2	
	Form of Seed		Colour of Albumen	
Plants	Round	Angular	Yellow	Green
1	45	12	25	11
2	27	8	32	7
3	24	7	14	5
4	19	10	70	27
5	32	11	24	13
6	26	6	20	6
7	88	24	32	13
8	22	10	44	9
9	28	6	50	14
10	25	7	44	18

As extremes in the distribution of the two seed characters in one plant, there were observed in Expt 1 an instance of 43 round and only 2 angular, and another of 14 round and 15 angular seeds. In Expt 2 there was a case of 32 yellow and only 1 green seed, but also one of 20 yellow and 19 green.

These two experiments are important for the determination of the average ratios, because with a smaller number of experimental plants they show that very considerable fluctuations may occur. In counting the seeds, also, especially in Expt 2, some care is requisite, since in some of the seeds of many plants the green colour of the albumen is less developed, and at first may be easily overlooked. The cause of this partial disappearance of the green colouring has no connexion with the hybrid-character of the plants, as it likewise occurs in the parental variety. This peculiarity [bleaching] is also confined to the individual and is not inherited by the offspring. In luxuriant plants this appearance was frequently noted. Seeds which are damaged by insects during their development often vary in colour and form, but, with a little practice in sorting, errors are easily avoided. It is almost superfluous to mention that the pods must remain on the plants until they are thoroughly ripened and have become dried, since it is only then that the shape and colour of the seed are fully developed.

Expt 3. Colour of the seed-coats – Among 929 plants 705 bore violet-red flowers and grey-brown seed-coats; 224 had white flowers and white seed-coats, giving the proportion 3·15 to 1.

Expt 4. Form of pods – Of 1,181 plants 882 had them simply inflated, and in 299 they were constricted. Resulting ratio, 2·95 to 1.

Expt 5. Colour of the unripe pods – The number of trial plants was 580, of which 428 had green pods and 152 yellow ones. Consequently these stand in the ratio 2·82 to 1.

Expt 6. Position of flowers – Among 858 cases 651 had inflorescences axial and 207 terminal. Ratio, 3·14 to 1.

Expt 7. Length of stem – Out of 1,064 plants, in 787 cases the stem was long, and in 277 short. Hence a mutual ratio of 2·84 to 1. In this experiment the dwarfed plants were carefully lifted and transferred to a special bed. This precaution was necessary, as otherwise they would have perished through being overgrown by their tall relatives. Even in their quite young state they can be easily picked out by their compact growth and thick dark-green foliage.*

If now the results of the whole of the experiments be brought together, there is found, as between the number of forms with the dominant and recessive characters, an average ratio of 2·98 to 1, or 3 to 1.

The dominant character can have here a *double signification* – viz. that of a parental character, or a hybrid-character.† In which of the two significations it appears in each separate case can only be determined by the following generation. As a parental character it must pass over unchanged to the whole of the offspring; as a hybrid-character, on the other hand, it must maintain the same behaviour as in the first generation [F_2].

§ [F_3] *The Second Generation [Bred] from the Hybrids*

Those forms which in the first generation [F_2] exhibit the recessive character do not further vary in the second generation [F_3] as regards this character; they remain constant in their offspring.

It is otherwise with those which possess the dominant character in the first generation [bred from the hybrids]. Of these *two-thirds* yield offspring which display the dominant and recessive characters in the proportion of 3

---

* [This is true also of the dwarf or 'Cupid' Sweet Peas.]

† [This paragraph presents the view of the hybrid-character as something incidental to the hybrid, and not 'transmitted' to it – a true and fundamental conception here expressed probably for the first time.]

to 1, and thereby show exactly the same ratio as the hybrid forms, while only one-third remains with the dominant character constant.

The separate experiments yielded the following results:

Expt 1. Among 565 plants which were raised from round seeds of the first generation, 193 yielded round seeds only, and remained therefore constant in this character; 372, however, gave both round and wrinkled seeds, in the proportion of 3 to 1. The number of the hybrids, therefore, as compared with the constants is 1·93 to 1.

Expt 2. Of 519 plants which were raised from seeds whose albumen was of yellow colour in the first generation, 166 yielded exclusively yellow, while 353 yielded yellow and green seeds in the proportion of 3 to 1. There resulted, therefore, a division into hybrid and constant forms in the proportion of 2·13 to 1.

For each separate trial in the following experiments 100 plants were selected which displayed the dominant character in the first generation, and in order to ascertain the significance of this, ten seeds of each were cultivated.

Expt 3. The offspring of 36 plants yielded exclusively grey-brown seed-coats, while of the offspring of 64 plants some had grey-brown and some had white.

Expt 4. The offspring of 29 plants had only simply inflated pods; of the offspring of 71, on the other hand, some had inflated and some constricted.

Expt 5. The offspring of 40 plants had only green pods; of the offspring of 60 plants some had green, some yellow ones.

Expt 6. The offspring of 33 plants had only axial flowers; of the offspring of 67, on the other hand, some had axial and some terminal flowers.

Expt 7. The offspring of 28 plants inherited the long axis, and those of 72 plants some the long and some the short axis.

In each of these experiments a certain number of the plants came constant with the dominant character. For the determination of the proportion in which the separation of the forms with the constantly persistent character results, the two first experiments are of especial importance, since in these a larger number of plants can be compared. The ratios 1·93 to 1 and 2·13 to 1 gave together almost exactly the average ratio of 2 to 1. The sixth experiment gave a quite concordant result; in the others the ratio varies more or less, as was only to be expected in view of the smaller number of 100 trial plants. Experiment 5, which shows the greatest departure, was repeated, and then, in lieu of the ratio of 60 and 40, that of 65 and 35 resulted. *The average ratio of 2 to 1 appears, therefore, as fixed with certainty.* It is therefore demonstrated that, of those forms which possess the dominant character in the first generation, two-thirds have the hybrid-character, while one-third remains constant with the dominant character.

The ratio of 3 to 1, in accordance with which the distribution of the dominant and recessive characters results in the first generation, resolves itself therefore in all experiments into the ratio of 2 : 1 : 1 if the dominant character be differentiated according to its significance as a hybrid-character or as a parental one. Since the members of the first generation [F_2] spring directly from the seed of the hybrids [F_1], *it is now clear that the hybrids form seeds having one or other of two differentiating characters, and of these one-half develop again the hybrid form, while the other half yield plants which remain constant and receive the dominant or the recessive characters [respectively] in equal numbers.*

HUGO DeVRIES
1848–1935

MUTATIONS ARE SUGGESTED AS THE MEANS
OF SPONTANEOUS HEREDITARY CHANGES

In gathering data to support his theory of natural selection as an explanation of the origin of species, Darwin studied the evidence for inherited variation in domesticated animals and the way in which animal breeders produced new varieties by selection. This led him to recognize the importance of variation in wild animals and plants and its inheritance to account for the new varieties. Darwin stressed small variations which, he felt, would build up by accumulation and thus lead to new types. He was unfamiliar with Mendel's discoveries, in which the inheritance of large variations was clearly set forth. It is ironic that, while the controversy over Darwin's ideas was at its height, evidence was clearly in existence which could have strengthened his arguments and caused the emphasis on slight variations to be shifted to larger, discontinuous variations.

Hugo DeVries was one of the three biologists who were led back to Mendel's original paper and revived his significant work. DeVries first experimented in plant physiology but soon became interested in the problem of variations in living things and their inheritance. It seemed that species in nature remained constant, an idea which was difficult to reconcile with Darwinian theory, supported as it was by so much evidence that, over the long sweep of geological time, new species undoubtedly have come into existence.

DeVries was born at Haarlem, the centre of the Dutch bulb-growing industry, where new varieties frequently added a fresh colour to the tulip fields, a likely stimulus to research into the reasons for change. He studied at the University of Würzburg in Germany, held a number of academic positions in Germany, and finally was appointed professor at the University of Amsterdam. It was there that he began his researches into the nature of variation.

DeVries chose as his experimental plant the evening primrose (*Oenothera lamarckiana*), which is native to North America but was grown as a garden flower in Holland. It had been observed that the primrose frequently produced new varieties following self-pollination and that these new varieties would often breed true. The new varieties were often so markedly different from the original plant that DeVries referred to them as new species.

To describe these discontinuous variations, DeVries used the term *mutation* and suggested that the mutation was the means by which new species originated. Those mutations that were favourable for the survival of the individual bearing the new traits persisted unchanged until there occurred further mutations, still more favourable to survival. The slight variations which resulted from environmental factors were considered insignificant in the evolutionary process: it was the mutation that provided the machinery of evolution.

T. H. Morgan, in his work with *Drosophila*, also encountered the unexpected new type which was capable of breeding true; he therefore assumed that the hereditary material (the gene) had been altered. This spontaneous change in a gene he called *mutation*, using DeVries's terminology. It has since been discovered that the mutations of DeVries were the result not of gene change but of changes in the chromosome number in the new species. The term *mutation* is used today to refer to any alteration of the genetic material and includes many additional types of change unknown to DeVries. H. J. Müller, a student of Morgan, has further shown that the rate at which mutation occurs can be noticeably increased by exposing organisms to powerful doses of radiation. This experimental technique has become a valuable tool of the geneticist, but since more than ninety per cent of all mutations are either harmful or lethal to the possessor, it has also demonstrated the dangers to our present age from increasing radioactivity.

The reading below is from Volume I, Part II, Chapter I, of *The Mutation Theory*, translated in 1909 by J. B. Farmer and A. D. Darbishire.

¶ Introduction

By the Mutation theory I mean the proposition that the attributes of organisms consist of distinct, separate, and independent units. These units can be associated in groups and we find, in allied species, the same units and groups of units. Transitions, such as we so frequently meet with in the external form both of animals and plants, are as completely absent between these units as they are between the molecules of the chemist.

It is perhaps unnecessary to remark that these generalizations refer to the animal as well as to the vegetable kingdom. In this book, however, I shall confine myself to the latter, in the belief that the truth of the principle will be granted in the case of the former as soon as it has been shown to apply in that of plants.

The adoption of this principle influences our attitude towards the theory of descent by suggesting to us that species have arisen from one another by a discontinuous, as opposed to a continuous, process. Each new unit, forming a fresh step in this process, sharply and completely separates the new form as an independent species from that from which it sprang. The new species appears all at once; it originates from the parent species without any visible preparation, and without any obvious series of transitional forms.

The Mutation theory affects not only our views on the

origin of species but in my opinion bears strongly on the whole question of hybridization. For it shows us that the units with which we deal in hybridization are not the species themselves but the single characters which compose them – the so-called elements of the species. This principle leads to an entirely new method of handling the subject, by enabling us to proceed gradually from the simpler to the more complicated phenomena instead of following the present custom which consists in dealing with the complex cases first.

This work therefore falls into two main parts of which the first treats of the origin of species and varieties by Mutation, and the second of the principles of hybridization.

The Mutation theory is opposed to that conception of the theory of selection which is now prevalent. According to the latter view the material for the origin of new species is afforded by ordinary or so-called individual variation. According to the Mutation theory individual variation has nothing to do with the origin of species. This form of variation, as I hope to show, cannot even by the most rigid and sustained selection lead to a genuine overstepping of the limits of the species and still less to the origin of new and constant characters.

Of course every peculiarity of an organism arises from a previously existing one; not however by ordinary variation, but by a sudden though minute change. It is perhaps appropriate to compare such a change with a chemical substitution.

The name I propose to give to this 'species-forming' variability is Mutability – a term in general use before Darwin's time. The changes brought about by it, the Mutations, are phenomena as to the exact nature of which we understand very little so far. The best-known examples of such Mutations are the so-called spontaneous variations (the 'single variations' of Darwin) by which new and distinct varieties arise. They are also termed, fitly enough, sports. In spite of the fact that they occur fairly often, they are usually not noticed until the new form has already appeared, when of course it is too late to study the phenomenon of its origin experimentally. These new forms can be sought for in cultivated species, which are seldom of pure origin; as well as in Nature. But as yet we have no power of inducing them at will.

It is my belief that all the simple characters of animals and plants arise in this way.

The methods of artificial selection correspond to these two types of variability. Ordinary variation, which is also known as individual, fluctuating, or gradual variation, is always present; and it can be described in terms of perfectly definite laws which have now been fairly completely formulated. It provides the breeder with material for his improved races. On the other hand he has to deal with Mutations which do not need repeated selection but, at the most, must be kept free from admixture, and which almost always breed true from the first.

Under the general term variation, then, are included two distinct phenomena: Mutability and fluctuation or ordinary variation. The latter forms a suitable object for statistical investigation. The epoch-making researches of QUETELET and GALTON on the anthropological side have raised this study to the position of an independent science. Among biologists, LUDWIG, WELDON, BATESON, DUNCKER, JOHANNSEN, MACLEOD, and others, have been active workers in this field. Fluctuation is either individual or partial: in the former case we are dealing with the statistical comparison of different individuals; in the latter with different but homologous organs of the same individual; for example with the leaves of a tree. In both cases the capacity for variation is regarded by those who are competent to judge as a means of adaptation to the environment. Single organs vary partly in mass and weight and partly in number. The former case is referred to by BATESON as continuous variation; the latter as discontinuous. But these terms are sometimes used by other authors with a different meaning.

The laws of Mutability are quite different from those of individual variation; but, so far as our scanty information reaches they are just as independent of the morphological nature of the mutating organ. We can distinguish between progressive and retrogressive Mutation. The former results in the origin of a new character; the latter in the loss of one already existing. It is, obviously, to progressive Mutation, according to this theory, that the main branches of the animal and vegetable genealogical tree owe their development; but the great majority of the cases of the departure of a single species from the type of the systematic group to which it belongs is due to retrogressive Mutation.

It is to considerations of this kind that the first part of this volume will be devoted. In the first place I shall give a critical revision of the facts on which the theory of Natural Selection of DARWIN and WALLACE and others is based. In the second I shall deal with some examples of the experimental study of new forms. The experiments to this end were begun in the autumn of 1886 and are now at least in one particular direction almost complete. A description of them will constitute most of the contents of the second part.

The critical revision to which I have referred will form the substance of the first section.

I shall confine my critique to the facts of selection and to the material, afforded by variability, on which selection operates. It will be shown that artificial selection is, as already mentioned, a twofold process. On the one hand it consists in the isolation of constant strains from their neighbours and, inasmuch as the best are chosen, in their improvement. On the other hand it improves races and is the source of those superior fruits which we can only propagate by grafting and other vegetative methods. But this selection, so far as our experience goes, never leads to the origin of new and independent types.

In this first selection then it will be our object to render the difference between these two types of variability as clear as possible. A correct apprehension of the nature of this difference will make clear the overwhelming importance of Mutability, as opposed to individual variation, in the production of new species. In connexion with this critical treatment I have tried, by experiments on numerous examples of individual variation, to discover the limits to the amount of alteration that can be attained in this way. And we shall see that these are much narrower than a belief in the theory of Selection, as commonly entertained, would lead us to expect.

For the main experiment I have chosen a plant in which I was enabled to follow in detail the phenomenon of Mutation through a number of years. This was *Oenothera Lamarckiana* which as long ago as 1886, formed the starting-point of this work. The second part will show that it has not disappointed me, and will give an account of the whole series of Mutations produced by it.

*

¶ *4. The Laws of Mutation*

I propose now to recapitulate the conclusions which I have drawn from my experiments. The various elementary species we have dealt with behave in essentially the same way; so also does a secondary branch of the family we have just considered, as well as two other primary families which will be described in Section 5; not to mention a number of subsidiary families and cultures. The main conclusion is that the facts of mutability can be described by laws just as definite as the laws of variability.

The following generalizations apply in the first instance to the new forms which have arisen from *Oenothera Lamarckiana*; but it should be stated that they are completely in accordance with a whole host of observations, for the most part of a horticultural nature, on other genera and families.

I. *New elementary species arise suddenly without transitional forms.* A great point in my experiments has been that the ancestors of the newly arisen forms have always been accurately known, and often for many generations back; and that they were either isolated as a group (1887–91) or that they flowered in isolating-bags and were artificially fertilized (1894–99). There is no mention of any such precaution in horticultural records. This precaution enables us to be certain that each new form arose from the seed of a normal specimen of *Oenothera Lamarckiana*. The new form always arises with all the characters proper to it. Once the identity of a seedling is recognized the characters which it will gradually assume can be predicted, and in every case the prediction has been fulfilled.

Many opportunities for testing the degree of certainty in identifying seedlings offered themselves during the course of the experiments, and especially when the chosen seedlings were planted out and flowered in my garden.

When there are hundreds of individuals to record, it is natural that one should occasionally be in doubt over some of them; particularly over such as happen to grow between others, and have not, on that account, sufficient space for their full development. I have usually given these plants an additional lease of life, in many cases the whole summer. They then very soon proved to be a pure type; or perhaps, to be compound forms such as *O. lata nanella*, *O. scintillans elliptica*, and so forth, or, lastly, new forms altogether. But they never turned out to be intermediate forms. Transitions between the various elementary species did not occur.

As a matter of fact I have thought on one or two occasions that I had discovered examples of such intermediates. For example I once noticed a plant which was like *O. lata* in many respects but bore plenty of pollen. I fertilized the plant artificially and raised 270 plants from its seed. These were all like their parent except for 1 per cent of them which were true *lata*, that is to say no larger percentage of

O. lata than the *Lamarckiana*-family itself can give rise to. I have called this form *O. semilata*. ... Other cases of a similar nature have been observed.

The seed of a newly arisen form will, if sown, always give rise to plants with exactly the same characters as their parents; and this purity of the new form is maintained in subsequent generations.

II. *New elementary species are, as a rule, absolutely constant from the moment that they arise.* The seeds set by an example of a newly arisen species after artificial self-fertilization give rise solely to plants like itself; without, as a rule, any trace of reversion to its parental form.

This is equally true of *O. gigas* which has only arisen three times, and of forms which have appeared as frequently as have *O. albida, O. oblonga, O. rubrinervis,* and *O. nanella.*

The point cannot be decided in the case of *O. laevifolia* or *O. brevistylis*, both of which were found on the spot where *O. Lamarckiana* was originally discovered, but have not arisen in my cultures. Both these, when self-fertilized, come perfectly true from seed. *O. brevistylis* breeds true in spite of its small fruits which sometimes set no more than a solitary seed. Indeed I thought at first that these fruits were absolutely sterile.

Oenothera scintillans and *O. lata* are exceptions to this rule. The seeds borne by self-fertilized plants of the first named form produce a generation only about one-third of which is *O. scintillans.* This is true of the seeds of three distinct individuals which have arisen quite independently of one another. From the seed of a fourth individual however 69 per cent of *O. scintillans* were raised; and these again in the next generation gave from 60 to 90 per cent.

This constancy of the new species is an extremely important characteristic. It has enabled *O. laevifolia* and *O. brevistylis* to maintain themselves in the spot where they arose – mere scattered examples among the host of *Lamarckianas* which surround them; and, what is more, pure in respect of all their characters (apart of course from accidental crossing).

That the struggle for existence is a pretty keen one in the field in question may be gathered from the fact that a vigorous *Lamarckiana* can bear 100 fruits and that each fruit contains between 200 and 300 seeds. The whole field contains no more than some thousands of plants, that is to say not much more than could be supplied by the seeds of a single individual. The seeds which do not produce adult plants either do not germinate or the seedlings which come up die young. Yet in spite of the severity of the competition, *O. laevifolia* and *O. brevistylis* have maintained themselves for more than twelve years.*

III. *Most of the new forms that have appeared are elementary species, and not varieties in the strict sense of the term.* Elementary species are distinguished from their nearest allies by nearly if not quite all their characters. The differences are often so slight as to escape notice by an eye not trained to observe them; and they are particularly apt, as systematists so often complain, to become lost in dried specimens. This latter is however fortunately not the case with the new forms whose origin I have witnessed; for they are distinguishable from one another and from *O. Lamarckiana* as herbarium specimens far more easily than, for example, specimens of this last species are from *O. biennis.*

This close familiarity with each form can only be attained by a careful and minute study and description of all the organs of the plant at every stage of its development. Once a plant is thoroughly known in this way it can be recognized at almost any stage.

Varieties are distinguished from the mother species usually by one single character or at most by two or three, whilst they resemble them in all others. Apart from this point, the difference between species and varieties is to a large extent arbitrary, since when tested experimentally the one is just as constant as the other.

* And afterwards until now (note of 1908).

It is rather curious that all the new forms which have arisen in my experiments should have been species in this sense and not varieties. I have always hoped to get a white flowered form or some other such distinct variety but so far in vain. *O. nanella* is perhaps the only form which can be called a variety in the horticultural sense of the term.

It is a characteristic of varieties that they crop up in a great number of unrelated species, genera, and families. For example the varieties *rosea, alba, laevis, inermis, laciniata, prolifera, bracteata,* and *pendula.* It is the same with monstrosities: e.g., var.: *plena, fasciata, torsa, adnata, fissa,* and so forth. The same is true of dwarfs or the var. *nana.*

But with the exception of *O. nanella* I cannot find in other families and genera any series of forms analogous to mine. It is for these reasons that I do not consider them varieties.

A very popular definition of varieties is that they are forms which are known to have arisen from other forms. This position is obviously untenable. The proof of their origin may exist in the case of some few horticultural varieties but with the vast majority of them and with all wild varieties this proof does not exist at all. Their origin is a thing of the past and when, as is usually the case, it was not witnessed by human eyes the so-called 'proof' of it is based on deduction or analogy.

And in all cases, where we are not dealing with direct observation, the origin of varieties is in no sense whatever more certain than that of collective species or genera.

I have dwelt on this point because I feel quite certain that many of my readers will regard my new forms as varieties *for the very reason that I have been able to observe their origin.**

IV. *New elementary species appear in large numbers at the same time or at any rate during the same period.*

* Fortunately, as a matter of fact, this has not been the case (note of 1908).

SCOTT's palaeontological results have led him to conclude that species-forming variability, or, as he also calls it, mutability must appear simultaneously in larger groups of individuals and that the causes of these changes have probably been working through long periods of time.

The palaeontologist investigates the problem of the origin of species only in broad outline. It is the experimental physiologist who deals with the separate individuals themselves and with their posterity, of whom not a millionth part would ever be preserved in the fossil state. We have no right therefore to expect more than a general agreement between the conclusions attained by these two lines of investigation.

And when we do find such agreement, as we do in the present instance, I think it is extremely desirable that it should be put on record.

Amongst the species which have arisen in my experimental garden *Oenothera gigas* has only been observed once. The others appeared every, or nearly every, year in varying, and often, indeed, in considerable numbers. More than 800 individuals of the seven new species we have described arose independently from one another from the *Lamarckiana*-family. And as about 50,000 plants were cultivated during this period of time the number of new forms amounted to between 1 and 2 per cent of the total cultivated.

In other words: *The new elementary species arose from the parent form in a ratio of 1–2 per cent. Sometimes more than, but oftener less than, this value.* And this ratio was maintained throughout the whole course of my experiment, so far, at least, as the difference in the methods of investigation which have been employed at different times permit me to estimate it.

This figure, 1–2 per cent, is more probably too small than too large. For it was only in the years 1895 and 1896 that I went to the labour of determining it accurately. In previous years the average was considerably lowered by other circumstances, the most important of which was the omission of such forms as *O. oblonga, O. rubrinervis,* and *O. scintillans* which at that time I could not recognize in their early stages. The table on page 224 shows, for the two years 1895 and 1896, 22,000 individuals of *Lamarckiana* and 711 of the new forms. *That is more than 3 per cent.*

O. laevifolia and *O. brevistylis* formed far smaller a percentage than 3 per cent of the number of *Oenotheras* growing on the original field at Hilversum; yet they, obviously, arose in quantities sufficient for them to maintain themselves. We may conclude therefore that a yearly appearance in the proportion of from 1 to 3 per cent would be sufficient for the establishment of a new species.

V. *The new characters have nothing to do with individual variability. Oenothera Lamarckiana* exhibits a degree of fluctuating variability in all its characters which is certainly not less than that exhibited by other plants. The new species fall right outside the range of this variability; as is evident from the fact that they are not connected with the parent type by intermediate or transitional forms.

New races can of course be evolved by repeated selection in one or another direction in *Lamarckiana* just as much as in any other plant. Indeed I have, myself, produced a long-fruited and a short-fruited form in this way. But such races remain dependent on selection and differ from their type only in one feature: they do not bear the slightest resemblance to elementary species.

Elementary species themselves exhibit fluctuating variability, and often indeed to a greater extent than the parent form. Nearly all their organs and characters vary, but never in such a way as to approach the original form.

VI. *The mutations, to which the origin of new elementary species is due, appear to be indefinite, that is to say, the changes may affect all organs and seem to take place in almost every conceivable direction.* The plants become stronger (*gigas*) or weaker (*albida*), with broader or with smaller leaves. The flowers become larger (*gigas*) and darker yellow (*rubrinervis*), or smaller (*oblonga* and *scintillans*) and paler (*albida*). The fruits become longer (*rubrinervis*) or shorter (*gigas, albida, lata*). The epidermis becomes more uneven (*albida*) or smoother (*laevifolia*); the crumples on the leaves either increase (*lata*) or diminish (*scintillans*). The production of pollen is either increased (*rubrinervis*) or diminished (*scintillans*); the seeds become larger (*gigas*) or smaller (*scintillans*), more plentiful (*rubrinervis*) or more scanty (*lata*). The plant becomes female (*lata*) or almost entirely male (*brevistylis*); many forms which are not described here were almost entirely sterile, some almost destitute of flowers.

O. gigas, O. scintillans, O. oblonga tend to become biennial more than *O. Lamarckiana*; and *O. lata* tends to become less so; whilst *O. nanella* cultivated in the usual way scarcely ever runs into a second year.

This list could easily be extended, but for the present it may suffice.

To regard the new forms from another point of view, some of them are fitter, some unfitter than the parent form, and others neither the one nor the other. Until experiments have been made with the new forms sown in the field it is obvious that no definite conclusion on this point can be arrived at: nor do the observations which have so far been made on the plants growing in the field at Hilversum throw any light on the subject.

Nevertheless it is evident that the female *O. lata* is at a great disadvantage; and that *O. albida* with its narrow leaves is, at any rate in its early stages, far too delicate. *O. rubrinervis* looks quite robust but is very brittle and liable to be broken. Annual plants of *O. oblonga* bear hardly any seeds, whilst *O. nanella* is very small and its petioles are often brittle. All these forms appear to me to be less fit as compared with *O. Lamarckiana*.

On the other hand *O. laevifolia* seems to be at least a

match for its parent; and *O. gigas* in many respects superior to it: all its organs are larger and stronger and apparently better adapted to perform their functions; the whole plant is stouter. Sowings of this species in the open should give favourable results.

The forms which have not yet been described (*O. spathulata, subovata*, etc.) are hampered in the struggle for existence by their almost complete sterility. *O. sublinearis* with its slender grass-like leaves is much too weak in its early stages – and so forth.

Many authors already hold that species-forming variability must be indiscriminate. We are strongly opposed to the conception of a definite 'tendency to vary' which would bring about useful changes, or at least favour their appearance. The great service which DARWIN did was that he demonstrated the possibility of accounting for the evolution of the whole animal and vegetable kingdom without invoking the aid of supernatural agencies. According to him species-forming variability exists without any reference to the fitness of the forms to which it gives rise. It simply provides material for natural selection to operate on. And whether this selection takes place between individuals, as DARWIN and WALLACE thought, or whether it decides between the existence of whole species, as I think, it is the possibility of existence under given external conditions which determines whether a new form shall survive or not.

We can go a step further and say that many more useless and unfavourable variations must arise than favourable ones. This becomes sufficiently evident when we consider the complexity of the conditions which an organism has to satisfy before it can supplant its fellows.

The mutability of *Oenothera Lamarckiana* satisfies all these theoretical conditions perfectly. Nearly all organs and all characters mutate, and in almost every conceivable direction and combination. Many combinations must obviously be fatal to the life of the germ within the ripening seed and cannot on that account be observed. Others hinder the development of the seedlings and the whole series of experiments with apparently mutated plants came to nothing in spite of every care on account of the premature death of the young plants. Many combinations reduce the fertility so much that we cannot go further than observe the mutated individual itself. A number of other combinations are, I suppose, lost in my experiments because they cannot be detected until the plants are fairly old, by which time the great majority have been weeded out to make more room.* Such considerations seem to me to explain how it was that I was able to cultivate only so small a number of new species through more than one generation. And it is of course open to question how many of those that I did cultivate could survive the struggle for existence.

I conclude therefore: Mutability is indiscriminate. Some mutations bear no offspring and disappear forthwith. Between the others and the species already established natural selection must decide, unless artificial selection steps in.

VII. *Mutability appears periodically.* I am led to this conclusion by my experiments; but I express it at present only tentatively. The fact that of all the species that I have examined so far, only one has proved to be in a state of mutation, appears to me sufficient evidence for this conclusion. But further investigations are necessary for the establishment of the generalization: and such I have only recently started. I am not of course now in a position to give experimental proof of the existence of mutable and immutable periods: but I have enunciated the hypothesis of their existence as the simplest explanation of the remarkable fact that I have so far observed mutations only in a single species; though plentifully enough in it.

The above generalizations refer in the first instance to

* For example *O. brevistylis* and *O. leptocarpa* are not recognizable until just before they flower.

the case which we have observed, namely the mutability of *Oenothera Lamarckiana*. But inasmuch as experimental investigation of other instances has not yet been published, we must, pending the acquisition of that knowledge, regard it as a typical case of the origin of new species.

VII
THE CONQUEST OF DISEASE

THE modern arsenal of vaccines, antibiotics, sulphon-amides, and other drugs has spectacularly reduced the lethal effects of many dread diseases. So thoroughly are these things taken for granted that it is difficult to realize that the germ theory of disease is hardly more than a hundred years old.

The idea of a living contagion (*contagium animatum*) is centuries old, and the notion of disease by contact goes back thousands of years to Biblical times. We have no information that the Greeks and Romans had a clear conception of what is now called 'infection' or 'contagion', but there are in the Bible (Leviticus XIII and XIV) a number of references to diseases such as leprosy, which were feared because it was known that direct contact with a victim or with objects he had touched could spread the disease. There was, however, no understanding of the cause of the contagion; some thought that it was a divine punishment for wickedness and offences against the Lord, or that it arose from natural phenomena such as earthquakes, floods, and miasmas which polluted the atmosphere. Hippocrates, for example, regarded bad air as an important causative agent of disease.

The Middle Ages experienced perennial epidemics, plagues, and pestilences which made the fact of contagion and infection an urgent problem. Boccaccio (1313–75) in his *Decameron*, for example, puts his stories into the mouths of a group of people who have withdrawn from contact with the plague-stricken populace.

The first serious suggestion that a living contagion was responsible for disease was made by Fracastorius (1483–1553), a student of Copernicus at Padua, who hinted at the existence of seeds or germs ('*seminaria*') of disease; but another century passed before Leeuwenhoek first saw bacteria and other microbic life through his microscope.

Another concept which could be traced back at least to Aristotle had to be refuted before the idea of a *contagium animatum* could be developed: this was the notion of spontaneous generation of living things. The first experimental attack on the idea of spontaneous generation was, as we have seen (p. 73), carried out by Francesco Redi, who proved that maggots do not arise spontaneously from decaying meat but develop from the eggs of flies deposited thereon. When Leeuwenhoek discovered bacteria (p. 80) the idea was revived, since microbes were thought to be spontaneously generated. This, too, was effectively disproved by Spallanzani (p. 86), who showed that protozoa and bacteria (microbes) enter infusions from the air and can be destroyed by heating. He further demonstrated that no microbes appear in sterilized infusions which are kept from the air.

There was no link, however, between these experimental observations and the belief of Fracastorius that living agents were responsible for disease. A number of developments, one technical, the other experimental, finally set the stage for the monumental achievements of Pasteur and Koch, the giants in the story of the germ theory of disease.

One significant step forward was the improvement of microscopic lenses, in which the father of Joseph Lister was one of the most important figures. The second was the discovery that yeast was a microscopic plant and that fermentation was a life process of yeast: this proved to be a major influence on Pasteur's studies. Then Agostino Bassi (1773–1856) discovered that the muscardine disease of silkworms was caused by a microbe (protozoan). This was the first demonstration that a microscopic living agent was responsible for a specific disease.

It was at this point that Pasteur entered the scene. His training as a chemist had introduced him to the microscope, and his facility with this instrument led him to his epochal discoveries. The agricultural communities of France, whose wines were spoiling and whose sheep and cows were dying of anthrax, called in Pasteur to solve these problems, which were bringing the industry to the verge of disaster.

When Pasteur examined the spoiled wine with his microscope, he found bacteria as well as the yeasts which produced the fermentation. He concluded that the microbes made the wines spoil and showed this spoilage could be prevented by heating the wine at the appropriate stage of fermentation. From there he went on to show that infection can cause disease in silkworms, cows, sheep, and men and women – in other words, he enunciated the germ theory of disease.

The concept of the bacterial origin of disease was not, however, immediately accepted, especially by the medical profession. Considerably more experimental proof was demanded before it could be established unequivocally. At about this time Pouchet revived the idea of spontaneous generation of microbic life. Pasteur determined to lay this error to rest for all time. In a dramatic lecture, he held a flask containing an infusion up to view and said, 'I did not publish these experiments; the conclusions which it was necessary to deduce from them were too serious for me not to have the fear that there existed some hidden cause of error in spite of the care which I had taken to make them irreproachable.' Pasteur was, in fact, doing little more than repeating Spallanzani's experiment but his vivid presentation finally persuaded the world that microbes have a natural origin by reproduction from pre-existing organisms conveyed by the air into material suitable for their growth.

Joseph Lister was impressed by Pasteur's demonstration and raised the question whether the sepsis of wounds after amputation was due to microbes from the air. Pursuing this hypothesis, Lister originated the era of antiseptic surgery as the first application of Pasteur's experimental results.

In the meantime Pasteur had moved on to other practical discoveries which were to save lives by minimizing the effects of many diseases. He produced vaccines from germs which were weakened by heating, drying, ageing, or by treatment with chemicals. Injected into an animal, they provided protection against future, more severe, infections by the same germs. He proved the value of inoculation of sheep to protect them from anthrax.

The second great figure of this period was Robert Koch (1843–1910), who established bacteriology as a science. Koch developed and perfected most of the basic techniques used in cultivating and studying bacteria, and in his four postulates he provided a set of procedures which are used to this day to relate specific bacteria to specific diseases. Koch's contributions complemented those of Pasteur, their unique discoveries extending man's control over a part of his environment which threatened his health and even survival. Koch discovered the organisms causing anthrax, cholera, and tuberculosis.

Discoveries followed one another rapidly. More and more human and animal diseases were traced to bacterial invasion – largely by students of Koch and Pasteur. Vaccines and antitoxins were evolved for the prevention or treatment of some of these diseases, notably, typhoid fever, diphtheria, and scarlet fever. The action of bacteria in the body and the body's defensive reactions were studied and described.

Although circumstantial evidence suggested that the great epidemic diseases of the tropics, including malaria, bubonic plague, and yellow-fever were spread by contagion, there were many unexplained and puzzling features in the epidemic pattern. The demonstration by Patrick Manson in 1877 of the transmission of *filariasis* by the mosquito initiated a series of investigations into the role of insects as the carriers of disease-causing organisms from host to host. Theobald Smith showed that Texas Cattle fever is transmitted by a tick, and Ronald Ross implicated the anopheline mosquito in the transmission of malaria. In both cases the parasite passes through certain stages of the life cycle in the insect which thus serves as its intermediate host and not as a simple carrier. Walter Reed was able to associate another type of mosquito with yellow-fever. Further researches established the role of an inter-mediate mammalian host, often serving as the natural reservoir of infection, in addition to the insect vector in the dissemination of diseases such as bubonic plague. The elucidation of the complex life cycles of the parasites has enabled man in many instances effectively to control the spread of diseases such as plague and malaria. It was the administrative genius of Gorgas, putting to practical application the discover of Ross, that made possible the construction of the Panama Canal.

The modern developments of bacteriology and virology culminating in the therapeutic triumphs of Alexander Fleming, Salman Waksman, and Jonas Salk and the profound probing of Macfarlane Burnet into the very nature of virus have stemmed from the solid foundations laid by the pioneers.

EDWARD JENNER

1749–1823

VACCINATION TO ESTABLISH IMMUNITY TO SMALLPOX IS DEMONSTRATED BY EXPERIMENT

•

EDWARD JENNER, as a country doctor in Gloucestershire, was naturally interested in the diseases that afflicted the country folk. One of these was cowpox, a virus infection transmitted from the udders of cows to the dairyman or milkmaid. While still serving his apprenticeship Jenner had learned of the tradition that an attack of cowpox would give protection against smallpox, at that time a prevalent disease which often left those who survived an attack severely disfigured. For centuries inoculation with smallpox had been practised in the East. Infective matter from a smallpox patient was inoculated in the hope that the resulting attack, induced when the sufferer was in good health, would prove less severe than the naturally occurring disease against which it gave him protection. This practice had long been employed in Wales but it first gained wide acceptance in England after its introduction from Turkey by Lady Mary Wortley Montagu in 1717. Its chief disadvantage was the unpredictable severity of the induced attack, which was sometimes fatal.

Jenner established the validity of the country tradition that an attack of the mild disease cowpox would give immunity against the dangerous smallpox. His report on twenty-three cases in which he had successfully used a 'vaccine' (from the Latin *vacca*, cow) to protect his patients against smallpox was published in 1796. In the face of strong opposition vaccination was rapidly adopted in Europe and the United States.

Jenner was unable to explain the reasons for his success. The understanding of the principles of natural and artificial immunity had to await the discoveries of the pioneer bacteriologists.

There were several claims from England and from Denmark and Germany that cowpox vaccination had been used before Jenner's experiments. The validity of these claims does not detract from Jenner's right to the credit of being the first to put to the test of careful experiment what was no more than a folk-lore tradition.

The selection that follows is taken from *An Inquiry into the Causes and Effects of the Variolae Vaccinae* (1798).

———————

The deviation of man from the state in which he was originally placed by nature seems to have proved to him a prolific source of diseases. From the love of splendour, from the indulgences of luxury, and from his fondness for amusement he has familiarized himself with a great number of animals, which may not originally have been intended for his associates.

The wolf, disarmed of ferocity, is now pillowed in the lady's lap. The cat, the little tiger of our island, whose natural home is the forest, is equally domesticated and caressed. The cow, the hog, the sheep, and the horse are all, for a variety of purposes, brought under his care and dominion.

There is a disease to which the horse, from his state of domestication, is frequently subject. The farriers have termed it *the grease*. It is an inflammation and swelling in the heel, from which issues matter possessing properties of a very peculiar kind, which seems capable of generating a disease in the human body (after it has undergone the modification which I shall presently speak of), which bears so strong a resemblance to the smallpox that I think it highly probable it may be the source of that disease.

In this dairy country a great number of cows are kept, and the office of milking is performed indiscriminately by men- and maidservants. One of the former having been appointed to apply dressings to the heels of a horse affected with the grease, and not paying due attention to cleanliness, incautiously bears his part in milking the cows, with some particles of the infectious matter adhering to his fingers. When this is the case it commonly happens that a disease is communicated to the cows, and from the cows to dairymaids, which spreads through the farm until most of the cattle and domestics feel its unpleasant consequences. This disease has obtained the name of the cowpox. It appears on the nipples of the cows in the form of irregular pustules. At their first appearance they are commonly of a palish blue, or rather of a colour somewhat approaching to livid, and are surrounded by an erysipelatous inflammation. These pustules, unless a timely remedy be applied, frequently degenerate into phagedenic ulcers, which prove extremely troublesome. The animals become indisposed, and the secretion of milk is much lessened. Inflamed spots now begin to appear on different parts of the hands of the domestics employed in milking, and sometimes on the wrists, which quickly run on to suppuration, first assuming the appearance of the small vesications produced by a burn. Most commonly they appear about the joints of the fingers and at their extremities; but whatever parts are affected, if the situation will admit, these superficial suppurations put on a circular form, with their edges more elevated than their centre, and of a colour distantly approaching to blue. Absorption takes place, and tumours appear in each axilla. The system becomes affected – the pulse is quickened; and shiverings, succeeded by heat, with general lassitude, and pains about the loins and limbs, with vomiting, come on. The head is painful, and the patient is now and then even affected with delirium. These symptoms, varying in their degree of violence, generally continue from one day to three or four, leaving ulcerated sores about the hands, which, from the sensibility of the parts, are very troublesome, and commonly heal slowly, frequently becoming phagedenic, like those from whence they sprung. The lips, nostrils, eyelids, and other parts of the body are sometimes affected with sores; but these evidently arise from their being heedlessly rubbed or scratched with the patient's infected fingers. No eruptions on the skin have followed the decline of the feverish symptoms in any instance that has come under my inspection, one only excepted, and in this case a very few appeared on the arms: they were very minute, of a vivid red colour, and soon died away without advancing to maturation; so that I cannot determine whether they had any connexion with the preceding symptoms.

Thus the disease makes its progress from the horse to the nipple of the cow, and from the cow to the human subject.

Morbid matter of various kinds, when absorbed into the system, may produce effects in some degree similar; but what renders the cowpox virus so extremely singular is that the person who has been thus affected is forever after secure from the infection of the smallpox; neither exposure to the variolous effluvia, nor the insertion of the matter into the skin, producing this distemper.

In support of so extraordinary a fact I shall lay before my reader a great number of instances.

Case I. Joseph Merret, now an under gardener to the Earl of Berkeley, lived as a servant with a farmer near this place in the year 1770, and occasionally assisted in milking his master's cows. Several horses belonging to the farm began to have sore heels, which Merret frequently attended. The cows soon became affected with the cowpox, and soon after several sores appeared on his hands. Swellings and stiffness in each axilla followed, and he was so much indisposed for several days as to be incapable of pursuing his ordinary employment. Previously to the appearance of the distemper among the cows there was no fresh cow brought into the farm, nor any servant employed who was affected with the cowpox.

In April 1795, a general inoculation taking place here,

Merret was inoculated with his family; so that a period of twenty-five years had elapsed from his having the cowpox to this time. However, though the variolous matter was repeatedly inserted into his arm, I found it impracticable to infect him with it; an efflorescence only, taking on an erysipelatous look about the centre, appearing on the skin near the punctured parts. During the whole time that his family had the smallpox, one of whom had it very full, he remained in the house with them but received no injury from exposure to the contagion.

It is necessary to observe that the utmost care was taken to ascertain, with the most scrupulous precision, that no one whose case is here adduced had gone through the smallpox previous to these attempts to produce that disease.

Had these experiments been conducted in a large city, or in a populous neighbourhood, some doubts might have been entertained; but here, where population is thin, and where such an event as a person's having had the smallpox is always faithfully recorded, no risk of inaccuracy in this particular can arise.

Case II. Sarah Portlock, of this place, was infected with the cowpox when a servant at a farmer's in the neighbourhood, twenty-seven years ago.

In the year 1792, conceiving herself, from this circumstance, secure from the infection of the smallpox, she nursed one of her own children who had accidentally caught the disease, but no indisposition ensued. During the time she remained in the infected room variolous matter was inserted into both her arms, but without any further effect than in the preceding case. . . .

Case IV. Mary Barge, of Woodford in this parish, was inoculated with variolous matter in the year 1791. An efflorescence of a palish red colour soon appeared about the parts where the matter was inserted and spread itself rather extensively, but died away in a few days without producing any variolous symptoms. She has since been repeatedly employed as a nurse to smallpox patients, without experiencing any ill consequences. This woman had the cowpox when she lived in the service of a farmer in this parish thirty-one years before.

Case XVII. The more accurately to observe the progress of the infection I selected a healthy boy, about eight years old, for the purpose of inoculation for the cowpox. The matter was taken from a sore on the hand of a dairymaid, who was infected by her master's cows, and it was inserted, on the fourteenth of May 1796, into the arm of the boy by means of two superficial incisions, barely penetrating the cutis, each about half an inch long.

On the seventh day he complained of uneasiness in the axilla and on the ninth he became a little chilly, lost his appetite, and had a slight headache. During the whole of this day he was perceptibly indisposed and spent the night with some degree of restlessness, but on the day following he was perfectly well.

The appearance of the incisions in their progress to a state of maturation were much the same as when produced in a similar manner by variolous matter. The difference which I perceived was in the state of the limpid fluid arising from the action of the virus, which assumed rather a darker hue, and in that of the efflorescence spreading round the incisions, which had more of an erysipelatous look than we commonly perceive when variolous matter has been made use of in the same manner; but the whole died away (leaving on the inoculated parts scabs and subsequent eschars) without giving me or my patient the least trouble.

In order to ascertain whether the boy, after feeling so slight an affection of the system from the cowpox virus, was secure from the contagion of the smallpox, he was inoculated the first of July following with variolous matter, immediately taken from a pustule. Several slight punctures and incisions were made on both his arms, and the matter was carefully inserted, but no disease followed. The same appearances were observable on the arms as we commonly see when a patient has had variolous matter applied, after having either the cowpox or smallpox. Several months afterwards he was again inoculated with variolous matter, but no sensible effect was produced on the constitution. . . .

After the many fruitless attempts to give the smallpox to those who had had the cowpox, it did not appear necessary, nor was it convenient to me, to inoculate the whole of those who had been the subjects of these late trials; yet I thought it right to see the effects of variolous matter on some of them, particularly William Summers, the first of these patients who had been infected with matter taken from the cow. He was, therefore, inoculated with variolous matter from a fresh pustule; but, as in the preceding cases, the system did not feel the effects of it in the smallest degree. I had an opportunity also of having his boy and William Pead inoculated by my nephew, Mr Henry Jenner, whose report to me is as follows: 'I have inoculated Pead and Barge, two of the boys whom you lately infected with the cowpox. On the second day the incisions were inflamed and there was a pale inflammatory stain around them. On the third day these appearances were still increasing and their arms itched considerably. On the fourth day the inflammation was evidently subsiding, and on the sixth day it was scarcely perceptible. No symptoms of indisposition followed.

'To convince myself that the variolous matter made use of was in a perfect state I at the same time inoculated a patient with some of it who never had gone through the cowpox, and it produced the smallpox in the usual regular manner.'

These experiments afforded me much satisfaction; they proved that the matter, in passing from one human subject to another, through five gradations, lost none of its original properties, J. Barge being the fifth who received the infection successively from William Summers, the boy to whom it was communicated from the cow.

I shall now conclude this inquiry with some general observations on the subject, and on some others which are interwoven with it.

*

Although I presume it may be unnecessary to produce further testimony in support of my assertion 'that the cowpox protects the human constitution from the infection of the smallpox,' yet it affords me considerable satisfaction to say that Lord Somerville, the president of the Board of Agriculture, to whom this paper was shown by Sir Joseph Banks, has found upon inquiry that the statements were confirmed by the concurring testimony of Mr Dolland, a surgeon, who resides in a dairy country remote from this, in which these observations were made. With respect to the opinion adduced 'that the source of the infection is a peculiar morbid matter arising in the horse,' although I have not been able to prove it from actual experiments conducted immediately under my own eye, yet the evidence I have adduced appears sufficient to establish it.

They who are not in the habit of conducting experiments may not be aware of the coincidence of circumstances necessary for their being managed so as to prove perfectly decisive; nor how often men engaged in professional pursuits are liable to interruptions which disappoint them almost at the instant of their being accomplished: however, I feel no room for hesitation respecting the common origin of the disease, being well convinced that it never appears among the cows (except it can be traced to a cow introduced among the general herd which has been previously infected, or to an infected servant) unless they have been milked by someone who, at the same time, has the care of a horse affected with diseased heels.

The spring of the year 1797, which I intended particularly to have devoted to the completion of this investigation, proved, from its dryness, remarkably adverse to my wishes; for it frequently happens, while the farmers' horses are exposed to the cold rains which fall at that season, that their heels become diseased, and so cowpox then appeared in the neighbourhood.

The active quality of the virus from the horses' heels is greatly increased after it has acted on the nipples of the cow, as it rarely happens that the horse affects his dresser with sores, and as rarely that a milkmaid escapes the infection when she milks infected cows. It is most active at the commencement of the disease, even before it has acquired a pus-like appearance; indeed, I am not confident whether this property in the matter does not entirely cease as soon as it is secreted in the form of pus. I am induced to think it does cease, and that it is the thin, darkish-looking fluid only, oozing from the newly formed cracks in the heels, similar to what sometimes appears from erysipelatous blisters, which gives the disease. Nor am I certain that the nipples of the cows are at all times in a state to receive the infection. The appearance of the disease in the spring and the early part of the summer, when they are disposed to be affected with spontaneous eruptions so much more frequently than at other seasons, induces me to think that the virus from the horse must be received upon them when they are in this state, in order to produce effects: experiments, however, must determine these points. But it is clear that, when the cowpox virus is once generated, the cows cannot resist the contagion, in whatever state their nipples may chance to be, if they are milked with an infected hand.

Whether the matter, either from the cow or the horse, will affect the sound skin of the human body I cannot positively determine; probably it will not, unless on those parts where the cuticle is extremely thin, as on the lips, for example. . . .

A medical gentleman (now no more), who for many years inoculated in this neighbourhood, frequently preserved the variolous matter intended for his use on a piece of lint or cotton which, in its fluid state, was put into a vial, corked, and conveyed into a warm pocket; a situation certainly favourable for speedily producing putrefaction in it. In this state (not infrequently after it had been taken several days from the pustules) it was inserted into the arms of his patients and brought on inflammation of the incised parts, swellings of the axillary glands, fever, and sometimes eruptions. But what was this disease? Certainly not the smallpox; for the matter, having from putrefaction lost or suffered a derangement in its specific properties, was no longer capable of producing that malady, those who had been inoculated in this matter being as much subject to the contagion of the smallpox as if they had never been under the influence of this artificial disease; and many, unfortunately, fell victims to it who thought themselves in perfect security. . . .

Thus far have I proceeded in an inquiry founded, as it must appear, on the basis of experiment; in which, however, conjecture has been occasionally admitted in order to present to persons well situated for such discussions objects for a more minute investigation. In the meantime I shall myself continue to prosecute this inquiry, encouraged by the hope of its becoming essentially beneficial to mankind.

———

ROBERT KOCH
1843–1910

THE METHODS FOR STUDYING DISEASE-
PRODUCING BACTERIA ARE DESCRIBED AND
ARE USED TO PROVE THAT TUBERCULOSIS
IS CAUSED BY A SPECIFIC BACTERIUM

ROBERT KOCH is regarded as the greatest of research
bacteriologists, just as Pasteur, by common consent, is the
greatest of applied bacteriologists. Koch was born in
Clausthal, Hanover, the son of a mining engineer. He
studied at the University of Göttingen, from which he
graduated as a doctor of medicine in 1886. Koch was a
pupil of Jacob Henle (1809–85), himself a pupil of the
great Johannes Müller.

Three years before Koch was born, Henle put forward
his hypothesis that infections were attributable to invasion of the body by micro-organisms. This pronouncement, when the idea was firmly established that such small
bodies were effects and not causes, was unlikely to gain
acceptance in the absence of proof, and this Henle could
not supply. Yet in 1835, Agostino Bassi (1773–1856)
demonstrated that the muscardine disease of silkworms
was caused by a microbe, and thus Bassi was actually the
first to propose the doctrine that microbes cause disease.
This doctrine did not gain wide acceptance, however, until
the convincing demonstrations of Louis Pasteur, who is
generally regarded as the originator of the germ theory
of disease.

Koch first practised as a country doctor with some success, but, with time on his hands, he took to the study of
bacteria, aided by a microscope he received as a gift from
his wife. He served as an army surgeon in the Franco-
Prussian war and later became a health officer in the town

of Wollstein, where he continued his studies of bacteria, especially the bacteria of anthrax.

A number of bacteriologists had observed that the blood of animals that had died of anthrax contained large numbers of minute, rod-shaped bodies which Koch attempted to study and to grow outside the body. By 1876 he had succeeded in demonstrating that the minute bodies were bacilli and were the cause of the disease anthrax – the first demonstration that a specific bacterium was the cause of a specific disease. This was followed by work to improve the techniques of examining bacteria and finally, in 1881, Koch succeeded in growing pure cultures of bacteria, now a basic procedure in bacteriological studies.

By this time Koch had become a member of the German Imperial Public Health Service in Berlin, where he established a school of bacteriology that attracted students from many countries and from which a flood of great bacteriological discoveries flowed.

The first of the selections below is taken from *On the Investigation of Pathogenic Organisms* translated by Victor Horsley in *Recent Essays on Bacteria in Relation to Disease*, published by the New Sydenham Society in 1886. In it we find a statement of Koch's postulates, a magnificently simple set of rules for proving that a specific bacterium is the cause of a specific disease and used to this day more or less as they were proposed by Koch. He also describes the technique of cultivating the bacteria and the procedures for staining bacteria to make them more easily visible for microscopic examination.

The second selection contains the announcement of Koch's greatest single discovery – the tubercle bacillus. This paper was originally published in the *Berliner Clinische Wochenschrift* in 1882 and was translated by Dr and Mrs Max Pinner. This illustrates the practical application of the postulates. A year later Koch announced the discovery of the cause of Asiatic cholera, a disease prevalent in the Far East but almost eliminated in the West.

Koch's achievements did not extend to the practical area of prevention and cure of disease. In 1890 he announced the development of tuberculin and suggested its use in preventing and curing tuberculosis. This announcement was premature and unfortunate, since use of the tuberculin was attended by disturbing and even fatal consequences. The new drugs evolved for the treatment of tuberculosis and the early detection of the disease by mass radiography have now greatly reduced its incidence.

¶ *On the Investigation of Pathogenic Organisms*

As a rule the following points must be observed in investigating microorganisms from the point of view of sanitary science. In the first place, it must be definitely determined whether the organisms are pathogenic at all, that is to say, whether they can cause disease. Following on that comes the proof of their inoculability, that is, of the possibility of their being transferred from one individual to another previously healthy; this transfer being attempted both on individuals belonging to the same species as those in whom the disease arose spontaneously or was artificially produced and on individuals of other species.

Next we have to trace out the mode in which the pathogenic organisms enter the animal body, to follow their behaviour outside the body in the air, water, and soil and finally to determine what influence reagents exert on them in the way of destroying them or preventing their development. . . .

Bacteria have one peculiarity which makes it possible to overcome the difficulties presented by their extremely small size. This peculiarity is simply the power of taking up and retaining the colours of certain dyes, especially the anilines. . . . The process of making the bacteria in fluids such as blood, pus, and lymph visible by means of stains, consists in spreading the fluid containing them in as thin a layer as possible on a cover glass, drying it, and then subjecting it to the action of the staining solution. . . .

By the methods described above the existence of microorganisms in animal tissues may be demonstrated, and if the investigation shows that they are present in large numbers, or that they have caused irritation or gangrene in the invaded tissues, their pathogenic power is thus made certain. A second question which interests us is whether these microorganisms, which are known to be pathogenic, are also infectious, that is whether they can be transferred from one animal to another. The terms infectious and pathogenic must not be confused with one another; it is perfectly possible to conceive the existence of organisms which, since they can penetrate in the tissues of the animal body and set up diseases therein, are truly pathogenic, but still have not the power of infecting, that is, of passing from one animal to another and causing disease in that one also. . . . The terms pathogenic and infectious are not, therefore, identical, and if a parasite is shown to be pathogenic it must be experimentally established in addition whether it is infectious or not.

In order that our procedures should be rewarded by a positive result, the conditions existing in nature must be adhered to as closely as possible, a precaution which was neglected in the early days of experimental research into infectious diseases. People have experimentally endeavoured in the most primitive way to communicate to dogs, cats, rabbits, guinea pigs, and the like, diseases which have hitherto only been observed in man. Experience has, however taught us that it is not a matter of indifference what species of animal is employed for the experiment, and that the method by which the inoculation is performed has the greatest influence on the success of the experiment. . . .

All instruments employed in infection experiments must, of course, be subjected to trustworthy disinfection which according to my experience in this sort of work is only to be obtained by prolonged heating at 150° C. and above. One often reads that disinfection was accomplished by the aid of alcohol, carbolic acid, and the like, but the experiments on the action of various disinfectants on the spores of *Bacillus anthracis* which are described elsewhere show how untrustworthy these substances are. . . .

There is still one indispensable condition attached to all experiments on infection, viz., that no reliance should be placed on one experiment, and that the requisite control experiments should never be omitted. How often one meets with the statement that some suspected substance or fluid had been inoculated into an animal, or injected subcutaneously; that the animal fell ill, and possibly died, and that this fatal result was clearly a direct result of the inoculation, and that the illness was an example of the affection in question. And yet it is quite evident that a single such experiment is as good as useless. For in the first place, it must be shown that this solitary result was neither a mistake nor an accident, and that the inoculation can produce in the animals experimented upon in every case, or in a very large majority of cases, the disease or death, so that every accidental circumstance may be excluded. A further point, and one on which I lay special stress, seeing how often it is omitted, is the necessity of first making certain that one has to do with a really infective material. The fact that a material when injected subcutaneously, or into a vein, or into the abdominal cavity or elsewhere, causes a pathogenic effect, does not in the least show that this material possesses infective power. . . . Only when it can be shown that a disease is successfully communicated from one individual to another by such a small quantity of the infective material that to have produced the disease it must have multiplied in the body, can such a material be regarded as infective. From this it follows that if anyone wishes to know for certain whether he is experimenting with an infective material he cannot possibly remain satisfied with one experiment, but must carry out a more or less extensive and continuous series of inoculations from one animal to a second, from that to a third and so on, before he can get rid of the just objection that he is only dealing with the symptoms of simple poisoning and not with those of an infective disease.

§ *Pure Cultivations*

After the presence of pathogenic organisms in the body has been definitely ascertained, as well as their capability of multiplying in the tissues, and their communicability from one individual to another, there yet remains a most interesting and most important hygienic problem, namely, the demonstration of the conditions of their growth. It has already been shown at the beginning of this paper that this problem is only to be solved by the aid of pure cultivations of the microorganisms, and it is no exaggeration to say that pure cultivations are the crux of all researches into infective diseases. . . . The essential principles of pure cultivation as it is practised may now be condensed as follows.

A sterile nutrient fluid is placed in a disinfected glass vessel, which is plugged 'fungus-tight' with disinfected cotton wool, and then this fluid is inoculated with the material containing the microorganisms of which a pure culture is to be obtained. If growth occurs in these first flasks, then further inoculation is performed from these into a second series of similarly prepared vessels by means of a disinfected instrument. In fact it is almost exactly the same process as in transmitting an infective disease from one animal to another.

Obviously, various precautions are employed in these methods, the first of which is to see that the cultivation vessel is really disinfected. . . . The second precaution must be to see that the wool plug really fits so closely as to exclude all fungi. . . . Thirdly, the nutrient fluid must be of suitable composition, and thoroughly sterilized. . . .

Fourthly, the substance to be inoculated must contain only the microorganism of which a pure cultivation is required and no other, for if there is the slightest contamination of the infective material with a more rapidly growing form of microorganism than that which one desires to cultivate, one cannot, as Buchner has very strikingly shown, possibly succeed in getting the desired pure cultivation. . . . Fifthly, precautions must be taken that no spores of extraneous organisms from the air fall into the culture fluid while the first inoculation, and indeed while every subsequent inoculation, is being made. This is a risk which no experimenter can ever protect his pure cultures from with absolute certainty. Even if he takes out the protecting wool plug only for an extremely short time, even though the early cultivations are successful, the probability increases with each further inoculation that a contamination will occur. . . .

I have abandoned the principles on which pure cultures have hitherto been conducted, and have struck out on a new path, to which I was led by a simple observation, which anyone can repeat. If a boiled potato is divided and then the cut surface exposed to the air for a few hours, and then placed in a moist chamber (as, for instance, on a plate under a bell jar lined with wet filter paper) so as to prevent drying, there will be found by the second or third day (according to the temperature of the room) on the surface of the potato numerous and very varied droplets, almost all of which appear to differ from each other. A few of these droplets are white and porcellanous, while others are yellow, brown, grey, or reddish; and while some appear like a flattened out drop of water, others are hemispeherical or warty. All grow more or less rapidly, and between them appears the mycelium of the higher fungi; later the solitary droplets become fused together and soon marked decomposition of the potato occurs. If a specimen is taken from each of these droplets so long as they remain distinctly isolated from each other, and is examined by drying and staining a layer of it on a cover glass, it will be seen that each is composed of a perfectly definite kind of microorganism. One, for example, will show enormous micrococci, another very minute ones, a third may show micrococci arranged in chains while other colonies, especially those which spread out flat like a membrane, are composed of bacilli of various size and arrangement. . . . The source of all these different organisms will not long remain a matter of doubt if another potato is taken, and peeled with a previously heated knife, so that none of the skin may remain which might contain, at least in the earth clinging to it, spores of bacilli which had not been killed by the brief boiling. It must not be exposed to the air, but kept in a disinfected vessel which is plugged with wool, under which circumstances it will be found that no droplets appear, no organisms settle on it, and consequently it remains unaltered, until after several weeks it becomes dried up. That the organisms which developed as small droplike colonies on the first potato fell on it from the air is obvious, and indeed one often finds a small particle of dust or thread in the centre of the small colony which has clearly served as a carrier of the organisms, whether as dry but still living bacteria, as spores, or as yeast cells. . . .

The question now arises, what do we learn from this observation of these colonies growing on potatoes? We learn this most striking fact, that with a few exceptions, every droplet or colony is a pure culture, and remains so until by growth it pushes into the territory of a neighbour, and the individuals of each colony mingle. . . . If an equally broad surface of a nutrient fluid, instead of the potato had been exposed to the influence of the air, numerous organisms would without doubt have fallen into it, indeed approximately as many kinds as in the case of the potato, but their development would have proceeded very differently. The motile bacteria would have dispersed themselves rapidly throughout the fluid, and would have become mixed with the immobile ones, which at first develop to some extent in small floating colonies. . . . To sum up: the whole fluid would from the beginning afford on microscopical examination a picture of a confused mixture of different forms and never even in the remotest sense of the word could be called a pure cultivation. In what lies the marked difference between the soil which is offered by the potato and by the fluid respectively? It only consists in this, that the former is a solid soil and prevents the different kinds of organisms (even those which are motile) from mixing with one another, whilst with regard to the latter, the fluid substratum, there is no possibility of the different species remaining separate from one another.

It becomes important to utilize further the advantages which a solid cultivation soil offers for pure cultivations. . . . I devoted my attention to discover how well-known and new nutrient solutions could be converted from the fluid into the solid condition; and I found the best way of accomplishing this was to mix gelatine with the nutrient liquid. . . .

The mixture of nutrient fluid and gelatine which I shall call 'nutrient jelly' is prepared in the following way: gelatine is soaked in distilled water and then dissolved by heat. To it is added the nutrient fluid in such quantity that the mixture shall contain in definite proportions the necessary quantities of gelatine and nutritive material. I have found the most convenient amount of gelatine in the nutrient-gelatine mixture to be about $2\frac{1}{2}$ to 3 per cent. . . .

The peculiarity of my method is that it supplies a firm, and where possible a transparent pabulum; that its composition can be varied to any extent, and suited to the organism under observation; that all precautions against the possibility of after-contamination are rendered superfluous; that subsequent cultivation can be carried out by a larger number of single cultures, of which, of course, only those cultures which remain pure are employed for further cultivation; and that finally, a constant control over the state of the culture can be obtained by the use of the microscope. In almost all these points my method differs from those hitherto employed, and especially also from the former attempts at cultivation with potatoes and isinglass referred to above.

¶ *The Aetiology of Tuberculosis*

Vellemin's discovery that tuberculosis is transmissible to animals has, as is well known, found varied confirmation, but also apparently well-grounded opposition, so that it remained undecided until a few years ago whether tuberculosis is or is not an infectious disease. Since then, however, inoculations into the anterior ocular chamber, first performed by Cohnheim and Salomonsen, and later by Tappeiner and others have established the transmissibility of tuberculosis beyond any doubt, and in future tuberculosis must be classed as an infectious disease.

*

There have been repeated attempts to fathom the nature of tuberculosis, but thus far without success. The so frequently successful staining methods for the demonstration of pathogenic microorganisms have failed in regard to this disease, and to date, the experiments designed to isolate and cultivate a tubercle virus cannot be considered successful, so that Cohnheim, in the recently published and newest edition of his lectures on general pathology had to designate 'the direct demonstration of the tuberculosis virus as a still unsolved problem'.

In my studies on tuberculosis I first used the known methods without elucidating the nature of the disease. But by reasons of several incidental observations I was prompted to abandon these methods and to follow other paths which finally led to positive results.

The aim of the study had to be directed first toward the demonstration of some kind of parasitic forms, which are foreign to the body and which might possibly be interpreted as the cause of the disease. This demonstration became successful, indeed, by means of a certain staining process, which disclosed characteristic and heretofore unknown bacteria in all tuberculous organs.

*

In several respects the bacteria made visible by this process exhibit a characteristic behaviour. They are rod-shaped, and they belong to the group of bacilli. They are very thin and one-fourth to one-half as long as the diameter of a red blood corpuscle, although they may sometimes reach a greater length – up to the full diameter of an erythrocyte. In shape and size they bear a striking similarity to leprosy bacilli. They are differentiated from the latter by being a bit more slender and by having tapered ends. Further, leprosy bacilli are stained by Weigert's nuclear stain, while the tubercle bacilli are not. Wherever the tuberculous process is in recent evolution and is rapidly progressing, the bacilli are present in large quantities; they usually form, then, densely bunched and frequently small braided groups, often intracellular; and they present at times the same picture as leprosy bacilli accumulated in cells. In addition, numerous free bacilli are found.

As soon as the height of tubercle-development is passed the bacilli become rarer, and occur only in small groups or quite singly, in the margin of the tuberculous forms and side by side with weakly stained and sometimes hardly recognizable bacilli which are presumably dying or dead. Finally, they may disappear completely; but they are but seldom entirely absent and if so, only in such places in which the tuberculous process has come to a standstill.

Under certain conditions to be mentioned later the bacilli form spores even in the animal body. Individual bacilli contain several, usually two to four spores, oval in shape, and distributed at even intervals along the entire length of the bacillus.

*

To prove that tuberculosis is a parasitic disease, that it is caused by the invasion of bacilli and that it is conditioned primarily by the growth and multiplication of the bacilli, it was necessary to isolate the bacilli from the body; to grow them in pure culture until they were freed from any disease-product of the animal organism which might adhere to them; and by administering the isolated bacilli to animals, to reproduce the morbid condition, which, as known, is obtained by inoculation with spontaneously developed tuberculous material.

*

Up to this point it was established by my studies that the occurrence of characteristic bacilli is regularly coincidental with tuberculosis and that these bacilli can be obtained and isolated in pure cultures from tuberculous organs. It remained to answer the important question whether the isolated bacilli, when again introduced into the animal body, are capable of reproducing the morbid process of tuberculosis.

§ *First Experiment*

Of six recently bought guinea pigs which were kept in the same cage, four were inoculated on the abdomen with bacillary culture material derived from human lungs with miliary tubercles and grown in five transfers for fifty-four days. Two animals remained uninoculated. In the inoculated animals the inguinal lymph nodes swelled after fourteen days, the site of inoculation changed into an ulcer, and the animals became emaciated. After thirty-two days one of the inoculated animals died, and after thirty-five days the rest were killed. The inoculated guinea pigs, the one that had died spontaneously, as well as the three killed ones, showed far-advanced tuberculosis of the spleen, liver, and lungs; the inguinal nodes were much swollen and caseated; the bronchial lymph nodes were but little swollen. The two non-inoculated animals displayed no trace of tuberculosis in lungs, liver, or spleen.

*

All these facts, taken together, justify the statement that the bacilli present in tuberculosis substances are not only coincident with the tuberculous process, but are the cause of the process, and that we have in the bacilli the real tuberculous virus.

———

LOUIS PASTEUR
1822–95

IMMUNITY TO RABIES IS SUCCESSFULLY
PRODUCED

PASTEUR was born in Dôle, Jura, where his father was a tanner. He received his scientific education at Besançon and at the Sorbonne in Paris. His first research after he received his doctorate in 1848 was an important study of the crystallographic forms of the tartrates. In 1854 he was appointed professor and dean of the faculty of science at Lille, where he studied alcoholic fermentation, and established that it was caused by minute organisms. His interest was thus aroused in the old problem of spontaneous generation.

In about 1859, Félix Poucher had revived that controversy by the announcement of a series of experiments which 'proved' that microbes could appear in a neutral broth. Pasteur's paper of 1862 ('The Organized Corpuscles which Exist in the Atmosphere') effectively answered Pouchet but when, in 1870, an English doctor, Bastian, again revived the old idea, Pouchet resumed his campaign. Pasteur, this time supported by John Tyndall (1820–93), an English scientist, put an effective end to the controversy. Out of the discussion it came to be realized that, as Koch points out in the preceding selection, effective sterilization involves prolonged heating at temperatures of 150° C. and above – a procedure requiring an instrument made in the days of Robert Boyle, known as Papin's digestor. This instrument has a much more familiar name today, for it is none other than the pressure cooker used in many kitchens to speed up the preparation of a meal. Incidentally, it is of interest to note that the question of spontaneous generation had, in effect, already been settled by another Frenchman some sixty years before. Nicolas Appert, a confectioner, discovered some time after 1800 that food packed in a glass bottle, boiled for some time, and closed while hot, would remain edible for a long period, a fact the significance of which Pouchet overlooked.

Pasteur's researches into the phenomena of fermentation and decay were often directed toward solving a specific problem presented to him by brewers, dairymen, vintners, silk growers – indeed, any sector of the agricultural processing industries. His stimulus was almost always a practical problem the solution of which was of economic importance. His account of his method of producing immunity to rabies, which was developed at first to be applied directly to dogs and was offered, in an emergency, to a young boy who had been bitten by a mad dog, resembles the matter-of-fact, practical work of Jenner; but Pasteur succeeding in developing scientific principles in all his work. His empiricism was a means to an end: to establish once and for all that disease, both human and animal, could be traced to microorganisms, some of which could be found 'living on the motes in a sunbeam'.

Pasteur's theories on fermentation led him into controversy with the great German physiologist and chemist Justus von Liebig (1803–73). Pasteur's emphasis was on the activity of *living* organisms; Liebig was preoccupied with chemical relationships. The details of the controversy are interesting but not important for our present purpose, but the occurrence of the controversy is very significant because of the tremendous impetus it gave to research.

The selection from Pasteur's researches on vaccination against rabies by means of the attenuated virus of the disease is taken from *Recent Essays on Bacteria in Relation to Disease*, edited by W. W. Cheyne and published in 1886 by the New Sydenham Society.

❡ A Method by which the Development of Rabies after a Bite may be Prevented

A real progress in the study of rabies was marked, without any doubt, by the papers in which I announced, in my own name and in the name of my fellow-workers, a prophylactic method; but the progress was scientific rather than practical. Accidents were liable to occur in its application. Of twenty dogs treated, I could not undertake to render more than fifteen or sixteen refractory to rabies.

Further, it was desirable, at the end of the treatment, to inoculate with a very virulent virus – a control virus – in order to confirm and reinforce the refractory condition. More than this, prudence demanded that the dogs should be kept under observation during a period longer than the period of incubation of the disease produced by the direct inoculation of this last virus. Therefore, in order to be quite sure that the refractory state had been produced, it was sometimes necessary to wait three or four months. The application of the method would have been very much limited by these troublesome conditions.

Finally, the method did not lend itself easily to the immediate treatment rendered necessary by the accidental and unforeseen way in which bites are inflicted by rabid animals.

It was necessary, therefore, to discover, if possible, a more rapid method, and yet one, I would venture to say, capable of affording perfect security to dogs. Otherwise who would have the temerity, before this progress had been achieved, to make any experiment on man?

After making almost innumerable experiments, I have discovered a prophylactic method which is practical and prompt, and which has already in dogs afforded me results sufficiently numerous, certain, and successful, to warrant my having confidence in its general applicability to all animals, and even to man himself.

This method depends essentially on the following facts:

The inoculation under the *dura mater*, after trephining, of the infective spinal cord of a dog suffering from ordinary rabies (*rage des rues*), always produces rabies in rabbits after a period of incubation having a mean duration of about fifteen days.

If, by the above method of inoculation, the virus of the first rabbit is passed into a second, and that of the second into a third, and so on, in series, a more and more striking tendency is soon manifested towards a diminution of the duration of the incubation period of rabies in the rabbits successively inoculated.

After passing twenty or twenty-five times from rabbit to rabbit, inoculation periods of eight days are met with, and continue for another interval, during which the virus is passed twenty or twenty-five times from rabbit to rabbit. Then an incubation period of seven days is reached, which is encountered with striking regularity throughout a new series extending as far as the ninetieth animal. This at least is the number which I have reached at the present time, and the most that can be said is that a slight tendency is manifested towards an incubation period of a little less than seven days.

Experiments of this class, begun in November 1882, have now lasted for three years without any break in the continuity of the series, and without our ever being obliged to have recourse to any other virus than that of the rabbits successively dead of rabies. Consequently, nothing is easier than to have constantly at our disposal, over considerable intervals of time, a virus of rabies, quite pure, and always quite or very nearly identical. This is the central fact in the practical application of the method.

The virus of rabies at a constant degree of virulence is contained in the spinal cords of these rabbits throughout their whole extent.

If portions, a few centimetres long, are removed from these spinal cords with every possible precaution to preserve their purity, and are then suspended in dry air, the virulence slowly disappears, until at last it entirely vanishes. The time within which this extinction of virulence is brought about varies a little with the thickness of the morsels of spinal cord, but chiefly with the external temperature. The lower the temperature the longer is the virulence preserved. These results form the central scientific point in the method.

These facts being established, a dog may be rendered refractory to rabies in a relatively short time in the following way:

Every day morsels of fresh infective spinal cord from a rabbit which has died of rabies developed after an incubation period of seven days, are suspended in a series of flasks, the air in which is kept dry by placing fragments of potash at the bottom of the flask. Every day also a dog is inoculated under the skin with a Pravaz' syringe full of sterilized broth, in which a small fragment of one of the spinal cords has been broken up, commencing with a spinal cord far enough removed in order of time from the day of the operation to render it certain that the cord was not at all virulent. (This date had been ascertained by previous experiments.) On the following days the same operation is performed with more recent cords, separated from each other by an interval of two days, until at last a very virulent cord, which has only been in the flask for two days, is used.

The dog has now been rendered refractory to rabies. It may be inoculated with the virus of rabies under the skin, or even after trephining, on the surface of the brain, without any subsequent development of rabies.

Never having once failed when using this method, I had in my possession fifty dogs, of all ages and of every race, refractory to rabies, when three individuals from Alsace unexpectedly presented themselves at my laboratory, on Monday the 6th of last July.

Théodore Vone, grocer, of Meissengott, near Schlestadt,

bitten in the arm, July 4th, by his own dog, which had gone mad.

Joseph Meister, aged nine years, also bitten on July 4th, at eight o'clock in the morning, by the same dog. This child had been knocked over by the dog and presented numerous bites, on the hands, legs, and thighs, some of them so deep as to render walking difficult. The principal bites had been cauterized at eight o'clock in the evening of July 4th, only twelve hours after the accident, with phenic acid, by Dr Weber, of Villé.

The third person, who had not been bitten, was the mother of little Joseph Meister.

At the examination of the dog, after its death by the hand of its master, the stomach was found full of hay, straw, and scraps of wood. The dog was certainly rabid. Joseph Meister had been pulled out from under him covered with foam and blood.

M. Vone had some severe contusions on the arm, but he assured me that his shirt had not been pierced by the dog's fangs. As he had nothing to fear, I told him that he could return to Alsace the same day, which he did, But I kept young Meister and his mother with me.

The weekly meeting of the Académie des Sciences took place on July 6th. At it I met our colleague Dr Vulpian, to whom I related what had just happened. M. Vulpian, and Dr Grancher, Professor in the Faculté de Médecine, had the goodness to come and see little Joseph Meister at once, and to take note of the condition and the number of his wounds. There were no less than fourteen.

The opinion of our learned colleague, and of Dr Grancher, was that, owing to the severity and the number of the bites, Joseph Meister was almost certain to take rabies. I then communicated to M. Vulpian and to M. Grancher the new results which I had obtained from the study of rabies since the address which I had given at Copenhagen a year earlier.

The death of this child appearing to be inevitable, I

decided, not without lively and sore anxiety, as may well be believed, to try upon Joseph Meister the method which I had found constantly successful with dogs.

My fifty dogs, it is true, had not been bitten before I brought them into the condition of being refractory to rabies; but I knew that that circumstance might be left out of my calculations, because I had previously rendered a large number of dogs refractory to rabies after they had been bitten. I have this year given the members of the Commission de la Rage evidence of this new and important advance.

Consequently, on July 6th, at 8 o'clock in the evening, sixty hours after the bites on July 4th, and in the presence of Drs Vulpian and Grancher, young Meister was inoculated under a fold of skin raised in the right hypochondrium, with half a Pravaz' syringeful of the spinal cord of a rabbit, which had died of rabies on June 21st. It had been preserved since then, that is to say, fifteen days, in a flask of dry air.

On the following days fresh inoculations were made. I thus made thirteen inoculations, and prolonged the treatment to ten days. I shall say later on that a smaller number of inoculations would have been sufficient. But it will be understood how, in the first attempt, I would act with a very special circumspection.

The days following, new inoculations were made, always in the hypochondrial region according to the conditions which I give in the following table:

July	Time	Cord taken	Dried for
7	9 a.m.	June 23	14 days
7	6 p.m.	June 25	12 days
8	9 a.m.	June 27	11 days
8	6 p.m.	June 29	9 days
9	11 a.m.	July 1	8 days
10	11 a.m.	July 3	7 days
11	11 a.m.	July 5	6 days
12	11 a.m.	July 7	5 days

13	11 a.m.	July 9	4 days
14	11 a.m.	July 11	3 days
15	11 a.m.	July 13	2 days
16	11 a.m.	July 15	1 day

In order to follow the condition as to virulence of the spinal cords, two fresh rabbits were inoculated, by trephining, with the various spinal cords employed.

Observation of these rabbits enabled us to ascertain that the spinal cords of July 6th, 7th, 8th, 9th, 10th, were not virulent, for they did not render the rabbits rabid; the spinal cords of July 11th, 12th, 14th, 15th, 16th, were all virulent, and the virulent material was present in larger and larger proportion. Rabies appeared after an incubation of seven days in the rabbits of July 15th and 16th; after eight days in those of the 12th and 14th; after fifteen days in those of July 11th.

On the last days, therefore, I had inoculated Joseph Meister with the most virulent virus of rabies, that, namely of the dog, reinforced by passing a great number of times from rabbit to rabbit, a virus which produced rabies after seven days' incubation in these animals, after eight or ten days in dogs.

When the condition of immunity has been attained, the most virulent virus can be inoculated, in considerable quantity, without ill effects. It has always seemed to me that the only possible effect of this must be to make immunity more assured.

Joseph Meister, therefore, has escaped, not only the rabies which would have been caused by the bites he received, but also the rabies with which I have inoculated him in order to test the immunity produced by the treatment, a rabies more virulent than ordinary canine rabies.

The final inoculation with very virulent virus has this further advantage, that it puts a period to the apprehensions which arise as to the consequences of the bites. If rabies could occur it would declare itself more quickly after a more virulent virus than after the virus of the bites. Since the middle of August I have looked forward with confidence to the future good health of Joseph Meister. At the present time, three months and three weeks having elapsed since the accident, his state of health leaves nothing to be desired.

What interpretation is to be given to this new method which I have just made known, of preventing rabies after bites? I have not at the present moment any intention of treating this question in a complete manner. I wish to confine myself to certain preliminary details essential to the comprehension of the significance of the experiments, which I am continuing, in order to adopt eventually the best of the various possible interpretations.

Bearing in mind the methods of progressively attenuating various lethal virus, and the prophylaxis in that way attained, and admitting also the influence of the air in bringing about this attenuation the first explanation to account for the effects of this method which suggests itself is, that while the morsels of spinal cord are left in contact with the dry air, the intensity of their virulence is progressively diminished, until it is entirely abolished.

This reflection would lead us to believe that the prophylactic method now described depended upon the employment at first of a virus without any appreciable activity, then of feeble intensity, and then of more and more virulence.

I will show that facts do not lend support to this view. I will prove that the increase in the length of the period of incubation of the rabies, each day, communicated to the rabbits, as I have just described, in order to test the virulence of the spinal-cords dried on contact with air, is an effect of a diminution of the quantity of the virus of rabies contained in the spinal cords, and not an effect of a diminution of its virulence. . . .

*

In conclusion I need not say that perhaps the most important of the problems to be solved at the present time is that of the interval which may be allowed between the occurrence of the bites and the commencement of the treatment. In the case of Joseph Meister this interval was two days and a half. But it must be expected to be often much longer.

On Tuesday last, October 20th, with the kind assistance of MM. Vulpian and Grancher, I commenced to treat a youth of fifteen years, bitten six full days before, on both hands, under exceptionally grave circumstances. I will promptly make known to the academy the result of this new trial.

JOSEPH LISTER

1827–1913

ANTISEPTIC PRINCIPLES ARE ESTABLISHED
FOR THE PRACTICE OF SURGERY

IT may seem strange that the work of Redi and Spallan-zani (p. 73 and p. 86) failed to suggest earlier a possible connexion between microbes 'in the air' and the appalling mortality in surgical wards. The history of science can provide many examples of the failure to appreciate the significance of such observations until the general intel-lectual climate becomes propitious. Not until the second quarter of the nineteenth century did some medical men begin to plead for greater cleanliness in the operating theatre. In Boston in 1843 Oliver Wendell Holmes, anat-omist and poet, agitated for improved conditions in maternity cases. Semmelweiss, an Austrian doctor, showed a few years later that he could reduce the number of deaths of mothers by forbidding his students from com-ing directly from the dissecting rooms to the maternity wards.

Joseph Lister, later Lord Lister, was the son of a wine merchant, an enthusiastic amateur scientist who perfected the achromatic lens and improved the compound micro-scope. He was born in London and studied medicine at University College. After a period in Edinburgh he was appointed Regius Professor of Surgery in Glasgow in 1860, and was subsequently Professor of Surgery in Edin-burgh. In 1877 he returned to London as Professor of Surgery at King's College Hospital. Lister realized that fermentation and suppuration were essentially similar processes. His familiarity with Pasteur's work led him to the conclusion that microorganisms carried in the air were responsible for suppuration. In 1867 after two years of experimentation he announced his discovery that carbolic acid applied to wounds would prevent suppuration.

Antisepsis, the control of infection by destruction of bacteria, was one of the greatest of surgical advances. Lister himself appreciated, however, that asepsis, the total exclusion of microorganisms, was the ideal. In 1870 he introduced a carbolic spray which was employed during operations. This procedure, criticized by Koch, was gradually abandoned as techniques of sterilization were improved and the attainment of something approaching asepsis became a practical possibility.

Lister left his mark on the whole field of surgery. He was honoured by governments and learned societies throughout the world. He was commemorated by the foundation, in 1891, of the Lister Institute of Preventive Medicine, modelled on the Pasteur Institute in Paris.

The reading is taken from Lister's paper *On the Antiseptic Principle in the Practice of Surgery* read before the British Medical Association in 1867 and published the same year in the *British Medical Journal*.

———

In the course of an extended investigation into the nature of inflammation, and the healthy and morbid conditions of the blood in relation to it, I arrived, several years ago, at the conclusion that the essential cause of suppuration in wounds is decomposition, brought about by the influence of the atmosphere upon blood or serum retained within them, and, in the case of contused wounds, upon portions of tissue destroyed by the violence of the injury.

To prevent the occurrence of suppuration, with all its attendant risks, was an object manifestly desirable; but till lately apparently unattainable, since it seemed hopeless to attempt to exclude the oxygen, which was universally regarded as the agent by which putrefaction was effected. But when it had been shown by the researches of Pasteur that the septic property of the atmosphere depended, not on the oxygen or any gaseous constituent, but on minute organisms suspended in it, which owed their energy to their vitality, it occurred to me that decomposition in the injured part might be avoided without excluding the air, by applying as a dressing some material capable of destroying the life of the floating particles.

Upon this principle I have based a practice of which I will now attempt to give a short account.

The material which I have employed is carbolic or phenic acid, a volatile organic compound which appears to exercise a peculiarly destructive influence upon low forms of life, and hence is the most powerful antiseptic with which we are at present acquainted.

The first class of cases to which I applied it was that of compound fractures, in which the effects of decomposition in the injured part were especially striking and pernicious. The results have been such as to establish conclusively the great principle, that *all the local inflammatory mischief and general febrile disturbance which follow severe injuries are due to the irritating and poisoning influence of decomposing blood or sloughs.* For these evils are entirely avoided by the antiseptic treatment, so that limbs which otherwise would be unhesitatingly condemned to amputation may be retained with confidence of the best results.

In conducting the treatment, the first object must be the destruction of any septic germs which may have been introduced into the wound, either at the moment of the accident or during the time which has since elapsed. This is done by introducing the acid of full strength into all accessible recesses of the wound by means of a piece of rag held in dressing-forceps and dipped in the liquid. This I did not venture to do in the earlier cases; but experience has shown that the compound which carbolic acid forms with the blood, and also any portions of tissue killed by its caustic action, including even parts of the bone, are disposed of by absorption and organization, provided they are afterwards kept from decomposing. We are thus enabled to employ the antiseptic treatment efficiently at a period after the occurrence of the injury at which it would otherwise probably fail. Thus I have now under my care in the Glasgow Infirmary a boy who was admitted with compound fracture of the leg as late as eight and a half hours after the accident, in whom nevertheless all local and constitutional disturbance was avoided by means of carbolic acid, and the bones were soundly united five weeks after his admission.

The next object to be kept in view is to guard effectually against the spreading of decomposition into the wound along the stream of blood and serum which oozes out during the first few days after the accident when the acid originally applied has been washed out, or dissipated by absorption and evaporation. This part of the treatment has been greatly improved during the last few weeks. The method which I have hitherto published consisted in the application of a piece of lint dipped in the acid, overlapping the sound skin to some extent, and covered with a tin cap, which was daily raised in order to touch the surface of the lint with the antiseptic. This method certainly succeeded well with wounds of moderate size; and, indeed, I may say that in all the many cases of this kind which have been so treated by myself or my house surgeons, not a single failure has occurred. When, however, the wound is very large, the flow of blood and serum is so profuse, especially during the first twenty-four hours, that the antiseptic application cannot prevent the spread of decomposition into the interior unless it overlaps the sound skin for a very considerable distance, and this was inadmissible by the method described above, on account of the extensive sloughing of the surface of the cutis which it would involve. This difficulty has, however, been overcome by employing a paste composed of common whitening (carbonate of lime) mixed with a solution of one part of carbolic acid in four parts of boiled linseed oil, so as to form a firm putty. This application contains the acid in too dilute a form to excoriate the skin, which it may be made to cover to any extent that may be thought desirable, while its substance serves as a reservoir of the antiseptic material. So long as any discharge continues, the paste should be changed daily; and, in order to prevent the chance of mischief occurring during the process, a piece of rag dipped in the solution of carbolic acid in oil is put on next the skin, and maintained there permanently, care being taken to avoid raising it along with the putty. This rag is always kept in an antiseptic condition from contact with the paste above it, and destroys any germs that may fall upon it during the short time that should alone be allowed to pass in the changing of the dressing. The putty should be in a layer about a quarter of an inch thick, and may be advantageously applied rolled out between two pieces of thin calico, which maintain it in the form of a continuous sheet, that may be wrapped in a moment round the whole circumference of a limb, if this be thought desirable, while the putty is prevented by the calico from sticking to the rag which is next the skin. When all discharge has ceased, the use of the paste is discontinued, but the original rag is left adhering to the skin till healing by scabbing is supposed to be complete. I have at present in the hospital a man with severe compound fracture of both bones of the left leg, caused by direct violence, who, after the cessation of the sanious discharge under the use of the paste, without a drop of pus appearing, has been treated for the last two weeks exactly as if the fracture were a simple one. During this time the rag, adhering by means of a crust of inspissated blood collected beneath it, has continued perfectly dry, and it will be left untouched till the usual period for removing the splints in a simple fracture, when we may fairly expect to find a sound cicatrix beneath it.

We cannot, however, always calculate on so perfect a result as this. More or less pus may appear after the lapse of the first week; and the larger the wound the more likely is this to happen. And here I would desire earnestly to enforce the necessity of persevering with the antiseptic application, in spite of the appearance of suppuration, so long as other symptoms are favourable. The surgeon is extremely apt to suppose that any suppuration is an indication that the antiseptic treatment has failed, and that poulticing or water dressing should be resorted to. But such a course would in many cases sacrifice a limb or a life. I cannot, however, expect my professional brethren to follow my advice blindly in such a matter, and therefore I feel it necessary to place before them, as shortly as I can, some pathological principles, intimately connected not only with the point we are immediately considering, but with the whole subject of this paper.

If a perfectly healthy granulating sore be well washed and covered with a plate of clean metal, such as block-tin, fitting its surface pretty accurately, and overlapping the surrounding skin an inch or so in every direction, and retained in position by adhesive plaster and a bandage, it will be found, on removing it after twenty-four or forty-eight hours, that little or nothing that can be called pus is present, merely a little transparent fluid, while at the same time there is an entire absence of the unpleasant odour invariably perceived when water dressing is changed. Here the clean metallic surface presenting no recesses, like those of porous lint, for the septic germs to develop in, the fluid exuding from the surface of the granulations has flowed away undecomposed, and the result is absence of suppuration. This simple experiment illustrates the important fact, that granulations have no inherent tendency to form pus, but do so only when subjected to a preternatural stimulus. Further, it shows that the mere contact of a foreign body does not of itself stimulate granulations to suppurate; whereas the presence of decomposing organic matter does. These truths are even more strikingly exemplified by the fact, which I have elsewhere recorded, that a piece of dead bone, free from decomposition, may not only fail to induce the granulations around it to suppurate, but may actually be absorbed by them; whereas a bit of dead bone soaked with putrid pus infallibly induces suppuration in its vicinity.

Another instructive experiment is to dress a granulating sore with some of the putty above described, overlapping the sound skin extensively, when we find in the course of twenty-four hours that pus has been produced by the sore, although the application has been perfectly antiseptic; and, indeed, the larger the amount of carbolic acid in the paste the greater is the quantity of pus formed, provided we avoid such a proportion as would act as a caustic. The carbolic acid, though it prevents decomposition, induces suppuration – obviously by acting as a chemical stimulus; and we may safely infer that putrescent organic materials (which we know to be chemically acrid) operate in the same way.

In so far, then, carbolic acid and decomposing substances are alike – namely, that they induce suppuration by chemical stimulation, as distinguished from what may be termed simple inflammatory suppuration, such as that in which ordinary abscesses originate, where the pus appears to be formed in consequence of an excited action of the nerves, independently of any other stimulus. There is, however, this enormous difference between the effects of carbolic acid and those of decomposition – viz. that carbolic acid stimulates only the surface to which it is first applied, and every drop of discharge that forms weakens the stimulant by diluting it. But decomposition is a self-propagating and self-aggravating poison; and if it occurs at the surface of a severely injured limb, it will spread into all its recesses so far as any extravasated blood or shreds of dead tissue may extend, and, lying in these recesses, it will become from hour to hour more acrid till it acquires the energy of a caustic, sufficient to destroy the vitality of any tissues naturally weak from inferior vascular supply, or weakened by the injury they sustained in the accident.

Hence it is easy to understand how, when a wound is

very large, the crust beneath the rag may prove here and there insufficient to protect the raw surface from the stimulating influence of the carbolic acid in the putty, and the result will be, first, the conversion of the tissues so acted on into granulations, and subsequently the formation of more or less pus. This, however, will be merely superficial, and will not interfere with the absorption and organization of extravasated blood or dead tissues in the interior; but, on the other hand, should decomposition set in before the internal parts have become securely consolidated, the most disastrous results may ensue.

I left behind me in Glasgow a boy, thirteen years of age, who between three or four weeks previously met with a most severe injury to the left arm, which he got entangled in a machine at a fair. There was a wound six inches long and three inches broad, and the skin was very extensively undermined beyond its limits, while the soft parts generally were so much lacerated that a pair of dressing-forceps introduced at the wound, and pushed directly inwards, appeared beneath the skin at the opposite aspect of the limb. From this wound several tags of muscle were hanging, and among them there was one consisting of about three inches of the triceps in almost its entire thickness; while the lower fragment of the bone, which was broken high up, was protruding four and a half inches, stripped of muscle, the skin being tucked in under it. Without the assistance of the antiseptic treatment, I should certainly have thought of nothing else but amputation at the shoulder-joint; but as the radial pulse could be felt, and the fingers had sensation, I did not hesitate to try to save the limb, and adopted the plan of treatment above described, wrapping the arm from the shoulder to below the elbow in the antiseptic application, the whole interior of the wound, together with the protruding bone, having previously been freely treated with strong carbolic acid. About the tenth day the discharge, which up to that time had been only sanious and serous, showed a slight admixture of slimy pus, and this increased till, a few days before I left, it amounted to about three drachms in twenty-four hours. But the boy continued, as he had been after the second day, free from unfavourable symptoms, with pulse, tongue, appetite, and sleep natural, and strength increasing, while the limb remained, as it had been from the first, free from swelling, redness, or pain. I therefore persevered with the antiseptic dressing, and before I left, the discharge was already somewhat less, while the bone was becoming firm. I think it likely that in that boy's case I should have found merely a superficial sore had I taken off all the dressings at the end of three weeks, though, considering the extent of the injury, I thought it prudent to let the month expire before disturbing the rag next the skin. But I feel sure that if I had resorted to ordinary dressing when the pus first appeared, the progress of the case would have been exceedingly different.

The next class of cases to which I have applied the antiseptic treatment is that of abscesses. Here, also, the results have been extremely satisfactory, and in beautiful harmony with the pathological principles indicated above. The pyogenic membrane, like the granulations of a sore, which it resembles in nature, forms pus, not from any inherent disposition to do so, but only because it is subjected to some preternatural stimulation. In an ordinary abscess, whether acute or chronic, before it is opened, the stimulus which maintains the suppuration is derived from the presence of the pus pent up within the cavity. When a free opening is made in the ordinary way, this stimulus is got rid of; but the atmosphere gaining access to the contents, the potent stimulus of decomposition comes into operation, and pus is generated in greater abundance than before. But when the evacuation is effected on the antiseptic principle, the pyogenic membrane, freed from the influence of the former stimulus without the substitution of a new one, ceases to suppurate (like the granulations of a sore under metallic dressing), furnishing merely a trifling amount of clear serum, and, whether the opening be dependent or not, rapidly contracts and coalesces. At the same time any constitutional symptoms previously occasioned by the accumulation of the matter are got rid of without the slightest risk of the irritative fever or hectic hitherto so justly dreaded in dealing with large abscesses.

In order that the treatment may be satisfactory, the abscess must be seen before it has opened. Then, except in very rare and peculiar cases, there are no septic organisms in the contents, so that it is needless to introduce carbolic acid into the interior. Indeed, such a proceeding would be objectionable, as it would stimulate the pyogenic membrane to unnecessary suppuration. All that is necessary is to guard against the introduction of living atmospheric germs from without, at the same time that free opportunity is afforded for the escape of discharge from within.

I have so lately given elsewhere a detailed account of the method by which this is effected, that it is needless for me to enter into it at present, further than to say that the means employed are the same as those described above for the superficial dressing of compound fractures – namely, a piece of rag dipped in the solution of carbolic acid in oil, to serve as an antiseptic curtain, under cover of which the abscess is evacuated by free incision; and the antiseptic paste, to guard against decomposition occurring in the stream of pus that flows out beneath it : the dressing being changed daily till the sinus has closed.

The most remarkable results of this practice in a pathological point of view have been afforded by cases where the formation of pus depended upon disease of bone. Here the abscesses, instead of forming exceptions to the general class in the obstinacy of the suppuration, have resembled the rest in yielding in a few days only a trifling discharge; and frequently the production of pus has ceased from the moment of the evacuation of the original contents. Hence it appears that caries, when no longer labouring, as heretofore, under the irritation of decomposing matter, ceases to be an opprobrium of surgery, and recovers like other inflammatory affections. In the publication before alluded to, I have mentioned the case of a middle-aged man with psoas abscess depending on diseased bone, in whom the sinus finally closed after months of patient perseverance with the antiseptic treatment. Since that article was written I have had another instance of success, equally gratifying, but differing in the circumstances that the disease and the recovery were both more rapid in their course. The patient was a blacksmith who had suffered four and a half months before I saw him from symptoms of ulceration of cartilage in the left elbow. These had latterly increased in severity, so as to deprive him entirely of his night's rest and of appetite. I found the region of the elbow greatly swollen, and on careful examination discovered a fluctuation point at the outer aspect of the articulation. I opened it on the antiseptic principle, the incision evidently penetrating to the joint, giving exit to a few drachms of pus. The medical gentleman under whose care he was (Dr MacGregor of Glasgow) supervised the daily dressing with the carbolic-acid paste till the patient went to spend two or three weeks at the coast, when his wife was entrusted with it. Just two months after I opened the abscess he called to show me the limb, stating that the discharge had for at least two weeks been as little as it then was – a trifling moisture upon the paste, such as might be accounted for by the little sore caused by the incision. On applying a probe guarded with an antiseptic rag, I found that the sinus was soundly closed, while the limb was free from swelling or tenderness; and, although he had not attempted to exercise it much, the joint could already be moved through a considerable angle. Here the antiseptic principle had effected the restoration of a joint which on any other known system of treatment must have been excised.

Ordinary contused wounds are of course amenable to the same treatment as compounded fractures, which are a complicated variety of them. I will content myself with mentioning a single instance of this class of cases. In April last a volunteer was discharging a rifle, when it burst, and blew back the thumb with its metacarpal bone, so that it could be bent as on a hinge at the trapezial joint, which had evidently been opened, while all the soft parts between the metacarpal bones of the thumb and fore-finger were torn through. I need not insist before my present audience on the ugly character of such an injury. My house surgeon, Mr Hector Cameron, applied carbolic acid to the whole raw surface, and completed the dressing as if for compound fracture. The hand remained free from pain, redness, or swelling, and, with the exception of a shallow groove, all the wound consolidated without a drop of matter, so that if it had been a clean cut, it would have been regarded as a good example of primary union. The small granulating surface soon healed, and at present a linear cicatrix alone tells of the injury he had sustained, while his thumb has all its movement and his hand a firm grasp.

If the severest forms of contused and lacerated wounds heal thus kindly under the antiseptic treatment, it is obvious that its application to simple incised wounds must be merely a matter of detail. I have devoted a good deal of attention to this class, but I have not as yet pleased myself altogether with any of the methods I have employed. I am, however, prepared to go so far as to say that a solution of carbolic acid in twenty parts of water, while a mild and cleanly application, may be relied on for destroying any septic germs that may fall upon the wound during the performance of an operation; and also that for preventing the subsequent introduction of others, the paste above described, applied as for compound fractures, gives excellent results. Thus I have had a case of strangulated inguinal hernia, in which it was necessary to take away half a pound of thickened omentum, heal without any deep-seated suppuration or any tenderness of the sac or any fever; and amputations, including one immediately below the knee, have remained absolutely free from constitutional symptoms.

Further, I have found that when the antiseptic treatment is efficiently conducted, ligatures may be safely cut short and left to be disposed of by absorption or otherwise. Should this particular branch of the subject yield all that it promises, should it turn out on further trial that when the knot is applied on the antiseptic principle, we may calculate as securely as if it were absent on the occurrence of healing without any deep-seated suppuration; the deligation of main arteries in their continuity will be deprived of the two dangers that now attend it – namely, those of secondary haemorrhage and an unhealthy state of the wound. Further, it seems not unlikely that the present objection to tying an artery in the immediate vicinity of a large branch may be done away with; and that even the innominate, which has lately been the subject of an ingenious experiment by one of the Dublin surgeons on account of its well-known fatality under the ligature from secondary haemorrhage, may cease to have this unhappy character, when the tissues in the vicinity of the thread, instead of becoming softened through the influence of an irritating decomposing substance, are left at liberty to consolidate firmly near an unoffending though foreign body.

It would carry me far beyond the limited time which, by the rules of the Association, is alone at my disposal, were I to enter into the various applications of the antiseptic principle in the several special departments of surgery.

There is, however, one point more that I cannot but advert to – namely, the influence of this mode of treatment upon the general healthiness of a hospital. Previously to its introduction, the two large wards in which most of my cases of accident and of operation are treated were among the unhealthiest in the whole surgical division of the Glasgow Royal Infirmary, in consequence, apparently, of those wards being unfavourably placed with reference to the supply of fresh air; and I have felt ashamed, when recording the results of my practice, to have so often to allude to hospital gangrene or pyaemia. It was interesting, though melancholy, to observe that, whenever all, or nearly all, the beds contained cases with open sores, these grievous complications were pretty sure to show themselves, so that I came to welcome simple fractures, though in themselves of little interest either for myself or the students, because their presence diminished the proportion of open sores among the patients. But since the antiseptic treatment has been brought into full operation, and wounds and abscesses no longer poison the atmosphere with putrid exhalations, my wards, though in other respects under precisely the same circumstances as before, have completely changed their character; so that during the last nine months not a single instance of pyaemia, hospital gangrene, or erysipelas has occurred in them.

As there appears to be no doubt regarding the cause of this change, the importance of the fact can hardly be exaggerated.

———

SIR RONALD ROSS

1857–1932

THE DISCOVERY OF THE ROLE OF THE MOSQUITO IN THE TRANSMISSION OF MALARIA

RONALD ROSS was born in India, where his father was serving in the British Army. He was educated in England and after studying medicine at St Bartholomew's Hospital, was commissioned in the Indian Medical Service in 1881. For almost twenty years he carried out the routine duties of the Service, devoting his leisure hours and his leaves to research, for he was at first given neither official encouragement nor special facilities. He retired from the Indian Medical Service in 1899 and after a period as lecturer at the Liverpool School of Tropical Medicine, he returned to London. He was awarded the Nobel prize in medicine in 1902. His versatility was remarkable; he was a mathematician of no ordinary ability, a poet, a novelist, and a musician.

Proof of the role of an insect in the transmission of disease had been provided in 1877 when Sir Patrick Manson demonstrated the transmission of *filariasis* by culicine mosquitoes and Theobald Smith in 1893 proved that Texas cattle fever was transmitted by a tick. Alphonse Laveran had discovered the parasite of malaria in red blood corpuscles in 1880. The American, A. F. A. King, suggested in 1883 that malaria was probably transmitted by mosquitoes and Manson elaborated this hypothesis, but it was not widely accepted and the validity of Laveran's observations was disputed. Ross himself in 1893 maintained that the suggested parasites were no more than post-mortem changes in red blood cells. On leave in London the following year Ross was shown the parasites by Manson who convinced him they existed and that the theory that they could be transmitted by mosquitoes deserved investigation. Returning to India Ross started his long series of studies on mosquitoes. The story of his progress, his frustrations, his failures, and his ultimate success are told in his correspondence with his wife and with Manson, who continued to assist him with advice and encouragement. In 1895 he found the sexual forms of the parasite (the so-called flagella) in the stomach of a mosquito which had fed on an infected patient and two years later he found the pigmented cells of the parasite also in the stomach. It still remained to show how the parasite was returned to the human host. At this critical point all officers of the Indian Medical Service were mobilized for active service in the Tirah Expedition. Fortunately Ross was soon given special facilities to resume his researches and in 1898 he discovered sporozoites in the salivary glands of the mosquito. In 1900 the final proof of the role of the mosquito was provided by Manson who let an infected mosquito bite his son, who two weeks later developed malaria.

This extract is taken from Ross's article in the *British Medical Journal*, 1897, 2, p. 1786.

———

¶ *On Some Peculiar Pigmented Cells found in Two Mosquitoes Fed on Malarial Blood*

For the last two years I have been endeavouring to cultivate the parasite of malaria in the mosquito. The method adopted has been to feed mosquitoes, bred in bottles from the larva, on patients having crescents in the blood, and then to examine their tissues for parasites similar to haemamoeba in man. The study is a difficult one, as there is no *a priori* indication of what the derived parasite will be like precisely, nor in what particular species of insect the experiment will be successful, while the investigation requires a thorough knowledge of the minute anatomy of the mosquito. Hitherto the species employed have been mostly brindled and grey varieties of the insect; but though I have been able to find no fewer than six new parasites of the mosquito, namely, a nematode, a fungus, a gregarine, a sarcosporidium (?), a coccidium (?), and certain swarm spores in the stomach, besides one or two doubtfully parasitic forms, I have not yet succeeded in tracing any parasite to the ingestion of malarial blood, nor in observing special protozoa in the evacuations due to such ingestion. Lately, however, on abandoning the brindled and grey mosquito and commencing similar work on a new, brown species, of which I have as yet obtained very few individuals, I succeeded in finding in two of them certain remarkable and suspicious cells containing pigment identical in appearance to that of the parasite of malaria. As these cells appear to me to be very worthy of attention, while the peculiar species of mosquito seems most unfortunately to be so rare in this place that it may be a long time before I can procure any more for further study, I think it would be advisable to place on record a brief description both of the cells and of the mosquitoes.

The latter are a large brown species, biting well in the daytime, and incidentally found to be capable of harbouring the *filaria sanguinis hominis*. The back of the thorax and abdomen is a light fawn colour; the lower surface of the same, and the terminal segment of the body a dark chocolate brown. The wings are light brown to white, and have four dark spots on the anterior nervure. The *haustellum* and *tarsi* are brindled dark and light brown. The eggs – at least, when not fully developed – are shaped curiously like ancient boats with raised stern and prow, and have lines radiating from the concave border like banks of oars – so far as I have seen, a unique shape for mosquito's eggs. The species appears to belong to a family distinct from the ordinary brindled and grey insects; but there is an allied species here, only more slender, whiter, and much less voracious. My observations on the characteristic of these mosquitoes were not very careful, as when I first obtained them I did not anticipate any difficulty in procuring more.

On August 16th eight of them were fed on a patient whose blood contained fair to few crescents (and also *filariae*). Unfortunately four were killed at once for the study of flagellate bodies (*flagellulae* cysts). Of the remainder two were examined on the 18th and 20th respectively, without anything being noted. The seventh insect was also killed on the 20th, four days after having been fed. On turning to the stomach with an oil-immersion lens I was struck at once by the appearance of some cells which seemed to be slightly more substantial than the cells of the mosquito's stomach usually are. There were a dozen of them lying among (or within?) the cells of the upper half of the organ, and though somewhat more solid than these, still very delicate and colourless. They were round or oval, 12μ to 16μ in diameter when not compressed (that is, considerably larger than the largest haemamoeba in man); the outline sharp but very fine; the contents full of stationary vacuoles; and no sign of apparent nucleus, contractile vesicle or amoeboid, or intracellular movement. So far it would have been impossible for any but a person very familiar with the insect's anatomy to have distinguished them from the neighbouring cells; but what now arrested attention was the fact that each of these bodies contained a few granules of black pigment absolutely identical in appearance with the well-known and characteristic pigment of the parasite of malaria (large quartans and crescent-derived spheres).

The granules were more scanty in comparison to the size of the cell than in the haemamoeba, and numbered from ten to twenty in each. They were not dispersed throughout the cells, but were collected in groups, or arranged in lines transversely or peripherally, or in a small circle round the centre (just as in some forms of the haemamoeba). They were black or dark brown, and not refractive on change of focus. In some cases they showed rapid oscillation within a small range, but did not change their position. Owing to the blackness, so different from the bluish, yellow, and green granules and debris found in and about the neighbouring cells, they arrested the eye at once; and it must clearly be understood that I have not confounded them with normal objects. In short (except perhaps that rods were shorter or absent) these granules of pigment were indistinguishable from those of the haemamoeba.

The eighth and last mosquito was killed the next day, five days after having been fed. The stomach contained precisely the same cells, twenty-one in all, again toward the oesophageal end of the organ. In this case, however, they were distinctly larger and more substantial than in the seventh mosquito, and had a decidedly thicker outline. The size (along the major axis) appeared now sometimes to reach nearly 20μ, on a rough computation made without a micrometer. There thus appeared to be a marked increase in bulk and definition between these cells of the fourth and fifth day, suggesting that they had grown in the interval.

Both specimens were irrigated with 40 per cent formalin, and sealed. The result of the formalin was, as anticipated, that the bodies became slightly more visible than before, as compared with the stomach cells.

In spite of all attempts, I have not yet succeeded in obtaining any more of the species of mosquito referred to. Thinking, however, that I may have overlooked these delicate cells in former dissections, I have again examined a large number of brindled and grey mosquitoes, fed on malarial blood. Their stomachs certainly contained no such cells. Next I caught by hand a number of the more slender and white, but allied, species already referred to (I have failed in finding their grubs also), and examined them. Some had not been fed at all, and others had fed themselves on (presumably) healthy blood, two, three, or four days previously. The results were again negative. I may add that I have not yet succeeded in getting this species fed on malarial blood.

To sum up: The cells appear to be very exceptional; they have as yet been found only in a single species of mosquito fed on malarial blood; they seem to grow between the fourth and fifth day; and they contain the characteristic pigment of the parasite of malaria. It would, of course, be absurd to attempt final conclusions as yet; but I think we may venture to draw some cautious inferences on these observations. First, as to the nature of the cells. Judging from the facts that the elementary cells of allied species of mosquitoes are always alike, or very similar, and that I have never observed such bodies in previous or subsequent dissections of mosquitoes (I suppose I must have examined quite a thousand more or less carefully by this time), we may reasonably conjecture that these are no normal physiological cells – in other words, that they are parasites; and this view is fortified by the comparative substantiality of the bodies, by the appearance of growth between the fourth and fifth days, and, most notably, by their possession of pigment, a substance in my experience certainly quite foreign to the physiological cells of the mosquito. Secondly, as to the connexion of these presumable parasites with the parasite of malaria: they have been found in two consecutive insects fed on malarial blood (owing to their delicacy, and to my attention not having been attracted by them, I may have overlooked them in the fifth and sixth mosquitoes), a fact which may encourage us to believe that they may exist in a large percentage of similar insects similarly fed; and as they have not been found in an allied species fed on presumably healthy blood, we may hazard a conjecture that their presence in the original species was due to the ingestion of malarial blood. These considerations, taken together with the remarkable fact that the cells contain pigment just like that of the haemamoeba (a characteristic product which is, I believe, unknown in any other protozoa except some allied haematozoa) seem to open the question of their being indeed the form of the haemamoeba we are in search of — namely, the alternative form in the mosquito of the parasite of malaria in man.

On the other hand, the parasitic nature of the cells cannot finally be accepted until certain facts as to structure, sporulation, and so on, have been demonstrated. Even if this be done, it remains to be seen whether the bodies are not parasites common in the particular species of mosquito referred to, and quite independent of the ingestion of malarial blood and of the haemamoeba in man. I must, however, confess to feeling personally that the presence of pigment, so distinctive of the haemamoeba, renders this last supposition rather unlikely.

In conclusion I may note that the pigment in the cells may be derived from the haemoglobin in the insect's stomach, in the walls of which the cells are situated. With reference to their being found as yet in only one species of mosquito, it may be remembered that Manson originally conjectured that each species of haemamoeba might require a special species of mosquito for development extraneous to man, just as *filaria* embryos do.

THEOBALD SMITH

1858–1934

THE ROLE OF A TICK IN TRANSMITTING TEXAS
FEVER IN CATTLE IS PROVED

IN Theobald Smith we find our first example of a new type of scientist, a type which is, in a sense, peculiarly American in origin – the government scientific adviser. Smith was born in Albany, N.Y., and obtained his medical degree at Albany Medical College in 1883. At the age of twenty-five, he was appointed Director of the Pathological Laboratory of the U.S. Department of Agriculture's Bureau of Animal Industry. His very age suggests that in those days the Bureau was not a very large organization. Smith's work there lasted for eleven years, and culminated in his study of the mode of transmission of Texas cattle fever. In 1895, he was appointed professor of bacteriology at George Washington University but soon after took over the directorship of the Massachusetts State Board of Health, which he held for twenty years. A year after he arrived in Massachusetts, he became Professor of Comparative Pathology at Harvard. The last eighteen years of his life were spent in the service of the Rockefeller Institute of Medical Research at Princeton, where he directed the Department of Animal Pathology.

Smith was probably America's greatest bacteriologist, and he made valuable contributions to many areas of this science. The selection describes one of the first demonstrations of an insect (or arthropod) vector of a microbic disease and is taken from *Bulletin No. 1* of the Bureau of Animal Industry, U.S. Department of Agriculture, 1893.

¶ *Investigations into the Nature, Causation, and
Prevention of Texas or Southern Cattle Fever*

§ *Historical Review*

A certain number of very important facts had already been
ascertained and repeatedly confirmed concerning the
nature of Texas or Southern cattle fever up to the time at
which these investigations were begun. There were also a
number of theories in the field concerning the causation
or etiology of this disease, based in part on investigations,
in part on speculation.

Of those definitely ascertained facts, we may mention as
the most important the one which traced the distribution
of the infection to cattle brought from a large but well-
defined territory, including most of the Southern States,
into more northerly regions. The Southern cattle bearing
the infection were, as a rule, free from any signs of disease.
It was likewise settled that this infection was carried only
during the warmer season of the year, and that in the
depth of the winter Southern cattle were harmless. It was
also known that the infection was not communicated
directly from Southern to Northern cattle, but that the
ground over which the former passed was infected by
them, and that the infection was transmitted thence to
susceptible cattle. All that was necessary for the production of disease was the passage of Southern cattle over a
given territory and the grazing of Northern cattle over the
same or a portion of the same territory during the same
season.

It was also discovered that Southern cattle, after remaining for a short time on Northern pastures, lost, in
some mysterious way, the power to infect other pastures
and were, for the remainder of their stay North, harmless.
Again, cattle driven over a considerable distance lost, after
a time on their way, the power to infect pastures. When
pastures and trails had been passed over by Southern
cattle, it was observed that the disease did not appear at

once in the Northern cattle grazing on them, but that a certain period of not less than thirty days elapsed before the native cattle began to die. More curious even than these facts was the quite unanimous testimony of stock-owners who had more or less experience with this disease, that native susceptible animals which had become diseased did not transmit the disease to other natives, and that they were harmless. We shall discuss this statement in detail, in connexion with experiments made to test its accuracy.

If we turn our attention to the opposite aspect of this interesting series of facts, which deals with the introduction of Northern cattle into Southern territory, we learn that such cattle may contract Southern cattle fever, and that it is only under considerable risks that Northern cattle can be introduced into what has been called the permanently infected territory.

*

In addition to this work of accurately defining the territorial distribution of the infection, nothing has been done to add materially to the permanently valuable knowledge concerning this malady. Although attempts have been made to discover the cause they were not successful, as we shall be able to show. In 1889 the first systematic experiments were made by the Bureau of Animal Industry, and these were at once fruitful in the discovery by one of us of a peculiar microorganism in the red blood corpuscles which corresponds in every respect with what we should expect as the true cause. At the same time the other showed by field experiments that the cattle tick was somehow necessary to the transmission of the disease. These observations were fully confirmed in 1890. In the fall of the same year it was observed that when young ticks hatched artificially are placed on cattle there is a sudden extensive loss of red blood corpuscles, accompanied by fever, which could in no way be explained by the simple abstraction of blood. This discovery, at once followed up by additional experiments, brought to light the remarkable fact that Texas fever is caused by putting recently hatched cattle ticks on susceptible cattle. All these results were reconfirmed in the summers of 1891 and 1892.

These investigations have thus far brought to light two important facts: (1) The constant presence of blood corpuscle-destroying microorganism in Texas fever, and (2) the transmission of the disease from cattle to cattle by the cattle tick. The various experiments and observations which have led to these results are embodied in the following report and appendix.

THE MICROORGANISM OF TEXAS FEVER (*Pyrosoma bigeminum, n. sp.*)

Although Texas fever is essentially a blood disease, and only secondarily affects the spleen, liver, and kidneys, most observers have failed to recognize this fact. R. C. Stiles was the earliest and the only observer who laid any stress upon the changed condition of the blood corpuscles. He says: 'The red blood corpuscles when examined immediately after removal from the body were shrivelled and *crenated* without artificial provocation.'

*

In 1888 during the examination of portions of the organs of cases Numbers three to six inclusive the destruction of the red corpuscles seemed to be the one prime phenomenon of the disease. The large quantity of haemoglobin in the urine, and the peculiar condition of the liver and the bile, indicative of hyper-secretion, could not but lead to the hypothesis that there was some destructive agency at work in the blood.

*

The outcome of the work in 1888 was the formulation of several theories as to how the blood corpuscles came to their destruction.

(1) There may be organisms in the blood which by the production of toxic products act directly on the corpuscles.

(2) There may be some toxic substance in the digestive tract which is absorbed into the blood and causes a dissolution of the red corpuscles. This substance may be the product of specific bacteria multiplying only in the digestive tract.

(3) There may be microparasites which invade the red corpuscles in a manner similar to those of malaria, and which by their growth disintegrate the containing corpuscle.

The first hypothesis was soon made improbable by the absence of any demonstrable organisms in the parenchyma of the various organs which are abundantly supplied with blood, such as the liver, spleen, and kidneys. To test the second, the contents of the digestive tract, more particularly the small intestine, were carefully examined microscopically in 1888, and many plates and rolls of gelatine were made with the intestinal contents without bringing to light any other than the ordinary intestinal bacteria. It is true that this method was merely preliminary and would have been followed by more exhaustive bacteriological studies of the digestive tract had not the third hypothesis furnished the clue. This, however, could not be tested in 1888, since no living animals were accessible, and the results of the study of the blood elements could not be considered reliable when obtained only from the organs of animals dead twenty-four hours or even longer. In the very first case which succumbed on the experiment station at Washington, in 1889, certain microorganisms were found within the red corpuscles which will now claim our attention.

§ *Peculiar Bodies Found in the Red Corpuscles of Healthy Cattle*

In endeavouring to prove the existence of specific parasites in the blood as causes of disease it becomes necessary to prove their absence during health. A large series of microscopic observations have been made upon the blood of cattle which were not infected as well as upon those which were infected before the disease had appeared and after it had passed away....

§ *The Nature of the Texas-Fever Microorganism and Its Relation to the Parasites of the Red Corpuscles of Other Animals and of Man*

It has been known since 1881 that the various types of malarial fever in man were accompanied by minute organisms living within the red corpuscles. This discovery by Laveran has been followed by confirmation in various parts of the world, and it is generally accepted that these intraglobular organisms are the cause of malaria. Stimulated by this important discovery, various observers have studied the blood of many animals (frog, turtle, and various birds) and have found therein certain minute parasites which likewise pass their life chiefly within red corpuscles.

*

The parasites found in the blood of birds and man first appear as minute, slowly enlarging amoeboid bodies in the red corpuscles. Soon pigment granules appear. When of a certain size these bodies break up within the corpuscles into a variable number of spores. These are set free and begin life as a new generation by entering other red corpuscles and undergoing the same development.

*

The Texas-fever parasite differs in many important respects from all those thus far described. Its morphology is quite unique. It contains no pigment. It probably runs through its whole development in a short time, otherwise it would be difficult to account for the rapid destruction of red corpuscles. Nevertheless, no distinctly reproductive phase has been seen during four years of observation of a great variety of cases.

§ *The Transmission of Texas Fever by Means of the Cattle Tick*
The Relation of the Cattle Tick to the Microorganism of Texas Fever

The hypothesis which seemed most plausible after the experiments of 1889 was that the tick, while withdrawing the blood from Southern cattle, drew out in it the Texas-fever parasite, which, entering into some more resistant state, perhaps some spore state, was disseminated over the pastures when the body of the mother tick became disintegrated. These spores were then supposed to enter the alimentary tract with the food and infect the body from this direction. The later experiments, however, completely demolished this conception. Neither the feeding of adult ticks and tick eggs nor the feeding of grass from infected pastures gave any positive results. On the other hand the unmistakable outcome of the experiments was that the young tick introduced the infection into the body. This fact implies two possibilities. Either the tick is a necessary or merely an accidental bearer of the microparasite.

*

Further investigations are necessary before the probable truth of one or the other of these hypotheses can be predicted with any degree of certainty.

§ *Conclusions*

(1) Texas cattle fever is a disease of the blood, characterized by a destruction of red corpuscles. The symptoms are partly due to the anaemia produced; partly to the large amount of debris in the blood, which is excreted with difficulty, and which causes derangement of the organs occupied with its removal.

(2) The destruction of the red corpuscles is due to a micro-organism or microparasite which lives within them. It belongs to the protozoa and passes through several distinct phases in the blood.

(3) Cattle from the permanently infected territory, though otherwise healthy, carry the microparasite of Texas fever in their blood.

(4) Texas fever may be produced in susceptible cattle by the direct inoculation of blood containing the micro-parasite.

(5) Texas fever in nature is transmitted from cattle which come from the permanently infected territory to cattle outside of this territory by the cattle tick (*Boophilus bovis*).

(6) The infection is carried by the progeny of the ticks which matured on infected cattle, and is inoculated by them directly into the blood of susceptible cattle.

(7) Sick natives may be a source of infection (when ticks are present).

(8) Texas fever is more fatal to adult than to young cattle.

(9) Two mild attacks or one severe attack will probably prevent a subsequent fatal attack in every case.

(10) Sheep, rabbits, guinea-pigs, and pigeons are insus-ceptible to direct inoculation. (Other animals have not been tested.)

(11) In the diagnosis of Texas fever in the living animal the blood should always be examined microscopically if possible.

———

INDEX

Accademia del Cimento, 74
Ahmes, 15
Alexander the Great, 17, 31, 41, 42, 48
Alexandria, 17, 18, 31, 42, 59, 61, 115; library at, 42; Alexandrian school, 59
Anatomy, animal, 195; human, 99–100, 103, 104, 105, 110, 111, 112, 113, 114, 115, 118, 167; microscopic, 100–101; minute, 128; plant, 100
Anaximander, 30
Anthrax, 333, 334, 347
Antibiotics, 331
Antisepsis, 370, antiseptic surgery, 334, 370, 381; antiseptic treatment, 371–82
Antitoxins, 334
Appert, Nicolas, 360
Aquinas, Thomas, 19, 237
Arabs, 18, 27, 28, 42, 59, 60, 99, 106, 113
Archimedes, 17, 27
Aristotle, 17, 18–19, 21, 27, 31, 41–7, 48, 59, 70, 99, 115, 168, 169, 175, 181, 183, 184, 237, 332; his concept of *psyche*, 168; his Lyceum, 41, 42, 48; his observations of marine animals, 41, 43–7
Asepsis, 370
Averroes, 18
Avicenna, 60

Babylonians, 15, 16, 27
Bacon, Francis, 172, 226, 242
Bacon, Roger, 19, 242
Bacteria, 22–3, 81, 332, 333, 334, 346, 347, 348, 353, 356, 370, 394
Banks, Sir Joseph, 138, 343
Bassi, Agostino, 332, 346
Bastian, H. C., 359

Bateson, William, 316
Bauhin, C., 251
Bell, Sir Charles, 169, 222, 223, 224
Bernard, Claude, 170, 225–34
Bestiaries, medieval, 32, 61–5
Blood, circulation of: Harvey's theory, 81, 172–91; Leeuwenhoek's observations, 81; Spallanzani's studies, 86; movement of: Empedocles' theory, 30–31; Galen's theory, 52–3; blood pressure, 203
Boccaccio, Giovanni, 331
Bock, 100
Bohr, Niels, 13
Bologna, University of, 99–100, 192
Borelli, Gian Alfonzo, 192, 194, 199
Boyle, Robert, 80, 359
Brown, Robert, 101, 138–41, 142
Brownian Movement, 138
Brunfels, 100
Bubonic plague, 334, 335
Buffon, G. L. L., 71
Burnet, Macfarlane, 335

Cabot, Sebastian, 20
Calendars, 15, 27
Capillaries, 81, 173, 193, 195–7, 203
Carbolic acid, 370, 371–82
Carrel, Alexis, 158
Catastrophism, theory of, 239
Cells, 101, 123–6, 142, 143–5, 148–57, 158–63; cell-nucleus, 138–41, 149, 154, 155, 156, 296; cell theory, 21, 101, 143, 148–9, 150, 152–7; cork cells, 123–5; growth of nerve cells outside living body, 158–63
Charles I, 172
Charles V, Emperor, 105

INDEX

*Some other Pelican and Penguin books
are described on the following
pages*

SCIENCE AND HUMAN VALUES

J. Bronowski

Dr Bronowski, as all those who have watched his stimulating programmes on television will have noticed, is equally at home in the world of science and of the arts. In these essays he describes the essence of the creative process – that leap of the imagination which distinguishes the mathematician as much as the poet – and develops an ethic for science, which he describes as a human progress and no mere mechanism. Among the propositions he puts forward are that the concept is more profound than its laws and the act of judging more critical than the judgement.

'A remarkable book, and the affirmation of a remarkable man. If I were trying to select six works, in order to explain to an intelligent non-scientist something of the deepest meaning of science, Bronowski's would be one of them. . . . Bronowski has built a structure of values, built them with what he himself has called the ethical enthusiasm of his rabbinical ancestors, but also with poetic feeling and a passionate identification with the human future' – Sir Charles Snow in the *New Statesman*

THE SCIENCE OF ANIMAL BEHAVIOUR

P. L. Broadhurst

For generations men have employed dogs and hawks to hunt, cormorants to fish, and performing animals for entertainment. Modern research, on scientific lines, may enormously widen the use of animals in human society. In this brief and fascinating study the director of the animal psychology laboratory of London University's Institute of Psychiatry recounts how, with the use of test apparatus, monkeys can learn to work for wages paid in token coins; how white rats can be trained to thread their way through a maze or taught specific drills in such devices as the 'shuttle box'. He describes too the scientific observations which have been made on the behaviour of penguins and crabs, for instance, in the wild, and the questions that these raise.

Such experimentation and observation, under approved conditions, can be shown to advance the treatment of human mental disorders and to help the study of such difficult problems as pre-natal influences. It might also lead to such extraordinary developments as the training of chimpanzees as engine-drivers or the employment of pigeons as production-line inspectors.

This authoritative book is the only one to explain clearly the meaning and purpose of modern research into animal behaviour.

THE ECONOMICS OF EVERYDAY LIFE

Gertrude Williams

'It is a measure of her success that she makes the whole subject sound like very little more than applied commonsense, but commonsense applied to familiar situations in a way that picks out a consistent pattern and shows the reader that the "economic aspect" is nothing more abstruse than a methodical selection from facts which, in a muddle-headed way, he knows already' – *Economist*

The title of this book reveals its intention – to analyse in plain, non-technical language some of the important economic issues which affect life today in Britain. Now revised and brought completely up to date to include the National Incomes Commission of 1962, the unemployment crisis of 1963, and other important economic developments, this book deals with matters that are of interest to everybody because they are closely allied to the daily life of the individual. Why do prices go up and down? Who really pays for advertisements? Is monopoly anti-social? These and many other vital questions are discussed in such a way that the reader is able to understand the complex factors involved in trying to reach sensible answers.

THE LIBERAL HOUR

J. K. Galbraith

Among the great dangers of today, the author of *The Affluent Society* picks on our solemnity in holding fast to economic illusions. As a counter-measure, Professor Galbraith selects a number of firmly entrenched myths – historical as well as economic – for relaxed scrutiny.

Does America compete effectively with Russia by producing more and more goods that nobody wants? Is capital really more important than talent nowadays? Must 'balancing the budget' always override all other economic priorities? Should a good business-man be so absorbed in his work that he has no time for art or leisure? And how clever was Henry Ford: was he in fact such a brilliant mechanic and business-man?

These and other topics, ranging from inflation to farming, from the American Civil War to the modern public relations 'build up', are surveyed with precision, irony, and good humour.

'He drives his points well home and imbues every theme he touches with interest' – Sir Roy Harrod in the *Listener*

'Professor Galbraith writes with the verve of a conversationalist in the top league of talkers' – *The Times*

IN DEFENCE OF POLITICS

Bernard Crick

'One of the most thoughtful products of the political dialogues of the London School of Economics since the great days of Tawney, Dalton, Wallas, and Hobhouse. Its sobriety, liberal spirit, and toughness of mind are rare qualities in any political work' – *Guardian*

At a time of brittle cynicism about the activities of politicians, this essay makes 'an attempt to justify politics in plain words by saying what it is'. In a civilized community, which is no mere tribe, the establishment among rival groups and interests of political order – of agreed rules for the game – marks the birth of freedom. In spite of the compromises, deals, half-measures, and bargains which prompt impatient idealists to regard politics as a dirty word – indeed, because of them – the negotiating processes of politics remain the only tested alternative to government by outright coercion.

'Original and profound. It is hard to think of anyone interested in politics at any level who would not benefit by reading it' – Max Beloff in the *Daily Telegraph*

SHAKESPEARE: A SURVEY

E. K. Chambers

'We listen to him with delight. . . . In ten pages Sir Edmund will show more of the quality and uniqueness of a given play of Shakespeare than other men will in a hundred' – *The Times Literary Supplement*

Sir Edmund Chambers was perhaps the most fluent and readable exponent of the 'Mind and art' approach to Shakespeare. Grouping the plays according to the stages of Shakespeare's psychological development, he studied the dramatist's progress, through lyric emotion, comic perception, and sceptical irony, to the 'philosophic insight' of the great tragedies.

His assessments of where each play stands in this progress are collected in *Shakespeare: A Survey*, which has become a classic. Behind the book lies a wealth of reflection on the structure and meaning of the plays. In it, Chambers advocates the 'scientific spirit' in the study of literature, and attacks gushing bardolatry and the essays of 'journalists and idle antiquaries'. Yet his own evident enjoyment of the plays warms every line of his criticism.

A SHAKESPEARE COMPANION

F. E. Halliday

'Nothing quite like this has been done before . . . the comprehensiveness, clarity, and reliability of the work as a whole are positive virtues which will make it extremely valuable to all students of Shakespeare' – *The Times Educational Supplement*

This volume provides a simple and handy index to all aspects of Shakespearian lore over three and a half centuries. As the author himself explains, 'It is a handbook not only to Shakespeare's life and works, to his friends and acquaintances, to his poems and plays and their characters, but also to the Elizabethan–Jacobean theatre, the other dramatists who wrote for it, their most important plays and the companies that performed them, and to the history up to the present day of Shakespeare's work both on the stage and in the study, to his printers and publishers, players and producers, editors and adapters, scholars and critics.'

'Everyone from sceptical schoolboys to devotees grown old in Shakespearian wisdom, will find a *livre de chevet* in Mr Halliday's "Companion" ' – *Sunday Times*

WHAT IS HISTORY?

E. H. Carr

'Simply to show how it really was.' Ranke, stating what he considered the proper aim of the historian, filled generations of historians after him with a burning zeal for objectivity.

But who is to say how things were? In formulating a modern answer to the question *What is History?* Professor Carr shows that the 'facts' of history are simply those which historians have selected for scrutiny. Millions have crossed the Rubicon, but the historians tell us that only Caesar's crossing was significant. All historical facts come to us as a result of interpretative choices by historians influenced by the standards of their age.

Yet if absolute objectivity is impossible, the role of the historian need in no way suffer, nor does history lose its fascination. Indeed, this published version of the 1961 Trevelyan Lectures at Cambridge confirms the vitality of both.

'E. H. Carr, author of the monumental *History of Soviet Russia*, now proves himself to be not only our most distinguished modern historian but also one of the most valuable contributors to historical theory' – *Spectator*

ECONOMIC PHILOSOPHY

Joan Robinson

This exceptionally stimulating book begins by showing how the basic human need for a morality on which the conscience can work has led to the necessity for a philosophy of economics in any society. It is stressed that economic values and money values are not identical and it is the task of the economist to justify the image of Mammon to man 'not to tell us what to do, but show why what we are doing anyway is in accord with proper principles'. The relations between science and ideology over the last two hundred years are traced from Adam Smith, through Marx and Keynes, to the dichotomy that exists in current economic thinking and the pressing fundamental problems which must now be faced.

'It would be difficult to think of a better book than this to place in the hands of the reader who thinks that economics is simply a matter of statistics, and who needs to be convinced of its intellectual interest and excitement' – Samuel Brittan in the *Observer*

MONETARY POLICY: ENDS AND MEANS

Paul Einzig

This book (formerly *How Money is Managed*) has now been revised and brought completely up to date. It incorporates the findings of the Radcliffe Committee on the Working of the Monetary System and other recent reports, and it contains important new chapters on economic growth, wages policy, and the new device of influencing the liquidity of the banks and of the entire community. It describes the manifold ends of monetary policy, and the even wider variety of means which may be employed in pursuing those ends. The author gives an account of the remarkable changes that have taken place during the last ten years in the objectives followed by governments in their monetary policy, and in the methods employed by them.

The subject of the book is of interest not only to the specialist, but also to the layman who wishes to understand the 'why' and 'how' of government action in the monetary sphere. Such action is of interest to everybody, because it is liable to affect his welfare.

'The language throughout is straightforward and nontechnical, the style discursive and readable. For all armchair Chancellors, this should be an ideal and inexpensive *vademecum*' – *Financial Times*

'The student as well as the general reader will find substance and enjoyment in this volume' – *American Economic Review*